Contents

Printed on Revive Silk

Diamond Publications
© **Copyright**

Published by Diamond Publications
PO Box 59, Bideford, Devon EX39 4YN.
Tel: 01271 860183 Fax: 01271 860064

Email: info@gethooked.co.uk   Web Site: www.gethooked.co.uk

Editor: Graham Sleeman   01566 785782   Advertising: Jane and Emma   01271 860183
Distribution: Jane Diamond   01271 860183   Printed by Broglia Press   01202 621621

Cover Pictures: Environment Agency (Salmon), Predator Publications (Pike), Russ Symons (Pandoras Bream), Mike Weaver (Grayling).

Special thanks to the team at the Environment Agency, annually understanding partners and children, Harry - our 'man on the ground' and everyone who contributed to this, the biggest and best so far.

ISBN 0-9527547-6-2

Welcome...

To the ninth annual edition of the Get Hooked Guide to Angling in South West England published in association with the Environment Agency.

Once again we have contacted EVERY fishery and association, offering day ticket fishing, known to us or the Environment Agency, throughout the area. Everyone who has responded is detailed in our directory section, now easier to use in full colour, which has increased yet again and has over 600 entries, re-affirming our position as THE DEFINITIVE guide to angling throughout the South West of England.

May we take this opportunity to ask those who we don't know of to contact us for insertion in next year's issue, a directory entry, in the guide and on the web site, costs you nothing. If you have access to the internet you can use the on line form to send us your details for inclusion on the web site database, or next year's guide as well as notifying us of any changes throughout the coming year. Updates to the paper guide will have to wait for the next edition but the website database will be updated on a regular basis. Use of the internet is becoming more widespread within the fishing fraternity with some 250 entries in the directory contactable by Email. If technology has not caught up with you yet we find the phone or fax still works perfectly!

Within our editorials this year we have the regular Environment Agency section, covering all the latest byelaws and licencing details and we have contributions from charitable groups and many organisations dedicated to improving and supporting the sport. Please take the time to read them. I know everybody just looks at the pictures on the first browse, but all of these organisations need our support.

A first this year is our tuition feature. There is a real feeling of enthusiasm throughout the guide, foot and mouth is behind us and many organisations are making a real effort to encourage new people, young and old, into the sport.

Our thanks go out to all the advertisers and contributors who help us make this publication what it is. We know the advertising is successful and hope the new advertisers will benefit as much as those who have been with us from our first edition.

An annual thank you is due to the tackle shops who have helped tremendously in finding previously unknown (to us) fisheries and clubs, enabling us to make the directory so comprehensive.

We have a great selection of pictures from the fisheries again this year, thanks to everyone who made the effort and apologies for not being able to get them all in. We would like to reiterate that the vast majority of pictures are supplied by anglers and fishery owners, not professional photographers, so don't be too critical if some of them aren't pin sharp! All photos of catches from fisheries in the guide are welcome (some more of species other than Carp would be great!)

Our Web Site 'Fish Finder' contains all the information published in our directory in a fully searchable format. There is no quicker way of finding fishing in the South West. We have some links on the site and welcome further enquiries. Fishing related sites only need apply.
Point your browser at:
www.gethooked.co.uk
Or Email us at: info@gethooked.co.uk

From some of the best sea fishing to a huge, and ever increasing, variety of coarse fishing plus quality game fishing, on stillwaters and rivers, to equal anywhere in the country. The South West has a huge amount to offer anglers from all branches of the sport.

We are sure you will find The Get Hooked Guide to Angling in the South West of England useful, informative and entertaining, whether you are local or visiting the area.

Enjoy your fishing

Graham Sleeman - Editor.

ENVIRONMENT AGENCY

The Environment Agency is the leading public agency for protecting and enhancing the environment in England and Wales.

Our vision is a healthy, rich and diverse environment for present and future generations.

We contribute to sustainable development through the integrated management of air, land and water. Sustainable development is about ensuring a better quality of life for everyone, now and for generations to come.

Specific responsibilities for the Agency are water resources, pollution prevention and control, waste management, flood defence, fisheries, conservation and recreation.

Visit our website at: www.environment-agency.gov.uk to find out more about the work of the Agency and your local environment.

A key element in our vision for the South West is looking after the region's important fisheries.

Fish are one of the best indicators of the state of rivers and lakes. Healthy and abundant freshwater fish stocks and populations will demonstrate the Agency's success in contributing towards sustainable development.

The work of the Agency helps fisheries in many ways. Pollution prevention, dealing with low river flows and habitat improvements are three good examples.

In addition, the Agency's fisheries staff carry out a number of vital tasks.
These include:
• Controlling the pressure on fisheries through issuing licences and making byelaws

• Preventing damage to fish and fish stocks by effective enforcement of fishery laws
• Ensuring the health and abundance of fish stocks through regular fisheries surveys
• Rescuing fish when pollution incidents occur and minimising damage to fish stocks
• Stocking fish to restore and improve fisheries
• Carrying out habitat improvement
• Constructing fish passes
• Monitoring of fish stocks i.e. catch returns, juvenile surveys and fish counters
• Carrying out fisheries research to allow future improvements and developments.

Fisheries operations are organised by staff based in the Agency's four South West areas.

They can be contacted as follows:

Cornwall:
    Environment Agency
    Sir John Moore House
    Victoria Square
    BODMIN PL31 1EB
    Tel: 01208 78301
    Fax: 01208 78321
Devon:
    Environment Agency
    Exminster House
    Miller Way
    EXMINSTER EX6 8AS
    Tel: 01392 444000
    Fax: 01392 316016
North Wessex:
    Environment Agency
    Rivers House
    East Quay
    BRIDGWATER TA6 4YS
    Tel: 01278 457333
    Fax: 01278 452985
South Wessex:
    Fisheries, Ecology and
    Recreation Manager
    Environment Agency
    Rivers House
    Sunrise Business Park
    Higher Shaftesbury Road
    BLANDFORD DT11 8ST
    Tel: 01258 456080
    Fax: 01258 455998

Strategic policy and planning issues are co-ordinated by fisheries staff at the Regional Office (Manley House, Exeter).

The Region is advised by the South West Regional Fisheries, Ecology, and Recreation Advisory Committee. The Committee usually sits four times a year and its meetings are open to the public and the media. Local fisheries forums also meet in each of the four areas.

AGENCY REORGANISATION

During the early part of 2002 the Environment Agency is undergoing a national reorganisation. The purpose of this is to enable the Agency to deliver improved environmental outcomes by operating more efficiently, regulating more effectively and consistently, whilst influencing and advising its customers.

The result of this reorganisation will bring some significant changes to the way the Agency works. The full picture will not be available until the summer, however the four main area offices are likely to remain as the main contact points for customers.

ANGLER PARTICIPATION

2002 sees the introduction of a new three-year scheme to promote angling, particularly for juniors and the disabled. The project is a joint venture with SPORTLOT to increase the number of anglers and involves working with national angling bodies and professional angling coaches.

Our target in the South West is to train 1200 new anglers in 2002 and establish/refurbish a major urban fishery for junior anglers and the disabled.

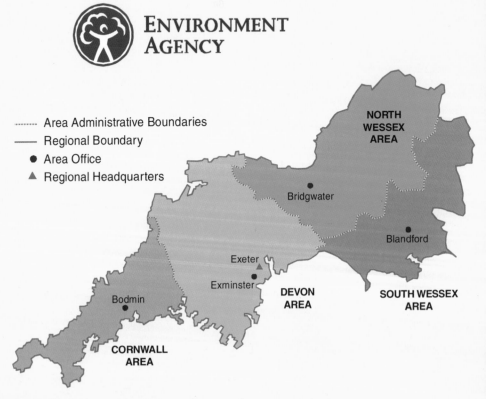

ENVIRONMENT AGENCY

- .... Area Administrative Boundaries
- —— Regional Boundary
- ● Area Office
- ▲ Regional Headquarters

NORTH WESSEX AREA

Bridgwater

Blandford

Exeter

Exminster

DEVON AREA

SOUTH WESSEX AREA

Bodmin

CORNWALL AREA

National Rod Licences

Before fishing for salmon, trout or freshwater fish (including eels) in any* water in England and Wales, it is necessary to have both a current Agency rod fishing licence and permission to fish from the owner of the fishery.

Except in waters where a general licence is in force - please check with the owner of the fishery in advance.

The area where a rod licence is required for fishing for salmon, trout and freshwater fish includes estuaries and the sea out to six miles from the shore.

In most cases a licence is not required to fish for freshwater eels in tidal water, though there are exceptions. Before fishing for eels in tidal waters, please check with your local Area Fisheries Office.

The Agency has a national rod fishing licence. This means that fishing in all regions is covered by one licence.

Licences are available for coarse fish and non-migratory trout or for all inclusive fishing, including salmon and sea trout.

The licence structure is aimed at raising approximately £14 million for essential fisheries work in addition to Government's grant-in-aid.

Coarse fish and non-trout

The price of the full annual licence (2002/2003) for coarse fish and non-migratory trout is £21 (£10.50 concessions [disabled anglers in receipt of invalidity benefit or severe disability allowance, and anyone aged 65 years and over]).

A short term coarse fish and non-migratory trout licence covers a period of eight consecutive days, giving anglers the benefit of being able to fish over two weekends. This costs £6.50 (no concessions). A one-day licence, aimed at beginners and casual anglers costs £2.50 (no concessions).

New Junior Licence

A full annual junior licence is available for coarse fish and non-migratory trout priced £5. Children under 12 years of age do not require a licence. Junior licences are available to anyone less than 17.

Salmon and sea trout

The price of the full annual licence (2002/2003) for salmon and sea trout (and also including coarse fish and non-migratory trout) is £60 (concessions £30 - including juniors). An eight-day licence costs £16.50 and a one-day licence is £5.50. There are no concessions on the eight - or one-day licence.

Licences are available from every Post Office in England and Wales or from a range of local distributors. A list of these local distributors is available from the Agency offices. If necessary, you may obtain your licence by post. A form to do this is available from Agency offices.

Alternatively a 'telesales' service operates from 8am to 8pm, seven days a week, except bank holidays, for full, junior and concessionary licences. The number to ring is 0870 1662662.

It is also now possible to obtain full licences - eight and one day and the new full junior licence - through the Agency's 'on-line licensing system'. Details are available on the fisheries web site: www.environment-agency.gov.uk/fish.

Payment by credit/debit card for 'telesales' and 'online': the licence will be immediately valid as the purchaser will be provided with a reference number to quote if challenged when fishing. Proof of identity will also be needed until the full licence has been received.

The 2002/2003 licences will be valid until 31 March 2003. Licences are issued on a 12-month basis and are subject to price reviews.

The licence has the following benefits:

* You can use a rod and line anywhere in England and Wales.
* You can use up to two rods per licence, subject to the National Byelaws (see page 12) and any local rules.
Your rod licence will help the Agency to continue and improve the vital work it carries out, including:
* Management of fish stocks.
* Surveys, essential for picking up changes and problems.

* Improvements in fisheries and the fish's environment.
* Fish rearing and stocking of rivers.
* Rescue of fish which would otherwise be lost through drought, pollution or other causes.
* Advice on fishing and management issues.
* Protection of stocks through enforcement activities, including anti-poaching patrols.

Please note that:

1. The licence gives you the right to use a fishing rod and line but does not give you the right to fish. You must always check that you have the permission of the owner or tenant of the fishing rights before starting to fish.

2. Your licence is valuable - if it should be lost, a duplicate can be issued from PO Box 432, National Rod Licence Administration, Environment Agency, Richard Fairclough House, Knutsford Road, Warrington, WA4 1HH. A charge of £5 will be made. Please make a note of the Licence Stamp Number.

3. The licence is yours alone; it cannot be used by anyone else. Please make sure that you sign the licence before you go fishing.

4. Your licence must be produced on demand to a water bailiff of the Agency who produces his or her warrant, a police officer or any other licence holder who produces his or her licence. Failure to do so is an offence and may make you liable to prosecution (maximum fine £2,500).

5. The licence is only valid if the correct name, address and date of birth of the holder, and the date and time of issue are shown without amendments, a stamp of the correct duty is attached and the licence is signed by the holder and the issuing agent.

6. A national rod licence is not required where a general licence is in force. Please check with the owner in advance.

7. The catch return form attached to the licence for salmon and sea trout is very important. This information is required by law and you should send in a return, even if you recorded a "nil" catch. Please fill in and return the form in an envelope when your licence expires, using the FREEPOST address.

8. Details of rod fishing byelaws and angling information can be obtained from Agency offices. Fishery byelaws may vary between different Agency Regions - if in doubt, check first. Details of the main byelaws applying to the Agency in the South West can be found on pages 7 to 12.

Salmon and sea trout kelts

Salmon and sea trout which are about to spawn, or have recently spawned but not recovered, are known as unclean. Fish in either condition, if caught, must by law be returned to the water with as little damage as possible. Fish about to spawn are identifiable by the ease with which eggs or milt can be extruded from the vent.

Those having recently spawned are called kelts and can be identified from clean fish by using the comparison given below.

KELT

1. Line of back and belly parallel
2. Gill maggots almost invariably present (salmon only)
3. Distinct "corner" or change of direction in profile of body at back of skull
4. Fins invariably frayed
5. Vent suffused and easily extruded by pressure
6. Belly normally black

CLEAN

1. Back and belly convex in relation to each other
2. Gill maggots only present in previous spawners or fish which have been some time in the river
3. Head tapers into body without a break
4. Fins entire; rarely frayed
5. Vent firm and compact
6. Belly normally pale

Smolts and parr

Young salmon known as parr look very similar to brown trout and are often caught by trout anglers. These parr are destined to run the rivers in a few years as adult salmon after feeding at sea. It is an offence knowingly to take, kill or injure these parr, and any which are caught by mistake must be returned to the water.

Salmon parr can be identified from trout by using the comparison given below. In March, April and May, salmon and sea trout parr begin to migrate to the sea. The spots and finger marks disappear and the body becomes silvery in colour. They are then called smolts and must be returned to the water if caught.

SALMON PARR

1. Body slightly built and torpedo-shaped
2. Tail distinctly forked
3. A perpendicular line from the back of the eye will not touch the maxillary bone
4. Eight to twelve finger marks, even in width, well-defined and regularly placed along the sides
5. No white line on leading edge of fins
6. No red colour on adipose fin

TROUT

1. Body thicker and clumsier looking
2. Tail with shallow fork
3. A perpendicular line from the back of the eye will pass through or touch the maxillary bone
4. Finger marks less numerous, uneven in width, less defined, irregularly placed along the sides
5. Normally white line on leading edge of fins
6. Adipose fin generally coloured with orange or red.

ROD FISHING SEASONS

The "Open Seasons", i.e. the periods when it is permitted to fish, are set out in the table opposite.

★ *There is no statutory close season for coarse fish and eels in still waters, but some clubs and fishery owners may impose their own close seasons.*

Gravel cleaning

FISHERY DISTRICT	MAJOR RIVERS WITHIN DISTRICT	ROD & LINE OPEN SEASON (dates inclusive)	
SALMON		**Starts**	**Ends**
Avon (Devon)	Avon (Devon)	15 Apr	30 Nov
	Erme	15 Mar	31 Oct
Axe (Devon)	Axe, Otter, Sid	15 Mar	31 Oct
	Lim	1 Mar	30 Sept
Camel	Camel	1 Apr	15 Dec
Dart	Dart	1 Feb	30 Sept
Exe	Exe	14 Feb	30 Sept
Fowey	Fowey, Looe, Seaton	1 Apr	15 Dec
Tamar & Plym	Tamar, Tavy, Lynher,	1 Mar	14 Oct
	Plym, Yealm	1 Apr	15 Dec
Taw & Torridge	Taw, Torridge	1 Mar	30 Sept
	Lyn	1 Feb	31 Oct
Teign	Teign	1 Feb	30 Sept
Frome (Dorset) & Piddle		1 Mar	31 Aug
	All other rivers in North & South Wessex Areas	1 Feb	31 Aug
MIGRATORY TROUT			
Avon (Devon)	Avon (Devon)	15 Apr	30 Sept
	Erme	15 Mar	30 Sept
Axe (Devon)	Axe, Otter, Sid	15 Apr	31 Oct
	Lim	16 Apr	31 Oct
Camel	Camel, Gannel, Menalhyl Valency	1 Apr	30 Sept
Dart	Dart	15 Mar	30 Sept
Exe	Exe	15 Mar	30 Sept
Fowey	Fowey, Looe, Seaton, Tresillian	1 Apr	30 Sept
Tamar & Plym	Tamar, Lynher, Plym, Tavy, Yealm	3 Mar	30 Sept
Taw & Torridge	Taw, Torridge, Lyn	15 Mar	30 Sept
Teign	Teign	15 Mar	30 Sept
	All rivers in North & South Wessex Areas	15 Apr	31 Oct
BROWN TROUT			
	Camel	1 Apr	30 Sept
	Other rivers in Devon & Cornwall Areas	15 Mar	30 Sept
	All rivers in North & South Wessex Areas	1 Apr	15 Oct
	All other water in Devon & Cornwall Areas	15 Mar	12 Oct
	All other waters in North & South Wessex Areas	17 Mar	14 Oct
RAINBOW TROUT			
	Camel & Fowey	1 Apr	30 Sept
	Other rivers in Devon & Cornwall Areas	15 Mar	30 Sept
	All rivers in North & South Wessex Areas	1 Apr	15 Oct
	Reservoirs, Lakes & Ponds ★ No statutory close season		
GRAYLING, COARSE FISH & EELS			
	Rivers, Streams and Drains including the Glastonbury Canal	16 Jun	14 Mar
	Enclosed waters - Ponds, Lakes & Reservoirs All other Canals	★ No statutory close season	

7

NATIONAL BYELAWS TO PROTECT SALMON STOCKS

National byelaws to protect spring salmon were introduced in April 1999.

A summary of the byelaws is as follows:

Mandatory catch and release of all salmon for all rivers before 16 June.

Fly and spinner only (where not already limited by existing byelaws) before June 16 for salmon fishing.

These measures replace some of the existing measures already in place.

Catch and release of salmon is mandatory to 16 June, removing the earlier bag limit of two salmon before 1 June on the Taw and Torridge. It also supersedes any early season voluntary bag limits.

Anglers are still encouraged to fish catch and release after 16 June and especially to return any large red fish late in the season which may be "springers". The 70 cm limit in August/ September on the Taw and Torridge still applies.

Permitted baits are restricted to artificial fly and artificial lure until 16 June. Exceptions where other restrictions remain include the Taw and Torridge (fly only from April 1) and North and South Wessex (fly only before 15 May).

These national byelaws are designed as a baseline and are considered to be the lowest common denominator across the country addressing the national problem of a decline in early-run large salmon.

Measures to address other local stock problems will continue to follow a river-by-river approach based on the programme of individual salmon action plans being developed by the Agency with local fisheries interests.

PERMITTED BAITS

The use of particular baits for fishing is regulated by byelaws and in some cases additional restrictions are imposed by the fishing association or riparian owner. The byelaw restrictions are shown in the table below:

★ *This restriction only applies to water where a statutory coarse fish close season is applicable. It does not apply to stillwaters. See also section on rod fishing seasons and the note on canal close seasons (page 12).*

★★ *All references to "Trout" include migratory trout and non-migratory trout.*

★★★ *This is a change introduced in 1998.*

No spinning for trout in waters included within the Dartmoor National Park, the Exe above Exebridge, Otter above Langford Bridge, Torridge above Woodford Bridge, Bray above

PERMITTED BAITS

FISHERY DISTRICT	SPECIES	BAITS (REAL OR IMITATION)
South West Region	Salmon	Artificial fly and artificial lure ONLY before 16 June
Avon (Devon)	Salmon & Trout ★★	No worm or maggot.
Axe (Devon)	Salmon & Trout	No shrimp, prawn, worm or maggot. Fly only after 31 July below Axbridge, Colyford.
Dart	Salmon	No worm or maggot. No shrimp or prawn except below Staverton Bridge. No spinning above Holne Bridge.
	Trout	Fly only.
Exe	Salmon & Trout	No worm or maggot.
Barnstaple Yeo (tidal)	All species (inc. sea fish)	No fishing
Taw & Torridge (except Lyn)	Salmon & Trout	No shrimp, prawn, worm or maggot. No spinning after 31 March. ★★★
Lyn	Trout	No worm or maggot before 1 June.
Teign	Trout	No worm or maggot before 1 June.
Camel & Fowey	Salmon	No byelaw restrictions on bait after 16 June
	Trout	No byelaw restrictions on bait
Tamar	Salmon & Migratory Trout	No worm, maggot, shrimp or prawn after 31 August.
North Wessex & South Wessex Areas	Salmon & Migratory Trout	Artificial fly only before 15 May.
North Wessex & South Wessex Areas	All species in rivers, drains and canals	No maggot (or pupae), processed product, cereal or other vegetable matter during the coarse fish close season. ★

Newton Bridge, Mole above Alswear Bridge, Little Dart above Affeton Bridge, and the whole of the Okement, Lyn and Barnstaple Yeo.

Artificial baits which spin: When fishing for salmon or trout in the Avon (Devon), Axe (Devon), Exe, Dart, Taw and Torridge and Teign districts, use of any artificial bait which spins is restricted to those with only a single, double or treble hook. The width of the hook must not be greater than the spread of the vanes of the bait.

SIZE LIMITS

Length to be measured from tip of the snout to the fork or cleft of the tail.

The size limits, below which fish must be returned, imposed by byelaws are set out in the table below. Riparian owners and fishing associations may impose further restrictions which anglers should familiarize themselves with before fishing.

These size restrictions do not apply to:

(a) Any person who takes any undersized fish unintentionally if he/she at once returns it to the water with as little injury as possible.

(b) Non-migratory trout in any waters included within the Dartmoor National Park, the Exe above Exebridge, the Otter above Langford Bridge, the Torridge above Woodford Bridge, the Mole above Alswear Bridge, the Little Dart above Affeton Bridge and the whole of the Rivers Okement, Lyn and Barnstaple Yeo.

MANDATORY BAG LIMITS

See section on National Byelaws to protect salmon stocks (page 8).

North Wessex Area. The bag limits set out in the table below are imposed by the byelaws, however, some riparian owners or angling associations obtain dispensation to increase their bag limits. Anglers should familiarize themselves with bag limits before fishing. Once a bag limit has been taken, the angler may continue fishing for the same species, provided that any fish caught are returned without injury. Freshwater fish other than grayling, pike and eels may not be permanently removed from the water.

TAW & TORRIDGE

The original size limit and bag limit byelaws introduced following a public enquiry in 1997 expired in September 2001. The Agency has applied to the Department for Environment, Food and Rural Affairs (DEFRA) for these byelaws to be renewed for the 2002 season and remain in place until 2008. Please check with the Devon Area office.

NOTE: Since 1 April 1999, with the introduction of national salmon byelaws, the bag limits apply after 16 June.

MANDATORY BAG LIMITS

RIVER OR AREA	SPECIES	PERIOD		
		24 HOURS	7 DAYS	SEASON
North Wessex	Non-migratory Trout	2	N/A	N/A
	Grayling	2	N/A	N/A
Taw	Salmon	2	3	10
	Migratory Trout	5	15	40
Torridge	Salmon	2	2	7
	Migratory Trout	2	5	20

SIZE LIMITS

AREA, DISTRICT OR CATCHMENT	MIGRATORY TROUT	NON-MIGRATORY TROUT	GRAYLING
Camel, Fowey, Tamar and Plym	18 centimetres	18 centimetres	N/A
Avon (Devon), Axe (Devon), Dart, Exe, Taw & Torridge, Teign	25 centimetres	25 centimetres	N/A
River Lim	N/A	22 centimetres	N/A
North Wessex (except By Brook)	35 centimetres	25 centimetres	25 centimetres
By Brook & tributaries	35 centimetres	20 centimetres	25 centimetres
South Wessex	35 centimetres	25 centimetres	N/A

VOLUNTARY BAG LIMITS

See section on National Byelaws to protect salmon stocks (page 8).

Spring salmon - In addition to the national byelaws, the Agency is encouraging salmon anglers to return any larger salmon, particularly red ones caught later in the season, as these are likely to be multi-sea-winter fish and valuable to the spawning stock. On many rivers a variety of voluntary measures have been adopted to protect fish stocks. All anglers should familiarize themselves with these rules before fishing. Details are provided below.

Rivers Camel/Fowey/Lynher (Cornish limit)

For the above Cornish rivers a maximum of: Salmon- 2/day, 4/week and 10/season. Sea trout- 4/day. Please check with club/association as more stringent rules apply on certain waters.

River Fowey

Fowey River Association: salmon 1/day, 2/week, 5/season. Sea trout 4/day-night. All to be returned in September.

Water quality sampling on the River Avon

River Camel

Same as Cornish limit above. No fishing in April. All sea trout to be returned in September.

River Tamar

Tamar and Tributaries Fisheries Association: 1 salmon/day followed by catch/release. All fish over 10 pounds returned from 1 September. Return red/unseasonable fish.

River Tavy

Tavy, Walkham and Plym Fishing Club: 1 salmon/day, return of all hen fish, limited fishing methods.

Rivers Plym, Tavy

Plymouth and District Freshwater Angling Association: 1 salmon/day, 3/season; 3 sea trout/day/night.

River Exe

River Exe and Tributaries Association: After 16 Aug salmon of 27.5" or over (8 pounds) to be returned unless injured, in which event, the next salmon caught **under** size limit to be returned. Red or coloured fish to be returned, no fishing by prawn or shrimp in September.

River Teign

Lower Teign Fishing Association: 4 sea trout/24 hours.

River Otter

All salmon to be returned. One mature sea trout and two school peal/season.

River Axe

Axe Fly Fishers: Catch and release only for salmon. Fly only.

River Avon (Hants)

Avon and Stour Riparian Owners and Wessex Salmon Rivers Trust. Catch and release only for salmon. No worm fishing.

Several river associations had not held their AGM prior to going to print. Please check with local club secretary for any voluntary measures that may have been agreed for other rivers before fishing.

CATCH AND RELEASE

With stocks of salmon under increasing pressure, the Environment Agency is seeking to do everything possible to protect the species for the future.

Catch and release is now becoming an established management technique for increasing spawning escapement, particularly where stocks are low. Salmon anglers are encouraged to consider this approach as a means of safeguarding salmon stocks in our rivers.

If you do decide to practice catch and release, the following guidelines may be useful to give your catch the best chance of surviving after you have returned it to the river:

Hooks - single hooks inflict less damage than doubles or trebles, barbless hooks are best. Flatten the barbs on your hooks with pliers.

Playing Fish - fish are best landed before complete exhaustion and therefore all elements of tackle should be strong enough to allow them to be played firmly.

Landing Fish - Fish should be netted and unhooked in the water, if possible. Use knotless nets - not a tailer or gaff.

Handling and Unhooking - Make every effort to keep the fish in the water. Wet your hands. Carefully support the fish out of water. Do not hold the fish up by the tail, this may cause kidney damage. Remove the hook gently - if necessary, cut the line if deeply hooked. Take extra care with spring fish, as they are more susceptible to damage and fungal infection.

Do not under any circumstances keep a fish which is to be returned out of the water for more than 30 seconds. Physiological changes affecting survival begin within one minute.

Reviving the Fish - Support an exhausted fish underwater in an upright position facing the current. Estimate weight and length in the water. Avoid weighing. Handle the fish as little as possible. Be patient and give it time to recover and swim away on its own.

TESCO SWAP A SALMON SCHEME

An arrangement, originally negotiated with Tesco for the Hampshire Avon, by Wessex Salmon Rivers Trust, entitles an angler catching and returning a salmon after 16 June to a voucher to be exchanged for a farmed salmon. This scheme now applies to other rivers as follows: Frome, Dart, Teign, Camel, Fowey, Tavy, Lynher, Plym, Otter and Fal. Contact your local fisheries office for further details.

WILD TROUT SOCIETY

Anglers are asked to return all brown trout caught on the East Dart above Postbridge, on the Cherry Brook and the Blackbrook; while on the West Dart between Blackbrook and Swincombe they are to return fish between 10" and 16" long.

USE OF OTHER TACKLE

Use of float. The use of a float when fishing for salmon or trout in any waters within the Avon (Devon), Axe (Devon), Dart, Exe, Taw and Torridge, and Teign districts is prohibited.

Use of gaff. See section on national byelaws Phase 1.

Limit on number of rods in use. See section on national byelaws Phase 1.

Prohibition of use of lead weights. No person shall use any instrument on which is attached directly or indirectly any lead weight (except a weight of 0.06 grams or less, or one of more than 28.35 grams) for the purpose of taking salmon, trout, freshwater fish or eels in any waters within the Agency's region.

Prohibited Fishing Area - Kilbury Weir. It is illegal to take or attempt to take by any means any fish in any waters within 50 yards below the crest of Kilbury Weir on the River Dart.

LANDING NETS, KEEPNETS AND KEEPSACKS

A new national byelaw was introduced on 1 April 1998 making it illegal to use landing nets with knotted meshes or meshes of metallic material.

Similarly keepnets should not be constructed of such materials or have holes in the mesh larger than 25mm internal circumference; or be less than 2.0 metres in length. Supporting rings or frames should not be greater than 40cm apart (excluding the distance from the top frame to the first supporting ring or frame) or less than 120cm in circumference.

Keepsacks should be constructed of a soft, dark coloured, non-abrasive, water permeable fabric and should not have dimensions less than 120cm by 90cm if rectangular, or 150cm by 30cm by 40cm if used with a frame or designed with the intention that a frame be used. It is an offence to retain more than one fish in a single keepsack at any time.

The retention of salmonids (adults or juveniles) in keepnets is illegal except when specially approved by the Agency for collecting broodstock.

THEFT ACT

The Theft Act 1968, Schedule 1, makes it an offence for anyone to take or attempt to take fish in private waters or in a private fishery without the consent of the owner.

The Agency may bring a prosecution under this Act on its own fisheries. It cannot do so on behalf of an individual, and any fishery owner who wishes such a prosecution to be brought should consult the police or a solicitor.

ATTENTION

SALMON AND SEA TROUT ANGLERS

Your catch return is needed by 1 January each year. Nil returns are also required. Send returns to:

Environment Agency, FREEPOST, P.O. Box 60, Patchway, Bristol, BS12 4YY.

NATIONAL BYELAWS

A number of national byelaws are now in place. These replace or modify regional byelaws that existed before.

A summary of the national byelaws is given below.

Phase I

1. The annual close season for fishing for rainbow trout by rod and line in all reservoirs, lakes and ponds has been dispensed with.

2. A close season for brown trout is to be retained on all waters.

3. Use of the gaff is prohibited at all times when fishing for salmon, trout and freshwater fish or freshwater eels.

4. The number of rods that may be used at any time is as follows:

a. One rod when fishing for salmonids in rivers, streams, drains and canals.

b. Two rods when fishing for salmonids in reservoirs, lakes and ponds (subject to local rules).

c. Up to four rods when fishing for coarse fish and eels (subject to local rules).

When fishing with multiple rods and lines, rods shall not be left unattended and shall be placed such that the distance between the butts of the end rods does not exceed three metres.

5. Catch returns for salmon and migratory trout should be submitted no later than 1 January in the following year.

6. See separate section on landing nets, keepnets and keepsacks.

Phase II

1. Crayfish of any species whether alive or dead, or parts thereof may not be used as bait for salmon, trout, freshwater fish or eels.

2. Livebait may only be retained and used at the water they were taken from.

3. All salmon, migratory trout or trout, hooked other than in the mouth or throat, shall be returned immediately to any river, stream, drain or canal.

4. The byelaw limiting the length of a rod to not less than 1.5 metres (that may be used in North or South Wessex) has been revoked.

5. A rod and line with its bait or hook in the water must not be left unattended or so the licence holder is unable at any time to take or exercise sufficient control over the rod and line.

COARSE FISH CLOSE SEASON ON CANALS

In March 2000 a new National byelaw removed the close season for coarse fish on canals within the region, with the exception of the Glastonbury Canal which is an open system with the South Drain.

FISH WITH ADIPOSE FINS REMOVED

As indicated on your rod licence, you may catch a fish from which the adipose fin has been completely removed. (These may carry a micro tag implanted within their nose - invisible to you.)

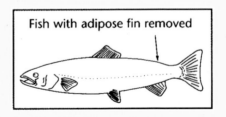

Fish with adipose fin removed

If this occurs, you should follow the licence instructions.

Any fish caught before 16 June without an adipose fin should be returned and reported to your local fisheries office.

* Dial 100 and ask the operator for FREEPHONE FISHWATCH. You will be put through to the Cardiff office where you should ask for the National Salmon Centre.
* Tell us your name, address and telephone number.
* Record details of your catch (where, when, size and species of fish).
* If the fish is caught after 16 June, keep the fish (or just the head) frozen if necessary and we will contact you to make arrangements for it to be inspected.

We will pay you a reward of £5 if it carries a micro tag and, of course, you keep the fish.

Details should be sent to the appropriate Area Fisheries Office.

PURCHASE AND RELEASE OF SALMON FROM LICENSED NETS

In recent years, the Wessex Salmon Rivers Trust has purchased salmon from the Mudeford nets for release to the Hampshire Avon as extra spawners to help boost stock recovery rates. Arrangements for the 2002 season are still under consideration.

Similar schemes have also operated on the rivers Tamar, Tavy, Lynher and Fowey, funded by a variety of sponsors including the Tamar and Tributaries Fisheries Association, Maristowe Estate and South West Water.

STOCKING FISH -
BUYER BEWARE

The Environment Agency has produced a free leaflet entitled "Buyer Beware - Your guide to stocking fish". The leaflet explains the Agency rules on fish introduction (Section 30, Salmon and Freshwater Fisheries Act 1975) and the common sense things fishery owners can do to protect themselves and their fisheries when buying/stocking fish.

Before introducing (stocking) any fish (or fish spawn) into inland waters, you must obtain written consent of the Agency. Failure to meet this obligation is a criminal offence and could lead to prosecution, with a fine of up to £2,500. In addition, the stocking of non-native species such as Wels Catfish or Grass Carp requires DEFRA approval under the Import of Live Fish Act - Prohibition of Keeping or Release of Live Fish Order 1998.

Mandatory health checks will be required where fish are to be moved into rivers, streams, drains or canals, or where the risk to other fisheries is high.

Health checks will not normally be required in waters where the risk of fish escape is minimal (e.g. enclosed waters). However, there may be occasions where the Agency will still insist on a health examination.

Regardless of the Agency's requirement for health checks, it should be stressed that establishing the health of fish before any stocking is essential. The Agency encourages everyone to follow the Agency's "Buyer Beware" code. Copies of the leaflet can be obtained from any of the Agency's Fisheries Offices.

LOOK OUT! - LOOK UP!
ADVICE ON SAFE FISHING NEAR OVERHEAD ELECTRIC POWER LINES

Several people have died and others have been seriously injured whilst using fishing rods and poles near overhead electric power lines. The following advice is designed to prevent these events recurring:

i   Because rods and poles conduct electricity, they are particularly dangerous when used near overhead electric power lines. Remember that electricity can jump gaps and a rod does not even have to touch an electric line to cause a lethal current to flow.

ii   Many overhead electric power lines are supported by wood poles which can be and are mistaken for telegraph poles. These overhead lines may carry electricity up to 132,000 volts, and have been involved in many of the accidents that have occurred.

iii   The height of high voltage overhead electric power lines can be as low as 5.2 metres and they are therefore within easy reach of a rod or pole. Remember that overhead lines may not be readily visible from the ground. They may be concealed by hedges or by a dark background. Make sure you **"Look Out"** and **"Look Up"** to check for overhead lines before you tackle up and begin fishing.

iv In general, the minimum safe fishing distance from an overhead electric power line is 30 metres from the overhead line (measured along the ground).

v When pegging out for matches or competitions, organisers and competitors should, in general, ensure that no peg is nearer to an overhead electric power line than 30 metres (measured along the ground).

vi For further advice on safe fishing at specific locations, contact your local Electricity Company.

vii Finally, remember that it is dangerous for any object to get too close to overhead electric power lines, particularly if the object is an electrical conductor, e.g. lead cored fishing line, damp fishing line, rod or pole.

ENVIRONMENT AGENCY AREAS

Devon Area

Fishery Districts (Rivers in parentheses):

Avon (Avon, Erme); Axe (Axe, Sid, Otter); Dart (Dart); Exe (Exe); Taw and Torridge (Taw, Torridge, Lyn); Teign (Teign). The River Lim is included in the Devon Area.

Cornwall Area

Fishery Districts (Rivers in parentheses):

Camel (Camel, other streams flowing into the sea on the North coast between Marshland Mouth and Lands End); Fowey (Fowey, East and West Looe, Seaton, Tresillian, other streams flowing into the sea on the South coast between Lands End and Rame Head); Tamar and Plym (Tamar, Lynher, Plym, Tavy and Yealm).

North Wessex Area

River Catchments:

Bristol Avon (including all tributaries), Axe (Somerset), Brue, Parrett, Tone, Yeo and all other rivers, drains and streams flowing into the Bristol Channel between Avonmouth and Foreland Point.

South Wessex Area

River Catchments:

Hampshire Avon (including all tributaries), Stour (including all tributaries), Dorset Frome, Piddle, Wey, Brit and Char and all other streams flowing into the sea between Christchurch Harbour and Charmouth.

ROD LICENCE

IN ORDER TO FISH FOR SALMON, TROUT (INCLUDING MIGRATORY TROUT), FRESHWATER FISH AND EELS IN ANY* WATERS IN THE SOUTH WEST REGION, ANGLERS WILL NEED AN ENVIRONMENT AGENCY NATIONAL ROD LICENCE AND PERMISSION FROM THE OWNER OF THE FISHERY.

ANGLERS MUST CARRY THEIR ROD LICENCES WITH THEM AT ALL TIMES WHILE FISHING.

* Except in waters where a General Licence is in force - please check with the owner of the fishery in advance.

The Agency's fisheries patrol vessel Nemesis.

ENVIRONMENT AGENCY

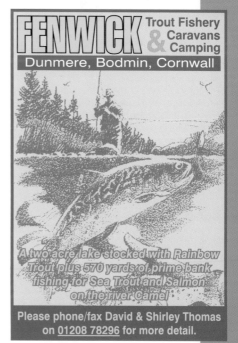

Grayling in the South West

Mike Weaver

A cool wind was blowing down the River Barle on that March day a quarter of a century ago. Around midday the trout had come to the surface and several good fish had taken my dry fly but by mid afternoon the surface activity had ceased and I was ready to call it a day. Then, as my fly drifted down a smooth run, I saw a shadow move up beneath it and drift back with the current for several feet before delicately taking the fly. My strike met a solid resistance and, as I saw the large upright dorsal fin holding the current, I realised that I was into my first grayling since coming to live in Devon. Two more casts produced two more grayling, both close to a pound, and I was reminded of something that I had learned on many other waters - grayling are shoal fish and like the company of other grayling.

Before moving to Devon some 30 years ago I had fished regularly for grayling on the rivers of the Welsh Marches and the chalk streams of Wessex, so I was pleased to re-establish my acquaintance with this lovely fish on the Barle. Grayling are not indigenous to the south west, but arrived as part of the fashion for extending the range of the species through artificial stocking that started in the late nineteenth century. In Devon and Cornwall the grayling is found in two river systems, the Exe and the Tamar, but its distribution is often patchy and unpredictable so locating the grayling hot spots can depend heavily on luck.

I recall an early spring day on the Ottery in Cornwall when I was fishing for trout on the topmost of the Arundell Arms beats. Conditions looked ideal for trout and fish were soon coming to my dry fly - a size 16 Adams. However, those rising fish were grayling with the trout strangely absent and when I called it a day I had caught 15 grayling and just one solitary trout. Since then I have fished that beat many times but failed to catch another grayling, though I have taken plenty further down the Ottery.

A similar experience occurred on another Arundell Arms beat, this time on the Lew. Once again it was spring and with nothing rising I was steadily catching trout on a weighted Hare's Ear Nymph. As I approached a small pool, I saw a swirl in the shallows at the tail and when my nymph dropped into the steam near the fish it was taken instantly and I had soon netted a lovely grayling of 14 inches. Two more grayling of the same size quickly followed, but I have never taken a grayling from the Lew since that spring day.

My most consistent sport with grayling on the Tamar system has been on the main river itself, especially in the Polson Bridge area. There I have often found shoals of rising grayling and settled down to picking them off with a small dry fly.

My most consistent sport on a Devon river has been on the lower Exe, where the grayling are of good average size and rise well on the right day - and the ideal day is when there is hardly a breath of wind. This is an exposed stretch of river and the surface is easily whipped up by the wind, making it difficult to spot the delicate rises of the grayling. On a calm day, however, you can locate big shoals of grayling sipping on the smooth stretches and enjoy first-rate dry fly fishing.

It is in Wessex, on the River Avon in the Woodford Valley between Amesbury and Salisbury, that I have taken some of my biggest catches of grayling, especially when nymphing in October and November. On a sunny autumn day when it has been possible to spot the fish in the clear water, stalking the grayling can be both productive and exciting. The trick is to locate a shoal against a patch of light-coloured

Game

gravel, which makes it possible to spot each fish and see it take your weighted nymph. By starting with the fish at the downstream end of the shoal and pulling each fish quickly downstream as soon as it is hooked, it is possible to take several grayling before the shoal is spooked. Those Avon grayling may not be the biggest, but there are plenty of them.

For big grayling, there are few better places than the Frome below Dorchester, where fish of well over two pounds are common. Permits for the Dorchester Fishing Club are restricted to the trout season but that gives you plenty of opportunity to catch the big grayling on this fishery. I recall fishing a clear pool where a big shoal of grayling up to over three pounds could be seen lying in about four feet of water. A heavily-weighted shrimp pattern was cast well upstream and allowed to drift through the shoal, with spectacular results. The first cast produced a "tiddler" of little more than a pound, but it was quickly followed by two fish of 2¾ pounds each, and another of the same size for my companion. It is in the winter, when club members fish with bait, that some of the really big Frome grayling of well over three pounds are caught.

In the south west, grayling are also present in the Bristol Avon, Tone, Brue and Stour, but I have yet to fish for them on these rivers.

Tackle and techniques for grayling fishing are really the same as those for river trout fishing. When the fish are rising I sometimes use the traditional grayling patterns like a Red Tag, Bradshaw's Fancy or Grayling Witch, with their brightly-coloured tags, but the more imitative flies that are normally used for trout are just as effective. On the chalk streams, where sight fishing with a weighted nymph is very effective, a size 12 or 14 leaded shrimp or a goldhead Hare's Ear Nymph will usually do the trick.

In the past, the grayling has often been loathed by those who manage our more famous trout streams and great efforts made to remove what has been seen as an unwelcome interloper. Fortunately, such efforts were always doomed to fail, as the grayling is a great survivor, and in recent years more and more anglers have come to realise its true value as worthy adversary for the fly fisherman. If you have yet to catch one of these beautiful fish, you have a treat in store.

Mike Weaver with a superb Grayling

PREMIER RAINBOW FISHERIES

KENNICK - Nr Christow, Devon.
Permits: Self Service Kiosk
Season: 23 March - 31 October
Best Flies: Black Gnat/Montana/Damsel Nymph
Biggest Fish 1997: 10lb 14oz Rainbow.
Information: (01647) 277587
WIMBLEBALL LAKE - Nr Dulverton, Somerset.
Permits: Self Service at Hill Farm Barn
Season: 23 March - 31 October
Best Flies: Montana/Soldier Palmer/Buzzer.
Biggest Fish: 10lb 12oz Rainbow.
Information: Office hours (01398) 371372
SIBLYBACK LAKE - Nr Liskeard, Cornwall.
Permits: Self Service Kiosk at Watersports Centre
Season: 23 March - 31 October
Best Flies: Viva/Black & Peacock/Montana
Information: Ranger (01579) 342366

PREMIER BROWN TROUT FISHERY

ROADFORD - Nr Okehampton, Devon.
Permits: Angling and Watersports Centre at Lower
Goodacre.
Season: 23 March - 12 October
Biggest Fish: 8lb 4oz Brown.
Information: (01409) 211514

BROWN TROUT BOAT FISHERY

TOTTIFORD - Nr Christow, Devon
BOAT ONLY
Permits: Kennick self service
Season: 15 March - 12 October
Information: (01647) 277587

INTERMEDIATE RAINBOW TROUT

STITHIANS - Nr Redruth, Cornwall.
Permits:
Stithians Watersports Centre (01209) 860301.
Sandy's Store, 7 Penryn St, Redruth (01209) 214877
Season: 15 March - 12 October
Information: Ranger (01579) 342366
WISTLANDPOUND - Nr Sth Molton, Devon.
Permits:
Post Office in Challacombe (01598) 763229.
The Kingfisher, Barnstaple (01271) 344919.
Lyndale News, Combe Martin (01271) 883283.
Variety Sports, Ilfracombe (01271) 862039.
Season: 15 March - 12 October
Information: Ranger (01288) 321262

LOW COST RAINBOW & BROWN

BURRATOR - Nr Yelverton, Devon.
Permits: Esso Garage, Yelverton.
Season: 15 March - 12 October
Information: (01837) 871565
COLLIFORD LAKE - Nr Bodmin, Cornwall.
Permits: Colliford Tavern.
Season: 15 March - 12 October
Information: Ranger (01579) 342366
FERNWORTHY LAKE - Nr Chagford, Devon.
Permits: Self Service Kiosk
Season: 1 April - 12 October
Best Flies: Black Gnat/Invicta/G&H Sedge
Information: (01837) 871565

FREE TROUT FISHING

MELDON - Nr Okehampton, Devon.
Free to holders of a valid E.A. Rod Licence and is
zoned into spinning, bait and fly.
Season: 15 March - 12 October
AVON DAM - South Brent, Devon.
Angling by spinning, fly or bait and is free to valid
E.A. licence holders.
Season: 15 March - 12 October
VENFORD - Nr Ashburton, Devon.
Free to holders of valid E.A. Rod Licence and can
be fished by spinning, bubble float and bait.
Season: 15 March - 12 October.
CROWDY RESERVOIR - Nr Camelford, Cornwall.
Free to holders of valid E.A. Rod Licence.
Season: 15 March - 12 October.

Success!

for the South West Rivers Association's partnership with the North Atlantic Salmon Fund

Michael Charleston
Secretary of the South West Rivers Association.

My forecast last year that the annual mass slaughter of European salmon by Irish drift nets would soon be greatly reduced was thought in some quarters to be too optimistic. For over three years, I was told, our Ministry of Agriculture had been pressing the Irish to spare these mixed stocks of salmon returning to several European countries - and had got nowhere.

So it is good to be able this year to report that my hopes have been vindicated. Quite suddenly on January 10th, after much delay and a great deal of international pressure, Ireland's Fisheries Minister, Frank Fahey, announced major restrictions on the drift nets. Up to now over 700 boats have been allowed to lay 700 kilometres of nets in the path of shoals of salmon returning from the North Atlantic feeding grounds to the rivers of several countries.

It could be the conservation breakthrough we have all wanted. If they are allowed to complete their migratiory journeys many of these salmon will return to our rivers. The rest will head for the many rivers of Ireland, Dorset, Hampshire, Wales, France, Spain and Germany. Mr Fahey plans to reduce the average catch by 40% and his officials calculate this will save the lives of nearly 80,000 fish. He is basing this on an official estimate that between 1997-2000 the drift nets took an average of 195,000 fish annually.

We think the results will be much better than that. In May last year I was a member of an international delegation from the North Atlantic Salmon Fund that went to Ireland. In Dublin some of the netsmen told me there had been a 50% under-declaration. If that is so, the average drift net catch in those years was actually about 300,000 fish .

The fishermen also say that there are now so many seals off the Irish coast that half the salmon that get enmeshed in the nets are eaten or ruined before the fish can be brought on board the boats. If that is so (when one takes the under-declaration into account, too) the number of salmon that actually died in the nets was well over 400,000. With stocks at the lowest levels ever known that is an enormous number to lose. The adverse effects on our rivers and those of our friends on the continent are obvious.

The Irish have now introduced a tagging scheme and it is illegal for anybody to be in possession of an untagged salmon. If Mr Fahey restricts the catch to 117,000 tagged salmon and if my arithmetic is correct, he may actually be saving the lives of perhaps 300,000 salmon. And it could get even better! The Minister said he will reduce the number of nets and that he will contribute to local set-aside schemes to compensate netsmen who give up salmon fishing for a year or more. Again, the effect on our rivers, this time wholly beneficial, needs little imagination!

That international NASF delegation last May can fairly claim to have changed the Irish Government's mind. Led by NASF's chairman, OrriVigfusson, we persuaded Mr Fahey's advisers, the Irish National Salmon Commission, that their huge drift net catch had to be greatly reduced if stocks were to survive..

If Whitehall had really been trying to do this for three years the civil servants will be amazed to learn it took the NASF delegation only only a

A pupil of Alex Henderson casting a double handed Salmon rod on the Torridge.

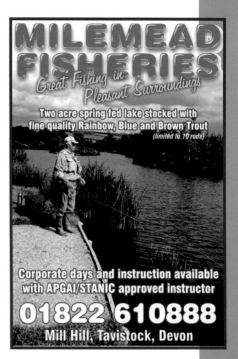

couple of hours. Orri talked the Irish Salmon Commission into passing an unanimous resolution advising their Minister to reduce commercial mixed stock fishing to a level that would protect salmon stocks for the future. The first cuts will be imposed this year so the benefits should be immediate.

Most of the credit must go to Orri Vigfusson, the Icelander who devotes so much of his life to trying to save the salmon. When the location of the salmon's northern feeding grounds were discovered in the 1980s the fishermen of Greenland and the Faroes began to catch vast numbers. Orri's first conservation campaigns stopped all that by offering fair compensation for those who give up commercial salmon fishing. In the last twelve months NASF has reached similar agreements that will end all English and Welsh drift netting. About 50,000 salmon a year were being netted off North East England and in the Bristol Channel. In addition, the Northern Ireland Assembly voted £1.5 million to partner NASF in ending salmon fishing off the coasts of the Six Counties. Nearer home Orri helped North Devon anglers to persuade most of the Taw and Torridge netsmen that they should stop fishing in return for compensation.

In much of this work, Orri Vigfusson has had the backing and practical help of the South West Rivers Association. In return he has consented to become the SWRA's Patron. Perhaps his greatest achievement last year was to convince almost all the drift net fishermen of Ireland that they would destroy their own fishery if they continued the slaughter. With their backing, Orri is determined to battle on. He hopes to persuade the Irish Government to follow the example of all other nations and end mixed stock salmon netting by partnering NASF in a complete buyout of the Irish drift nets.

Orri Vigfusson will be speaking at the SWRA's annual general meeting at the Arundell Arms Hotel, Lifton, on Saturday, April. 6. Why not come to hear this remarkable man who has been called the living saint of salmon conservation? All anglers are welcome.

The SWRA is the regional voice of the 17 rivers associations of Devon and Cornwall. For more information and a newsletter phone me at 01822 853293 or e-mail: mwcharl@aol.com

West Country Federation of Fly Fishers

Fish for England by Lake and River

The WCFFF provides eligible adults with a yearly chance to fly fish for England. Qualifiers from Devon and Cornwall compete in the National Championships aiming to be in England's international squad for the following year. The competitions are against Ireland, Scotland and Wales in events called the Home Internationals. This is fishing to International Rules on either rivers or by boat on stillwaters.

2002 Rivers eliminator:
River Teign Sunday 28 April.

2002 Loch Style eliminator:
Wimbleball Lake Sunday 26 May.

Both eliminators are routes into England's European and World Teams.

The WCFFF also runs an annual informal, make a new friend, event by boat and bank. This year, Wimbleball on Sunday 25 August. Everyone welcome. Arrive around 9 am.

Put your name on the mailing lists for the eliminators!

Contact Peter Page (Chairman WCFFF), Woodlands House, Woodland, Ashburton TQ13 7LN Tel/Fax 01364 654395; Email: PetePageUK@aol.com

Westcountry Rivers Trust

WRT at the Royal Cornwall Show.

Objective One Funding Heralds New Era for Cornwall Fisheries!

The Rivers Trust team has settled in well to the Trust's office headquarters at Lifton (opposite the Arundell Arms Hotel). The Trust has also opened a new Department of Fish & Wildlife for 2002 led by Simon Evans (Head of Fisheries) and Dr Dylan Bright (Head of Research). Although important project work continues on a number of Devon rivers including the Taw, Torridge, Tamar, Dart, Exe, Tale (Otter) and Axe a large part of the Trusts resources will now focus on Cornwall.

Cornwall Rivers Project

After a lengthy application process under the new EU Objective One structural funds now available in Cornwall, the Westcountry Rivers Trust is delighted to announce an exciting new three year partnership project- The Cornwall Rivers Project.

The new innovative project builds on previous work by the Rivers Trust and will contribute to key Objective One themes:

To increase absolute prosperity

To support agricultural adjustment

To support communities faced with change; and

To enhance regional distinctiveness

The 3 year £1.8 million river and fisheries restoration and rehabilitation project for Cornwall will include work on the rivers: Ottery, Inny, Lynher, Fowey, Camel, East & West Looe, Seaton, Neet & Strat, Fal and Cober. This exciting project will give a real boost to angling opportunities in the Duchy and will focus on increasing juvenile recruitment through water quality and habitat improvements, including reducing soil erosion and sediments, optimising farm inputs and river- bank fencing. The project team will be working closely with farmers and angling clubs to achieve the targeted outputs which include the production of around 700 integrated Farm & River Plans covering some 40,000 hectares and erection of over 100 kilometres of riverbank fencing. The project will also seek to improve access for anglers, particularly the disabled and encourage new entrants to angling as well as raising awareness of the importance of our rivers and their wildlife. Cornwall Rivers Project partners, collaborators and supporters include: EU, Government Office South West, DEFRA, Royal Holloway Institute for Environmental Research, BDB Associates, Environment Agency, Pennon, SWW, Imerys and County Environment Trust (to be confirmed).

The Trust will be fundraising in Cornwall over the next few years to provide matching funds to draw down the all important European grant to deliver this ambitious project. So please help by joining the Trust as a Supporter, or why not consider running an event yourself to raise funds.

Angling 2000- building on success!

For 2002 the Westcountry Rivers Trust's Angling 2000 flexible day permit scheme expands into Cornwall with a new choice of hitherto un-fished beats. Further beats are expected to enter the scheme throughout the summer. Farmers and both local and visiting anglers have all benefited from the Angling 2000 scheme during 2001 where beats were mainly concentrated on the Trusts former project areas on the Tamar and Taw Torridge tributaries. Notable catches included a wild 4 lbs 8 oz brown trout from beat 11, two sea trout of 5 lbs 8 oz and 6 lbs 8 oz on beat 10, sixteen wild brownies

G Smith with a 6lb 10oz Salmon caught from the Taw in August last year on beat five. Eggesford Hotel

between 9 and 16 inches from beat 8 and a 6lb 4oz escapee rainbow that surprised an angler on beat 9. As well as offering angling access to some wonderful natural stretches of river it has also provided a welcome boost to farm incomes and a number of farm B&B's in each area adding value and extending the season. Anglers can buy books of ticket tokens from the Rivers Trust or from local tackle shops and then using the Angling 2000 booklet select a beat to fish for salmon, sea trout or grayling.

Once at their chosen location the angler leaves the appropriate number of tokens in the collection box next to the parking area and proceeds to fish the waters. The income from the scheme goes mainly to the farmers or beat owners with a small amount retained by the trust to contribute to printing and marketing expenses. Angling 2000 allows farmers and riparian owners to get a modest income from their river beats and helps provide a return for the effort they have put into on farm river restoration and fisheries improvement. Angling 2000 also provides local opportunities for youngsters and others to fish in their parish through the controlled access offered by the scheme as well as valuable diversification opportunities for on farm and other local farm based tourism enterprises.

For details of the Angling 2000 scheme and beats for 2002 contact: Simon Evans on 01566-784488.

Your support is vital

To continue it's important work improving fisheries and helping rivers, wildlife and communities in the region, the Trust needs your help. You can join the Westcountry Rivers Trust as a "Supporter" for £50 a year (less that £1 per week). In return the Trust will send you its Newsletter and invitations to its events, river walks and other activities including "Angling 2000".

Please ring or write for your free information pack. You can also find out more about the work of the Trust and talk to our Scientific Team at the Westcountry Rivers Trust stand at the Devon County Show, Royal Cornwall Show and the Cornwall & Devon Countryman's Fair, we look forward to seeing you there!

For further information please contact:

Westcountry Rivers Trust,
Fore Street, Lifton, Devon, PL16 0AA
Telephone: 01566-784488
Fax: 01566-784404
Web address: www.wrt.org.uk
E-mail: wrt@wrt.org.uk

Trout Fishing in the South Wessex Area

By Matt Carter

Rivers

The South Wessex Area encompasses many 'chalk streams' which are nationally famous for fly-fishing for trout. These include the Upper Avon at Salisbury and associated tributaries, the Rivers Frome, Piddle and River Allen a tributary of the River Stour.

Fishing access to these waters is generally controlled by local owners, estates, syndicates and in a limited way by local angling clubs.

Many of these waters are currently stocked with brown trout, however several fisheries are now turning away from this to catch and release, promoting natural production and 'wilder' fish populations. Further details regarding access are given in this guide.

Stillwaters

There are several stillwater 'put and take' fisheries spread across this area. These are generally stocked with rainbow trout although a few specialise in brown trout.

In the north of the area good stillwater fly fishing can be found at Steeple Langford Fisheries near Salisbury. In the West of the area good fly fishing can be found at the Wessex Chalk streams Ltd site near Tolpuddle.

Other notable fisheries can be found at Damerham and Rockford near Ringwood.

The assistant manager about to release a 20lb Rainbow - someone is going to be lucky! Manningford

The Salmon & Trout Association

Guardians of Game Fishing since 1903

exists to protect an endangered species...You!

Trout, sea trout and salmon fishing are under threat from all directions. Can game angling survive? Can the game angler survive?

That's up to us - and to you.

S&TA achievements

Developed the machinery to monitor applications to abstract water or make discharges.

Spoke for anglers in the campaign which abolished the open-ended right to abstract water.

Persuaded the Government to review outdated fisheries legislation.

Marshalled the views of 13 leading angling organisations into a set of major proposals to the Government's Fisheries Review.

As a result, the Government has allocated £750,000 towards the buy-out of the north-east drift nets.

Successfully resisted the proposal to allow access to the waterside by all and sundry.

Set up a countrywide programme to introduce young people to the joys of fly fishing.

Our priorities for the future.

Better control of fish-eating birds.

Force the Scottish Executive to recognize the damage caused by sea lice and bring salmon farming under independent legislation.

Ensure that the Government acts on the key recommendations of its Fisheries Review, including:

To properly fund the Environment Agency's fisheries programmes.

To assist in the buy-outs of all remaining salmon nets in the UK and Ireland.

Successfully fight the game angler's corner in the competition for water and the waterside.

During 2002, expand and encourage the number of youngsters and other newcomers introduced to the sport by our fly fishing courses and follow-up initiatives.

Why the S&TA needs your support

The Government and other bodies recognise the S&TA as the voice of game angling - and the more members we have, the more we'll be listened to.

Members' subscriptions pay for vital fact-finding, publicity and lobbying.

The threats to game angling are real and game anglers must speak with a united voice.

S&TA is also leading the work of the National Angling Alliance in providing a robust and unified voice for all anglers.

Together we can make the difference.

For further information on membership please contact Debbie Creasy on 020 7283 5838.

www.salmon-trout.org

Local Contact details:
Bristol & West
Mr JS Tennant, Littlefield, The Village, Burrington, Bristol BS40 7AD
01761 462947 (h) 01275 852143 (w)

Wessex
Mr T Atkinson Willow Cottage, 1 Tolbury Mill, Bruton, Somerset, BA10 0DY
Tel: 01749 813699

Somerset
Mr DJ Greenshields, Park Farm, Wellington, Somerset TA21 9NP Tel: 01823 663409

North Devon
Lt Col D Michie, The Round House, Webber Hill Farm, Sampford Courtnay, Okehampton EX20 2RU Tel: 01837 54698

South & East Devon & Tamar
Mr C Hall, Higher Sticklepath Farm, Belstone, Okehampton, Devon, EX20 1RD
Tel: 01837 840420

Cornwall
Mr A Hawken, 5 Meadow Close, St Stephen, St Austell, Cornwall, PL26 7PE
Tel: 01726 822343. Fax: 01726 824175

or come and meet us at the following shows:
16th-18th May: Devon County Show, Exeter
29th May-1st June:
Royal Bath & West Show, Shepton Mallet
6th-8th June:
The Royal Cornwall Show, Wadebridge
For further information phone 020 7283 5838
www.salmon-trout.org

Steve Burt of Torquay with a nicely conditioned 11lb 12oz Rainbow. Watercress

FOSFELLE

COUNTRY HOUSE HOTEL

A 17th Century Manor House set in six acres of peaceful surroundings.

Fully Licenced - Excellent Cuisine

Trout and Coarse Fishing at The Hotel

HARTLAND, BIDEFORD, DEVON.

TEL: 01237 441273

Game

~HIGHBULLEN~
~ Country House Hotel ~

CHITTLEHAMHOLT, N. DEVON
Telephone: 01769 540561

OVER 6 MILES OF SALMON, SEA TROUT & WILD BROWN TROUT FISHING...

.. on the rivers Taw and Mole.

Easily accessible beats set in totally unspoilt countryside with an abundance of wildlife. Ghillie & tuition available.

Pre book for professional tuition with Roddie Rae.

55 Salmon caught in 2000!

Indoor and outdoor heated pools, outdoor and INDOOR tennis. Squash, croquet, billiards, sauna, steam room, sunbed, massage.

UNLIMITED FREE GOLF ON our 18 holes, par 68 golf course (Resident Professional).

*Secluded yet marvellous views *Highly rated Restaurant *45 En Suite bedrooms *In all the impartial Hotel Guides *4 Crowns Highly Commended. *Rates from £75 pppn including dinner, breakfast, service.

www.highbullen.co.uk   Email: info@highbullen.co.uk

29

The Wessex Salmon and Rivers Trust

Michael Twitchen

A fisherman at the start of the 21st Century who wants to catch a Salmon weighing over 30lbs will probably dream of visiting the wild torrents of Norway or the midnight sun lit rivers of Russia's Arctic Circle. Forty years ago a fisherman could almost have guaranteed a 30lbs salmon with a two hour drive from London to Hampshire's River Avon.

During most of the 20th Century the Hampshire Avon, Dorset Stour and Dorset Frome produced a race of immense salmon the equal of any river in the world. Today, all that remains of these great fish is a remnant population and memories.

The objective of the Wessex Salmon and Rivers Trust is to restore the salmon populations of these Wessex Rivers to their former glory. To appreciate the greatness we have lost, we need to look back at the catch records of these three rivers in their heydays the middle of the 20th Century.

The Avon's largest rod caught salmon weighed 49½lbs and was captured by Mr G M Howard spinning on the Royalty fishery in 1952. In 1951 he had a 41½lb and a 41lb salmon also from the Royalty fishery. The average weight of rod caught salmon reached 23lbs in some years. The late Sir John Mills, the owner of Bisterne Fishery on the Avon caught 310 Avon salmon during his life, of which two weighed 40lbs, three weighed 38lbs and 25 other fish weighed over 30lbs.

The Dorset Stour's salmon fishing was at its best at the old Throop weir and was largely ruined by dredging of the river for land drainage. The Stour's record fish weighed 48½lbs.

The most Westerly of these three rivers is the Dorset Frome. The size of its salmon in past years is reflected by the catches of Mr R C Hardy-Corfe who took seven Frome salmon of over 40lbs including one of 48½lbs.

Today these three rivers are mere shadows of their past greatness. The Stour has no rod catch of salmon although a handful of fish may run the river, the Avon yields maybe 30 to 50 salmon per year to rod fisherman and the Frome slightly more.

How did such a great angling resource and such a noble race of large salmon become reduced to such a pitiful remnant? There are many views, theories and vested interests wishing to avoid responsibility. All Atlantic salmon rivers in Europe and America have seen reductions in the numbers and average size of returning spawners. This is probably due to high seas netting and climatic change affecting the richness of sea feeding available for growing salmon. These reasons only account for part of the collapse of salmon stocks in the Wessex rivers over the last 30 years.

The rivers themselves have been changed by man into a far less hospitable environment for salmon to spawn, their eggs to hatch and young salmon to be nurtured, prior to their migration to the ocean. Man's diverse acts of damage can be examined by looking at how the Hampshire Avon has changed. This river carries less water than in past decades. Clean chalk filtered water is abstracted out of bore holes to supply garden sprinklers and car washing rather than the springs that feed the Avon. Dredging and drainage work encourages the river's water to race to the sea. The effect of this abstraction and drainage work has been to shrink the river and leave less pure water to dilute pollutants and silt that enter the Avon from many sources.

Water running off agricultural land carries residues of nutrients, insecticides and herbicides into the river. These affect the aquatic ecology upon which young salmon and many other forms of water life depend. Subsidised changes in farming from pasture to autumn sown arable have seen old meadows ploughed up and silt from fields washed into the Avon. Silt deposits on the river bed and chokes the porous gravel salmon need for spawning.

Industrial, domestic and Trout farm

Roger Prowse of Plymouth with a superb trio of
Rainbows to 9lb 8oz.
Bake Lakes

abstractions and discharges impact upon flow regimes and chemical and biological conditions to a so far unknown extent and are in urgent need of examination. Fish farm escapee rainbow trout abound as aliens competing with young salmon for food.

Imagine the hostile river that greets a pair of adult salmon returning to spawn in the Avon. They have travelled from the Arctic to the south coast of England escaping predators and miles of Irish drift nets and now enter the river Avon to answer their urge to spawn. Their heroic journey is almost over and they should be welcomed by the river of their birth. Instead they swim upstream through a river invisibly tainted with a cocktail of chemicals and obstructions that might affect their whole breeding cycle.

The hen salmon looks for clean gravel in which to dig a nest or redd for her eggs. Much of their river's gravel has been dredged away and what remains is choked with silt. Her eggs are laid and some are fertilized by her partner's milt. The eggs lie in the gravel of the riverbed during the winter. Invading silt prevents clean oxygenated water from bathing the eggs and most are suffocated. In the Spring as few as 3% of the eggs hatch.

The depleted number of young salmon try to feed on micro invertebrates that themselves depend upon pure water to thrive. As the young fish search for food they are mercilessly eaten by predatory chub, perch, rainbow trout, birds pike and trout, including stocked fish and farm escapees. Only a pathetic number of young salmon ever live to leave the Avon and face the perils of the sea and the long journey to their Arctic feeding grounds. Even in the deep ocean they are at risk from pelagic fisheries and starvation by over fishing of their food sources.

How can all these problems affecting the Hampshire Avon and the other salmon rivers of Wessex be solved? In an ideal world the whole catchment area of a river would be managed as a single entity.

Land management and agricultural practices would have to be designed to minimise chemical and silt entry into the river. Water abstraction would be limited to what the river could withstand and would cost the water

companies the real cost of the water's loss from the river. Trout farms would only be licensed to operate if they could prove no damage from their discharges and no escaping of their trout into the river. Unfortunately we are a long way from such an enlightened management of Wessex's chalk stream salmon rivers.

Statutory responsibility for preserving these special rivers and their genetically distinct salmon population lies with the Environment Agency, English Nature and MAFF, now re spun as DEFRA. If too many cooks can spoil a broth then too many organisations can certainly spoil a river. Funding for conservation is relentlessly cut by Government. Commercial interests and riparian owners argue and little is done.

Amidst this chaos of neglect and inaction, the Wessex Salmon and Rivers Trust stands as a body with a clear sense of purpose to act for the salmons benefit. We have worked to form a consensus for conservation with the licensed salmon netsmen in the Avon's estuary at Mudeford. This has lead to the netsmen releasing alive all their salmon catch each year so the fish can ascend the river to spawn. For a decade this effective conservation measure has been generously funded by Tesco Supermarkets.

To encourage rod anglers to return salmon to the river, Tesco run a "swap a salmon scheme" across the south and west of England where an angler voluntarily returning a salmon alive to the river receives a farmed salmon from Tesco as compensation. The support of Tesco for Avon salmon is a practical measure that all anglers should appreciate. Here we have a commercial company putting many public bodies with statutory conservation duties to shame.

The lead taken by Avon anglers in returning salmon is now being mirrored across the whole of south and western England. The Wessex Salmon and Rivers Trust funds research into river improvement, but we are presently frustrated in our desire to support salmon stocks with assisted spawning or hatchery work by long running discussions with the Environment Agency as to whether this work is effective. At every turn we fight the salmon's cause. To prevent a generation growing up in Wessex with no knowledge of the past beauty of their rivers

A fin perfect Rainbow for Gary Judd of Bodmin. Innis

and their salmon heritage we are developing an education programme that we can take into schools.

Is the presence of wild salmon in the rivers of Wessex worth the frustrations and problems of their conservation? The answer has to be yes. Salmon are a barometer of river health and a river that supports salmon will be rich in otters, wildlife and plants for everybody to enjoy. Coarse fisherman will remember that when the Hampshire Avon was a good salmon river, it was the greatest coarse fishery in Britain.

I caught one Avon salmon in 2001 after many days of hard fishing. The sight of this 14lb chrome silver fish in the river made me tremble. The knowledge that he had seen sights in the deep ocean I can only imagine and had survived so many obstacles to return home humbled me.

Releasing him back into the river, with the hope he will spawn another generation of magnificent fish, made me glow with pleasure. His memory will sustain my efforts to preserve him and his river over coming years.

The loss of these fish would diminish our rivers and in the process diminish us.

Anyone wishing to help our work can join the Wessex Salmon and Rivers Trust and should contact our membership secretary: -

Mr John Levell,
4 Forestside Gardens,
Poulner,
Ringwood,
Hants.
BH24 1SZ

VRANCH HOUSE SCHOOL FLY FISHING CHARITY CHALLENGE 2002
In aid of the Devon & Exeter Spastics Society

Pairs of anglers are invited to enter the 11th Fly Fishing Charity Challenge to raise funds for children with cerebral palsy at Vranch House School & Centre, Exeter.

The Challenge raised £13,008 in 2001 - over £200 more than in 2000 and has raised a magnificent £88,478 since 1992.

Heats and semi-finals will take place from March to September at Bake Lakes, Bellbrook Valley, Kennick, Roadford, Stithians, Tavistock, Temple, Tree Meadow and Watercress.

The semi-finals are at Bake, Kennick and Temple and the finals, at Tavistock, are on the first two Sundays in October.

There are over £3,000 worth of prizes including M&S vouchers, lines, day tickets, garden statues and hooks. Entry is free provided the minimum sponsorship of £20 per person is raised.

Anglers who wish to enter please contact the fisheries or Sue Gould, Marketing Manager of the Devon & Exeter Spastics Society: Tel: Exeter 01392 873543.

Heat Dates:

Stithians	Redruth	01209 821431	Sun 17 March
Bake Fishery	Saltash	0498 585836	Sun 7 April
Watercress	Chudleigh	01626 852168	Sun 28 April
Kennick Reservoir	Bovey Tracey	01626 353551	Sun 6 May
Bellbrook Valley	Tiverton	01398 351292	Sun 12 May
Temple	Bodmin	01208 821730	Sun 7 July
Tavistock Trout	Tavistock	01822 615441	Sun 1 Sept
Tree Meadow	Hayle	07971 107156	Sat 7 Sept
Roadford Lake	Okehampton	01392 873543	TBA

Lewis into a big one in the dark!
Bellbrook

The Saltwater Experience

Fly fishing in saltwater

Derek Aunger

As a lad, about 45 years ago I owned a fabulous little rod, about 8ft long, split cane, with a handle that you would reverse, making the reel seat either at the very end, or about a foot up the rod. This made it a great all-rounder, a fly rod, spinning rod and short bait rod and everything else in between. I was very lucky, growing up in the town of Bude, on the North Cornish Coast with a variety of fishing on my doorstep.

I would walk up the canal tow path to a little stream known as Sharlands, at it's widest no greater than 10ft where I could fish for magic little brownies with either fly, or spin with the proverbial Devon minnow. Sharlands then ran into a feeder, which divided into the Bude Canal and into the River Neat, which ran for about 2 miles before reaching Bude. At this point if you chose the canal you could coarse fish for roach, rudd and the like, and if you could keep well out of sight of the farmer, you could either fly fish, or trot a worm down through some swims on the Neat.

As river and canal met the sea I would fish with fly for mullet, and then off the breakwater into the surf for bass. It was as natural to me then, to fly fish in saltwater as it is to fish for trout in still waters today, yet we are led to believe it's a whole new 'ball game'.

Most of today's information, tackle and literature on saltwater fly-fishing is based on fishing abroad, for game fish used to warmer climes, but do not despair we have fine opportunities for fishing the fly in saltwater here in the U.K

As a professional game angler and instructor, and after experimenting over the many years with many combinations of rods, from double-handed salmon rods to heavy single-handed trout rods, I finally came up with the ideal rod for fly fishing from the rocks or from a boat. I have been using the superb Bruce & Walker fly rods for my casting demonstrations for some considerable time and after talking over my ideas for a fly rod specifically for saltwater use in the U.K they are now manufacturing a rod to my design. It is called the Bruce & Walker 'Derek Aunger Saltwater' rod and is now included in the Bruce & Walker brochure.

I suppose the word 'fly' is something of a misnomer. They are in fact fairly large streamers or lures, some up to about 8.5 cms long (that's about 4 inches in old money). The flys are best cast on a rod with a shooting head #9 line. You could be fishing just below the surface for top feeding bass, or deeper for mackerel or pollack.

The excitement comes in knowing that you do not know what may take your lure.

It's often the case that you only know what it is when it reaches the surface. One problem I wanted to overcome was to be able to fish two lures on one leader, as you would imagine this does present some problems with casting so after hours of experimenting I have finally come up with the solution, which I have named the 'Kernow Slider' and this is how it works.

The Kernow Slider

This set up consists of 2 parts.
1. The Main Leader With the Point Lure:
On the end of your fly line you attach 4ft of leader material (about 10-12lbs) and at the end of this tie on a barrel swivel (about size 6), on the other end of the swivel you attach a further 3ft of leader and to that your main lure. You now have a lure on the end of about 7ft of cast, with a swivel part way up the cast, this you will be able to cast quite easily.
2. The Slider or Dropper Lure:
The dropper is made up separately by tying about 6 inches of leader onto a hooked snap swivel, and the other end to your dropper lure.

The Method:

You first cast your main lure, and when it is below the surface of the water, and the fly line is taut, you clip your slider dropper onto the fly line and it will then slide down the line until it hits the swivel on the leader. You then do your retrieve, but now fishing with 2 lures, about 3ft

apart, with the dropper, or slider lure achieving the main purpose, as an attractor for the point lure. Try it....... It really works!

Because of the limitations of space, I am not able to go into any great detail about specific methods for particular species of sea fish but there are a few general tips.

Fishing from sea washed rocks is perfect for bass, a typical lure would be a blue and silver streamer of about 3 inches long, cast into the foaming surf or eddies and retrieved at a good steady pace. Have a chat with the local sea anglers for best conditions and states of tide in you area. Be very safety conscious, fishing in these conditions you need to be ever aware of the tide and conditions underfoot. I would advise you to fish with friend until you are really conversant with the ever-changing surroundings and conditions. If you are fishing from a boat, or not sure where to fish have a look around for feeding birds, but once again local knowledge is unbeatable.

I hope this has given you a little taster into the exciting world of saltwater fly fishing and makes you want to get out and have a go. The locals may look at you a little oddly at first but don't worry, you would be amazed how interested they are when they come and chat.

If you would like to find out more about saltwater fly fishing around the East Cornish Coast please do not hesitate to contact me.
Tel: 07812 360764
Email:
flyfishingexperiences@breathemail.net

Bass Lures

The South West Federation of Fly Fishers

The South West Federation of Fly Fishers belongs to the Confederation of English Fly Fishers. The Confederation is, amongst other things, responsible for running National and International Fly Fishing Teams and Competitions. The grassroots of all the National and International Competitions are the Regional Eliminators run by Federations all over the Country.

The South West Federation runs Eliminators at Chew Valley Lake. This years dates are as follows

FIRST ELIMINATOR: SUNDAY 28 APRIL
SECOND ELIMINATOR: SUNDAY 26 MAY
FINAL ELIMINATOR: SUNDAY 23 JUNE

Competitors can ONLY enter ONE of the first two eliminators and if successful would qualify for the Final Eliminator.

Thirty competitors compete in the Final Eliminator. In 2001 there were sixteen places available for the Loch Style National, and we would hope for a similar number in 2002.

The Loch Style National in 2002 is at Chew Valley on Saturday September 21st.

ELIGIBILITY

Anyone can enter provided that they are over 18 years of age, and have been domiciled in ENGLAND for 3 years.

Competitors can ONLY enter eliminators in ONE Region in any one year. Anyone who has previously fished at International Level for another Country is NOT eligible to fish.

If you are interested in competitive Fly Fishing, with the chance to fish for England, write to me at the address below or give me a ring.
J.A. Loud,
153/155 East Street,
Bedminster,
BRISTOL BS3 4EJ
Tel (Daytime) 0117 9872050
Tel (Evenings) 0117 9232166

Spring fishing on the Fowey.
Liskeard & District A.C.

CHEW VALLEY LAKE
BLAGDON LAKE
THE BARROWS

Catch rates were again very high at our fisheries in 2001, despite the late start forced upon us by the outbreak of foot and mouth, with anglers catching over 3 trout on average, per visit. Since nearly 60,000 hard fighting rainbow and brown trout were landed over the season this meant an awful lot of enjoyable visits and a huge number of happy anglers!

Woodford Lodge is now firmly established as a very popular venue. Rebuilt in 2000, the lodge provides excellent facilities for anglers such as the full scale tackle shop, as well as a comfortable lounge and restaurant serving breakfasts, lunches and evening meals and a bar.

We continue to offer a friendly and helpful fishery service to all from the Lodge even though it is now open to the public as well as to anglers. Those seeking a quieter venue can still visit Blagdon which still caters only for anglers.

Disabled anglers may fish from a special wheely boat, at reduced rates, at Blagdon and we have priority bank fishing spots, suitable for those with limited walking ability, marked out at Chew and Blagdon. Our Lodges are all accessible to wheelchair users.

CHEW

at 1200 acres, is our largest lake and it lies some seven miles due south of Bristol. It is most renowned for loch style boat fishing and has a fleet of 32 motor boats, each equipped with an outboard motor. There is plenty of room on the lake for expert and pleasure angler alike and the scenery and bird life are a real bonus for those with time to look around. May and June are usually, but not always, the best months and

are the time of year when a variety of buzzers hatch and bring the trout to the surface. Casting to rising fish and hooking and playing our superb, home-grown rainbows, which average well over 2lbs, is the pinnacle of stillwater fly fishing.

Bank fishing can also be very good at Chew, particularly early in April, through May and June and then again in September and October. There are many miles of uncrowded lake margins to choose from and though the main season ends in mid October we continue for winter fishing up until the end of November.

BLAGDON

is 440 acres in area and has 15 rowing boats. Anglers are welcome to use their own electric outboards and a local pub operates a hire service. With no noisy petrol engines the fishery is a peaceful and beautiful place to fish. In recent seasons there have been less buzzers than at Chew but more sedges and damsel flies and the nature of the fishing is thus slightly different.

The banks provide very good sport and there are numerous hot-spots from where you will find ample space to cast a line. The surrounding meadows support cowslips and native orchids and overhead you will often see buzzards riding the thermals and hoards of swallows and martins competing with the trout to take the flies; fishing at Blagdon is about more than just catching fish!

THE BARROWS

are three reservoirs of 60, 40, and 25 acres lying close to Bristol on either side of the A38 some three miles out of the city. They are bank only fisheries, though we allow some float tubing by arrangement. All the lakes contain a mixture of brown & rainbow trout. We stock slightly smaller fish, so permit prices cost less, but the Barrows perhaps provide the most reliable bank sport of all our fisheries. The evening rise can be a very profitable time with buzzer and sedge hatches giving great sport to rising fish.

LITTON

gives fishermen the chance to have exclusive use of a fishery for a day's fishing. There are two lakes; the lower is 8 acres and is the main fishery stocked with rainbows and browns, while the upper is 11 acres but reduces in size through the summer and is stocked mostly with brown

Game

Tom Pullen with a 14lb 2oz Rainbow.
Newhouse

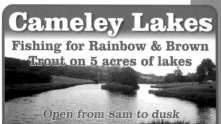

41

trout. There is a rowing boat on each lake and a permit will allow you to fish at both. The limit is 5 trout per person. The fishery is available on Thursdays, Fridays, Saturdays and Sundays and bookings are made at Wooford Lodge.

PERMITS.

The centre for bookings, enquiries and tackle Sales is Woodford Lodge at Chew. All kinds of permit are issued here. At Blagdon our half-timbered lodge offers a lesser range of facilities but is still a comfortable place to eat your lunch or warm up in front of a log fire and the building is staffed during the morning for permits, enquiries, small tackle sales and advice. At the Barrows there is a self-service kiosk for permits and separate lavatories and shelters.

SPECIAL OFFERS.

This year we offer the following special deals:

1 Any experienced angler can take a junior angler fishing on his day bank permit at no extra cost. (limit bag is shared).

2 In August all bank permits will entitle the permit holder to a free bank permit to be taken during August.

3 In August if you purchase two days boat fishing you will be entitled to a third day FREE OF CHARGE!

4 For people on holiday in July, August and September, we offer three mid-week boat permits at Chew or Blagdon taken within a single week at a 15% discount.

TUITION.

We are keen to encourage all ages to take up fly fishing and offer a range of lessons backed up by half price permits for your first few visits after a lesson. Casting lessons are held on most Saturday mornings and cost just £5.00, (tackle can be provided) Following one of these you can have 2 bank permits at half price to get you going. Many beginners will also want a full fishing lesson, (normally held once a month on a Saturday) in order to move on from casting to actual fishing and these cost £15 and entitle you to 4 half price permits. Our tutors hold the Stanic qualification and we will continue to give advice and help on subsequent visits for as long as it takes you to feel confident about your fishing. We can also put you in touch with private tutors and particularly recommend Mike Gleave for tuition at our lakes or elsewhere and England International John Horsey who offers a coaching service for boat fishing at Chew or Blagdon.

We run two highly popular Beginners Days for all ages. The first will be on Sunday April 28th and the second on May 26th. These combine basic teaching with you having a go at bank and boat fishing at only £5 for juniors and £10 for adults. You also get two half price permits for your next two visits. Booking is essential.

YOUTH COMPETITION.

On Wednesday the 5th June we will hold our annual Youth Fishing Competition. Open to all anglers between 12 and 19 years, this is a boat competition at Chew with a local expert as a boat partner, and a top prize of a tackle voucher for £200. The entrance fee of £15 includes permits and an evening buffet. Details and booking forms from Woodford Lodge.

ENQUIRIES AND BOOKINGS.

Phone or write to Bristol Water Fisheries, Woodford Lodge, Chew Stoke, Bristol. BS40 8XH. Telephone or fax: 01275 332339 for a free brochure, for all enquiries and for bookings.

You can e-mail us at bob.handford@bristolwater.co.uk

or visit our web site for regular updates on the fishing at, www.bristolwater.co.uk and www.chewvalleylake.org.uk

Richard and Niamh with a superbly conditioned Rainbow.
Bake Lakes

Pleasure Carp Fishing

Marcus Watts

One of the most rewarding days coarse fishing you can have is to spend a day on a well-stocked commercial fishery. If you pick the correct lake good sport can be enjoyed 12 months a year with fish that average between 3lb and 7lb. These are a nice size because they give a good fight but allow you to use normal tackle.

This type of fishery is a relative newcomer, as over the last decade many smaller lakes have been built to meet the growing demand for coarse fishing. The lakes are usually between 1 and 4 acres, not too deep and have easily accessible swims. The stock is predominantly of mirror and ghost carp that have been artificially reared at a fish farm, and it is this that holds the key to success.

In normal fishing location is the prime factor in catching species by design. You go to your local lake for Tench or Bream and pick a spot you know (or hope) will produce them. Once there you choose the appropriate method, be it pole, waggler or feeder and bait or baits that you know they will eat if you're in the right place. The commercial carp fishery is stocked with between 1000lb and 2200lb of fish per acre, or 30 to 75 fish for every swim on the lake. With this head of young, hungry fish you don't strictly need to locate them, as they will soon find you once you start putting in feed. They are not easily scared away by your presence either, as these lakes are fished nearly every day, often with large matches too.

Foremost, the key to success lies with choosing the right baits for the day, half a pint of mixed maggots will not really unlock the full potential of these fisheries very often. For warm water carp fishing a one kilo bag of frozen sweet corn is better value than tins, next on the shopping list is meat. Cheap luncheon meat is best left on the shelf, buy the Bacon Grill as the fish are far more sensitive to poor quality foodstuffs than people are, your success or failure in carp fishing can be down to bait quality more often than not. If you can stand the smell on your fingers one bait will out fish the previous ones and that is cat food. You need the chunks in jelly so the rubbery pieces of meat can be picked out and used on the hook. For several months now cat food has dominated the main match carp lakes in Cornwall, and with so many brands and flavours it should have a long life span.

Lastly we have the most important bait of all, pellets. These carp remember their fish farming background and a good quality fish rearing diet will out fish most of the brightly coloured and flavoured fishing pellets. The pale brown standard trout pellet isn't bad for un-pressured fish, the darker winter or high oil diets are better but the one that's head and shoulders above them all is the Marine fish farm Turbot pellets. These are used to farm Turbot and Halibut, both of which are so fussy about eating pellets that only the highest-grade ingredients are used to make them. If this pellet has not been used on your lake yet it will out-fish all that went before.

The pellets will make up half your feed and if used in conjunction with an elastic pellet band alternative hook bait too. A very good alternative is the soft pellets and these can be put on the hook in the normal manner. By carrying a selection of pellet sizes from the tiny 3mm up to the 13mm you can cover all requirements and offer the fish a varied diet that can keep them interested all day.

Arriving at the lake I'd pick a swim with a little marginal weed to the left and right but I wouldn't worry about wind direction. Set up your chosen tackle, the pole is very effective but the waggler is good, especially if the fish go over 10lb. Use the smallest float conditions will allow on about 4lb line with a barbless carp hook in a size 12. Plumb the depth EXACTLY on a spot in the margin to one side, and then find a similar spot on the other side that is the same depth. While getting ready feed a handful of pellet and a dozen hook bait samples to each side. Start fishing on the left hand spot but don't feed around the float, this will lead to line bites and foul hooked fish. The bites should come within 30 seconds to 10 minutes. If not move the float to the second area and only then feed the spot you've just fished. Keep this rotation going,

A real result for this young angler Milemead

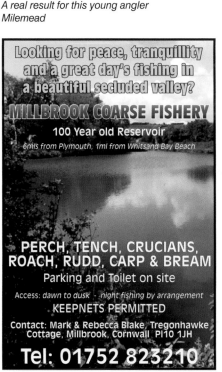

Coarse

feeding one spot while fishing the other, even when you are catching as it lets the fish settle on the bait and feed confidently before you drop your tackle in.

The margin method will be very reliable until the water cools down and the fish move out into deeper water. When this happens a small ground bait swimfeeder comes into it's own. Use a quality fishmeal ground bait with no additional food items in as you are aiming to put a smell in the water not too much bait. Tie up a short hook length of 6lb line to a strong 16 hook with three red maggots, this will out fish any other hook bait.

Cast out practically anywhere and after 5 minutes twitch the feeder along the bottom once, if an immediate bite does not materialise instantly wind in and repeat. Never leave the feeder in the water more than 10 minutes as the fish respond to the noise of the feeder hitting the water. It doesn't pay to cast too accurately to one spot, if you've just fished an hour in one place with no bites why cast back there? You must hunt around the swim looking for the fish.

To use the float in winter set it slightly over depth at a distance of 10-12 meters. Feed very sparingly with the micro pellet and use corn or maggot on the hook. I'd leave the luncheon meats at home in the winter as the cold water solidifies the fats and makes them un-digestible. Three small balls of fishmeal ground bait at the start will be enough to keep the fish mooching for the day, after that rely on loose feed. The carp will probably take an hour or two to respond on the float line so fish the feeder at the start but have a look every 20 minutes and feed a little every 15 minutes until you start getting bites.

The methods I've outlined will regularly produce 100lb pleasure catches as long as you've chosen the correct venue. This is critical because you can't catch fish that don't exist, so watch the match results on your local venues, as these cannot be exaggerated for publicity purposes. Multiple 75lb weights and top weights of 100lb+ show that the lake has enough fish to go round and not just one good swim.

Be lucky, Marcus

Marcus - being lucky?

Christopher Bennet with a 4lb Eel
Private Devon Water - Manadon Angling

Bernard Venables *by Chris Yates*

To celebrate his 90th birthday, Bernard Venables and I went pike fishing on the Dorset Stour and, after several hours of concentrated casting, Bernard landed a tigerish ten pounder. Last year, (his birthday was February 14th) he was 94 and once again we planned to go fishing to celebrate the event. He was just as enthusiastic as ever and we agreed to go back to the Stour as soon as the winter floods had subsided. But before that had happened he suddenly fell ill. Up to that moment I'd been convinced, as Bernard himself had been, that he would still be casting a line when [not if] he was 100. I never thought of him as an old man. He was simply an angler whose passion could never fail. But we did not have that 94 year old cast. The illness could not be cured and Bernard died on the 21st of April, 2001.

As well as being a good friend of mine, Bernard, through his writing, was also the friend of millions of other anglers. He was the Isaak Walton of the Twentieth Century, who had inspired a whole generation of fishermen through his book, Mr Crabtree Goes Fishing. First published in 1949, it went on to become an enormous best seller, going through many editions and two million copies. At one time, just about every angler in the country was reading Mr Crabtree and even nowadays if you mention the book to any angler over 40 he will go misty eyed at the memory. It was a great delight to Bernard that, because of the continuing interest in the book, a facsimile of the first edition was published by the Medlar Press in 2000 and, once again, Mr. Crabtree became a best seller.

Though he travelled widely and fished in some very exotic places, Bernard always returned to the waters he loved best, the rivers of South West England. Much of the fishing that he described and illustrated in Crabtree was based on his own experiences on the Hampshire Avon and Dorset Stour, though Bernard would be the first to admit that he was never quite as successful an angler as his fictitious character. For the last decade of his life he lived within walking distance of the upper Avon, just north of Amesbury.

Bernard wrote many other fishing books beside Crabtree, all of them imbued with a lovely, almost magical sense of wonder at the beauty of the waterside and the gloriousness of the fish. His love of nature had inspired him to become an angler when he was a child, before the First World War, but it was not until the end of the Second World War that he began to write about his experiences. Until then he had made a precarious living through painting and illustrating, but it was his talent for writing as well as drawing which eventually led him into journalism. He worked for various Fleet Street papers, including the Daily Mirror, which is where Mr Crabtree first appeared, as a daily strip cartoon. Such was its instant popularity it was inevitable that the cartoon should make the famous leap into a full colour book and subsequent mythic status. Buoyed by this success, Bernard left Fleet Street and went on to found the Angling Times, in 1953, a weekly newspaper which soon became the most popular fishing journal in the country [it still is]. And ten years later, he launched Creel, which many still regard as the best monthly angling magazine ever produced. It made me very chuffed when, thirty years later, I created my own fishing magazine, Waterlog, and Bernard not only became a regular contributor, but also said that it was the only natural successor to Creel. Bernard never missed a single deadline.

But apart from all his achievements as a writer and artist, Bernard will be remembered as a true angler because of his appreciation of the real essence of fishing. For him, what made fishing so fascinating was not the striving for consistent catches or perfect technique, but the way it drew him into a very real and yet very magical relationship with Nature. His life's work was an expression of the joy that relationship gave him.

Mr Crabtree goes fishing is available from The Medlar Press on 01691 623225 Price £9.99

A classic 32lb Mirror Carp.
Valley Springs

sw lakes trust

Success for these youngsters

The South West Lakes Trust is an independent charity formed to promote and enhance sustainable recreation, access and nature conservation on and around inland waters in the South West of England for the benefit of the general public.

In spite of the Foot and Mouth outbreak, last season proved to be very successful for South West Lakes Trust anglers. The newly formed South West Angling Association coarse fishing team, captained by Billy Knott, fished and won The Embassy National Championship, Division 5. Wimbleball Junior angler, Lewis Hendrie, successfully fished the National heats to qualify for the England Junior team, and Kennick and Wimbleball angler John Gollop not only qualified for the England team, but won the National final. We plan to build on last year's success, and aim to offer something for all levels of competence (from complete novices through to international match anglers) in both coarse and game disciplines.

The Trust continues with its drive to introduce the sport to all newcomers, from children to pensioners. We intend to follow up on last year's successful introductory and training days in various aspects of coarse angling, (including our specialist pike and carp days), with the help of the E.A., N.F.A. accredited instructors, and local specialists. Fly fishing tuition and introductory days for both adults and juniors will be available at Wimbleball, Kennick, and sites in Cornwall, all run by qualified professional instructors, throughout the season. All aspects of the sport will be covered, as will the promotion of a responsible and healthy interest in the environment. Juniors again will be encouraged to fish for trout — the parent/child ticket allows the youngster to fish for free and share the parent's bag limit. We will also be holding a series of Ladies' Days, starting off at Roadford

on 28th April, run by professional instructors Anne Champion and Sally Pizzi.

The 'Peninsula Classic' bank competition will be held at Kennick on the 19th May, in which there will be a special junior prizes category. The 'Wimbleball 2000' boat competition will be held on 15th September. There will also be an Open Day for juniors on 22nd September at Siblyback — all youngsters will be welcome to try their hand at fly-tying, casting competitions, boat fishing, and professional instructors will be on hand for coaching and advice.

We have continued to move fish up from College to Argal ,where they thrive — a number of pike and carp in excess of 30lb were landed last season, as well as excellent bream.

Following on from the success of float-tubing at Kennick last year, the Trust will again organise float tubing days on the first and third Sundays in each month from May onwards. These will be held at Kennick, with local suppliers Snowbee and Orvis helping to promote this aspect of the sport, providing demo equipment on the first Sundays (self-launch only on the third Sundays).

The Trust remains committed to angling and customer care, and welcomes all comments to help us provide what the angler really wants.

For further information, including instruction and competition information, please contact:
Chris Hall, Head of Fisheries on
01837 871565
Or E-mail: chall@swlakestrust.org.uk
Or visit our website:
www.swlakestrust.org.uk

swlakestrust *Coarse Fishing*

Coarse

COARSE FISHING PERMIT AGENTS:

A: The Liscawn Inn, Crafthole, Nr Torpoint, Cornwall PL11 3BD Tel: (01503) 230863

B: Variety Sports, 23 Broad Street, Ilfracombe, Devon. Tel: (01271) 862039

C: Summerlands Tackle, 16-20 Nelson Road, Westward Ho!, Devon, EX39 1LF. Tel: (01237) 471291

D: The Kingfisher, 22 Castle St, Barnstaple, Devon, EX1 1DR. Tel: (01271) 344919

E: Powlers Piece Stores, Powlers Piece, East Putford, Holsworthy, Devon EX22 7XW Tel: (01237) 451282

F: Bude Angling Supplies, 6 Queen Street, Bude, Cornwall. Tel: (01288) 353396

G: Bideford Tourist Information Centre, The Quay, Bideford, Devon Tel: (01237) 477676

H: Whiskers Pet Centre, 9 High Street, Torrington, Devon. Tel: (01805) 622859

I: Exeter Angling Centre, Smythen St, Exeter, Devon EX1 1BN Tel: (01392) 436404

J: Exmouth Tackle & Sports, 20 The Strand, Exmouth, Devon EX8 1AF. Tel: (01395) 274918

K: Knowle Post Office, Budleigh Salterton. Tel: (01395) 442303

L: Newtown Angling Centre, Newtown, Germoe, Penzance, Cornwall TR20 9AF. Tel: (01736) 763721

M: Sandy's Tackle, 7 Penryn St., Redruth, Cornwall TR15 2SP. Tel: (01209) 214877

N: Ironmonger Market Place, St Ives, Cornwall. TR26 1RZ. Tel: (01736) 796200

O: Heamoor Stores, Heamoor, Gulval, Nr Penzance. TR18 3EJ. Tel: (01736) 65265

P: Turner's Tackle, 19 Fore St., Holsworthy, Devon EX22 6EB Tel: (01409) 259300

LOWER SLADE - Ilfracombe, Devon
Stocked with mirror and common carp to 20lb plus bream to 5lb plus, perch to 2.25lb, roach, rudd, gudgeon and pike.
Fishing Times:Open all year, 24 hours per day
Permits: From agents: B,C,D. Tel: (01288) 321262

JENNETTS - Bideford, Devon
Best fish: Common 22lb, Mirror 23lb. Produces quality bags of smaller carp, roach, and tench to float & pole.
Fishing Times: Open all year, 6.30am to 10pm.
Permits: From agents: C,F,G,P. Tel: (01288) 321262

DARRACOTT - Torrington, Devon
Roach up to 1lb. Mixed bags to 20lb plus of roach, rudd, bream, tench, perch to 2.25lb, carp to 15lb.
Fishing Times: Open all year, 24 hours per day.
Permits: From agents: C,D,F,G,H,P.
Tel: (01288) 321262
Seasons Permits - (01837) 871565

MELBURY - Bideford, Devon
Best mirror 27.75lb. Good mixed bags of roach, rudd, bream to pole, float and feeder.
Fishing Times: Open all year. 6.30am - 10pm.
Permits: From agents: C,D,E,F,G,P.
Limited season permits from our office.
Tel: (01288) 321262

TRENCHFORD - Nr Christow, Devon
Pike weighing up to 30lbs.
Fishing Times: Open all year -
1 hour before sunrise to 1 hour after sunset.
Permits: Self service kiosk at Kennick Reservoir
Tel: (01647) 277587

UPPER TAMAR LAKE - Bude, Cornwall
Carp to 28lbs. 50lb plus bags of bream and 30lb bags of rudd. Regular competitions.
Fishing Times: Open all year, 24 hours a day.
Permits: From agents: C,D,F Tel: (01288) 321262

SQUABMOOR - Exmouth, Devon
Good head of carp to 25lb, roach to 3lb 2oz, Tench.
Fishing Times Open all year, 24 hours a day.
Permits: From agents: I,J,K
Season Permits from our office Tel: (01837) 871565

OLD MILL - Dartmouth, Devon
Carp to over 20lbs, roach to 2lb, tench and bream.
Fishing Times: Open all year, 24 hours a day.
Permits: Season permits from our Office
Tel: (01837) 871565

PORTH - Newquay, Cornwall
Bags of 130lb plus have been caught. Best bream 9lb 2oz, tench 9lb 12oz. rudd to 3lb, roach to 1.25lb plus. Mixed bags of roach, rudd/skimmers to 60lb.
Fishing Times: Open all year, 24 hours a day
Permits: Agent L. Self service at Porth car park.
Season permits from our Office. Great competition water. Tel: (01637) 877959

BOSCATHNOE - Penzance, Cornwall
Common, mirror and crucian carp with fish into the low 20lb range. Roach and bream also stocked.
Fishing Times: Open all year, 1 hour before sunrise to 1 hour after sunset. Season permits from our Office.
Permits: From agents: L,M,N,O. Tel: (01579) 342366

ARGAL - Nr Falmouth, Cornwall
Carp to 20lb plus. Best fish: carp 26lb, bream 8lb 6oz, tench 8lb 8oz and eel 7lb, Pike over 30lb.
Fishing Times: Open all year, 24 hours per day.
Permits: From agents: L,M and self service unit at Argal Reservoir car park. Tel (01579) 342366
Season permits from our Office (01837) 871565.

BUSSOW - St Ives, Cornwall
Rudd to 1.5lb, roach bream and carp.
Fishing Times: Open all year, 24 hours a day.
Permits: From agents: L,M,N. Season permits from our Office. Tel (01579) 342366

CRAFTHOLE - Nr. Torpoint, Devon.
Stocked with carp and tench.
Quality Carp up to 30lb.
Fishing Times: Open all year
1hr before sunrise to 1hr
after sunset.
Limited permits from agent A.
Season permits from our
office (01837) 871565

51

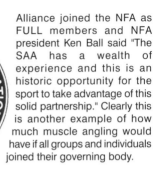

The National Federation of Anglers

STATISTICS prove that angling is the biggest participant sport in the UK and with an influx of new junior recruits last year the sport has an exciting future.

The National Federation Of Anglers (NFA) can take some credit for the junior section increasing. The Federation, which was established in 1903, has more than 100 qualified coaches nationwide and they make themselves available to coach at Road Shows, special functions or privately and usually do not charge for their services. The coaches have been a great success story and many 'lapsed' anglers, as well as new recruits, have been pleased to seek advice from them to enable them to enjoy the sport in all its peculiar facets.

The NFA is the governing body for coarse fishing and the organisation has around 200,000 members mainly through its 400 clubs and Individual Members. The NFA is recognised by Sport England as a governing body and the appropriate funding is provided through a 'four-year Plan' structure. Representatives from the NFA regularly meet government ministers (president Ken Ball and media consultant Rodney Coldron met the Minister for Sport, Richard Caborn, recently) and the NFA is represented on other important committees including British Waterways, Environment Agency, The Moran Committee and the *National Anglers Alliance (NAA) where important topics are discussed for the benefit of individual anglers and the sport as a whole.

*The NAA recently issued a press release warning angling clubs about the government paper 'The Right to Roam."

The NFA has signed a 'Memorandum of Understanding' with the Welsh Federation and more recently with the Countryside Alliance. Recently the powerful Specialist Anglers' Alliance joined the NFA as FULL members and NFA president Ken Ball said "The SAA has a wealth of experience and this is an historic opportunity for the sport to take advantage of this solid partnership." Clearly this is another example of how much muscle angling would have if all groups and individuals joined their governing body.

The NFA joined the European Anglers Alliance in 1994 - this organisation was formed to maintain a watchful eye on any European legislation that is likely to affect our rights as anglers, our sport and the aquatic environment: It may well be that in this high 'corridor of power' the cormorant "problem" may be resolved!

The NFA spent £20,000 on a research project which looked into the design of keepnets and their effect on fish and more recently issued a statement warning anglers of the dangers of using the maggot dye Chrysoidine Y. The NFA was also instrumental in ensuring that a tiny Nottinghamshire stream, which had a good head of roach, chub and dace, who restocked following a serious pollution.

No angler should take their sport for granted. In many European countries no-one can go fishing without first purchasing a licence or permit from the governing body and it is impossible for a competition to take place without an endorsement by the governing body. This is not the case yet in the UK where the sport is fragmented: Power and influence comes from numbers which is why all clubs and individual anglers should join the National Federation Of Anglers.

The NFA will soon have a new streamlined management structure with a 'Board' of just eight members (one from each region) one President and one vice-president (previously there were three) and the organisation will be run by the new Membership Services Manager, Bob Clark who is responsible to the President. Already new clubs, organisations and individuals have joined the 'new look' NFA and they clearly believe the NFA is entering a new era with a firm promise that they intend to deliver.

Coarse

The benefits enjoyed by member clubs and individual members of the NFA are: Protection of riparian rights, whether owned or controlled under a tenancy agreement; Provision of coaching to promote the level of excellence as identified by Sport England and to impart the basic skills necessary to enjoy our sport; Legal Advice; Environmental Research; Fishery Advice; Newsletter; Insurance Cover; Travel Club; Exclusive Visa Credit Card; Entry into Competitions; Entry into International Events for 'outstanding members.'

Coarse anglers concerned about the future of the sport should join the NFA. Individual membership costs £10.00 per year and details for club membership can be obtained from central office. The full details are:

National Federation of Anglers,
Halliday House, Egginton Junction,
Derbyshire DE65 6GU.
Telephone 01283 734735:
Fax: 01283 734799:
e-mail: office@nfahq.freeserve.co.uk
Web site: http://www.the-nfa.org.uk

Coarse

The Gift of Angling

by Wayne Thomas

If you are a keen angler with children I feel it is only fair to introduce them to the sport of angling with the many benefits it can bring. In this day and age many anglers it would seem do not make an effort to give kids the start they need. Angling will hopefully give a lifelong interest in the environment and a means to unwind in an ever stressful world.

I have been an angler for as long as I can remember and have never regretted my obsession with the pastime I love. Of course not everyone is destined to like fishing, I mean it must be in the genes or something. Your child may not be cut out for it but many are if given a good start.

So how do we go about introducing our children to our hobby? First of all you must try to see the world through a child's eyes. A couple of hours fishing is all you should aim for at first. Bites and plenty of fish are essential if interest is to be maintained. Children especially boys have short attention spans. So for this reason choose a venue that has an abundance of small fish. At first do not fish yourself, give all your attention to assisting your child with the task at hand. You will inevitably spend a considerable time sorting out tangles, don't lose your cool just keep calm and encourage. Spend the session shouting at your pupil and they will

never want to go again. Have regular breaks for a snack. If the going is slow try a new spot. If the fish are really not having it go home, do something else and try again another day. When they do catch try to show enthusiasm, a tiny Roach or Rudd may not excite you but it will probably thrill a child.

Tackle

Well I guess I jumped the gun a little with the above introduction as they will need to have some tackle with which to catch a few fish. Now they could use yours but that probably isn't a good idea. If its good gear it may get damaged and lead to frayed tempers, if its old cast offs it may hinder them not being suitable for the job at hand. Now I am assuming that your child is aged five to ten years. My son James is seven now and has been fishing for a couple of years. I started him off with a 3 metre Whip which he could use to catch small Roach, Carp, Rudd etc. A tackle box, a few hooks, Floats, split shot, disgorger, a bait box full of maggots and a permit will be all you require for that first trip. This should all cost you £25.00 or less.

Whip	£6.00
Packet barbless hooks (16)	£1.00
Split shot	£2.00
Floats	£2.50
Disgorger	£0.50
Spool of line	£4.00
Bait Box and Maggots	£4.00
Permit	£5.00

Compare this to the price of a playstation game or similar and I am sure you will agree its not that dear.

The main consideration when taking a child fishing is of course safety. Many children drown by lakes and rivers every year so you must supervise at all times and choose a safe venue. It would obviously be foolish to take a child fishing on a flooded river. Hygiene is also important. Many venues are infested with rats which unfortunately carry the very real threat of Wiels Disease. Make sure that you carry some anti bacterial wipes for washing of hands prior to eating and to clean any cuts or grazes picked up on the waterside.

Get it right and you'll enjoy teaching them as much as they enjoy learning!

Stuart Bray

Early Retirement

Stuart Bray, Fisheries, Recreation, Conservation and Navigation Manager for the Environment Agency, retires in May 2002 after 36 years with the Agency and its predecessors.

Stuart, who has a degree in Zoology and is a Fellow of the Institute of Fisheries Management, began his career as a biologist with Lincolnshire River Authority in 1965. Whilst there he worked on the coarse fish populations of the river Witham and other Fenland systems.

In 1968 he moved to Cornwall as Deputy Fisheries Officer to Cornwall River Authority. In 1974 he became Fisheries and Recreation Officer to SWW for North and West Devon. Then for a brief spell in the early 1980's he returned to manage the Cornish rivers before taking up the position of Recreation Officer to SWW, which involved managing all the reservoir fisheries in Devon and Cornwall. In 1990 he joined the National Rivers Authority as Regional Fisheries, Recreation and Conservation Controller and then in 1994, with the merger of South West and Wessex regions, he became FRCN manager for the whole of the South West.

During his career Stuart has been involved in many fisheries issues and improvements across the region benefiting game and coarse fish. Some of the more notable ones include: Introducing byelaws to control illegal coastal netting, building Monkokehampton fish pass on the R. Okement to allow salmon to spawn after being denied access for almost 100 years, project managing early work to establish the problems of silt deposition on egg survival of salmon and trout and developing Fisheries Action Plans for all the rivers of Devon and Cornwall.

His period of management of the reservoir fisheries was regarded as the heydays of reservoir trout fishing in the West Country and during the same period he was responsible for developing the large reservoir coarse fisheries at Tamar Lakes and Porth. He produced a coarse fish strategy for the region and set a national precedent by removing the close season for coarse fish on still waters and promoting local management.

During the past 10 years as well as becoming involved in dealing with issues from the chalk streams of Dorset and Hampshire, Stuart has been helping to develop national policy and strategy on a whole range of fisheries issues and has served on several project groups. He has also represented the Agency nationally on Sea Fisheries matters and has chaired the Eel Group.

Stuart has been a keen fisherman all his life, now fishing mainly for salmon, trout, pike and carp. In his retirement he plans to add fly-fishing for bass to this list.

He wishes to thank all those anglers and riparian owners who have helped him during his career in fisheries. Without their help much of the above would not have been possible.

Editors Note: On a personal level we at Get Hooked would like to thank Stuart for his enthusiastic contribution to the guide. Enjoy your fishing.

Nickei Pullen with a cracker caught last
September from peg 15.
Follyfoot Farm

The British Disabled Angling Association

Peter Thompson

With the implementation of the 2004 Disability Discrimination Act fast looming on the horizon, water owners are under pressure to ensure anglers with disabilities have the same access rights as able-bodied people.

And thankfully help is at hand in the form of the British Disabled Angling Association and a newly published 'Information Guide to Disability Angling' which deals with access and facilities required by water owners prepared to make the sport truly 'open to all'. With almost 9 million disabled people in the UK, the British Disabled Angling Association (BDAA) are out to ensure that every one - be they at beginner or expert level, has the opportunity to cast a line.

It was in 1996 that Walsall based Terry Moseley set up the charity Angling Link, designed to help and encourage disabled

Terry Moseley brings a fish to the net

people to at least try fishing and to encourage others to improve and excel in the sport. After five years of hard work and a growing list of members which was fast approaching 1000, last year the name Angling Link was changed to the British Disabled Angling Association, and since then has come recognition in the form of alliances with Government and major Agency's who approve of the valuable work being carried out.

It was therefore appropriate that as the name changed, so did the status of the man who began the quest, Terry Moseley becoming the first disabled person to be awarded the prestigious Anglers Conservation Association's Dick Walker Award, a title and trophy voted on by the general angling public - Terry winning the award on an unprecedented number of nominations sent in to honour his tireless work. Terry is now the BDAA secretary and still deals with the day to day running of an organisation which often garners upwards of 200 enquiries a day from people interested in their work. With this new charity now created and approaching the end of its first full year, the likes of the Environment Agency and the Countryside Alliance have committed their full support for the BDAA.

There is now a coveted place for the BDAA on the unique Environment Agency 'Angling Participation Project Group', which brings together Government, Sport England, the Angling Governing Bodies, Angling Trade Association and many others in a bid to promote the sport of angling, and which aims to put half a million new converts onto the banks of rivers and stillwaters over a three year period. Terry Moseley had a vision that would see an organisation learning all the time, not only about people's needs - but also how to gain funding to give disabled people suitable venues and increased opportunities to sample angling. That is now a reality!

It goes without saying that the BDAA do not expect all 9 million disabled people to go fishing, but they are out to give them all the chance to try it if they so desire. Hence the new booklet on access and facilities which will give water owners an insight of the needs of disabled people, and give those possible new converts a less hazardous start than in days of old when

wheelchairs often became stuck in rutted farmers fields - or even worse the potential angler found themselves in hairy confrontations with deep and cold water as they slipped or slid their way to what they had always believed from the outside to be a quiet gentile sport!

Not that coarse fishing is the only side of the sport that the BDAA have become involved in, now they have active groups who regularly take to the sea, tackle trout and seek specimen sized conquests - or to put it bluntly they have become the active voice for all and now represent a growing band that has a bigger voice in the sport. And on the drawing board now at the ever active BDAA is a second disability angling guide, concerning the various adaptations from around the world to help people with disabilities, and with a price the same as the Access guide at £1.50 it is sure to get more on board.

More recently the BDAA have been working with the Disability Rights Commission on accessibility, ready for the implementation of that important Disability Discrimination Act 1995 which comes gradually into force and takes full effect in the year 2004.

Under the act fishery bosses will have to provide for the disabled the same access and facilities they operate for able bodied people, and that could mean millions of £'s worth of work having to be carried out on existing venues. Tackle dealers will have to build ramps for access and re-arrange their shops to allow better inspection of goods for sale, because The Disability Discrimination Act aims to end the discrimination which many disabled people face and give them rights in the areas of access to goods, facilities and services, and that includes fishing!

The BDAA have an important role to play at this stage by giving guidance and information on what will be required, hence the new series of guides which have been endorsed and backed by the Government sponsored agency 'The English Federation of Disability Sport.'

Say's Terry Moseley, " For many years there has been very little in the way of access to fisheries of which many are owned by commercial companies or local authorities and the Environment agency, and we have pleaded with people within angling to make provision for disabled people to be able to gain access to waters, so we too can enjoy fishing despite the severity of disability."

"Through the BDAA we are prepared to work with fisheries and authorities, explaining the difficulties people with disabilities have, and to rectify and change the necessary facilities."

Added Terry "Until now there has been no standard approved platform design to hand or commissioned which would provide the requirements needed to access a fishery or charter boat for disabled people, that is something we are constantly working on."

The British Disabled Angling Association charity is willing to offer advice to anyone who wishes to improve their facilities before 2004. The telephone number to call is 01922 860912.
Web site: www.bdaa.co.uk

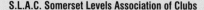

Coarse

Coarse

A Wealth of Fishing for the All-Rounder

Mike Winter

Editors Note: This editorial was submitted by Mike and the following is an extract from the accompanying letter. I feel it encapsulates the principles of Get Hooked - anglers working together, putting something into the sport for other anglers to enjoy.

'.... First I want to congratulate you on the Get Hooked Angling Guide. I have a copy of every edition and it has gone from strength to strength, it is as invaluable to me as my fishing Diary. Now I want to put something back into it and enclose a small piece for your consideration' ....

Born, bred and living as I do in East Devon there is a breadth and width of fishing so great that it is often difficult to decide where to go and what to fish for.

In the 'good old days' of Carp fishing back in the late fifties and sixties I was a founder member of the original 'Devon Carp Catchers Club' and seldom fished for anything else. Carp waters were few and far between here in those days. That was until I spent several weekends fishing the Upper Great Ouse at the invitation of Richard Walker at his fishing hut on its banks at Beachampton. Those experiences and his influence broadened my outlook and I've never spent a whole season fishing for just one or two species again.

In January I now spend my 'angling time' fishing for flatties in the Exe and Teign estuaries and for Pike in the Exeter and Tiverton canals. During January and the first half of March I spend as much time as possible fishing the Hampshire Avon and Dorset Stour for Chub, Pike and Roach. As a biologist I voluntarily observe the old coarse fish close season on all freshwaters. The latter half of March and April is devoted to trout fishing on Dartmoor streams,

chalkstreams and small stillwaters. These I fish with the dry fly and nymphs, some of my home tied 'killers' being the Dark Blue Upright, Kite's Imperial and, on the odd trip later in the summer, Tup's Indispensable, Blue Winged Olive and Caperer. Also Crowherl, Green Damsel, Pheasant Tail, Hare's Ear and Mayfly nymphs work well for me.

By May and early June the Mackerel and Bass are usually back inshore at Sidmouth, Branscombe, Beer and Seaton. Fishing for these from the shore and a small dinghy gradually takes over from sport with the Trout.

From 'the glorious 16th' of June until the middle of August I mostly fish for Carp, Tench, Bream, Eels, Crucians and Chub - interspersed with some Trout and sea fishing as the freezer empties! I love 'Chub chasing' with freelined slugs and lobworms, hiding in the lush bankside growth of summer, as much as watching the needle bubbles burst around my Tench float on a muggy, overcast dawn. I fish for Carp in the 'primitive' ways, with floating baits and with float tackle and centre-pin reel, scouring the margins.

Come late August I return to the rivers to fish for Barbel interspersed with some time on stillwaters. This style of fishing continues into November, if the weather is right, with the addition of sport with Perch and the first of the year's Pike fishing. Autumn is also the time for big Bass and I manage to squeeze in a night or two on East Devon beaches when the tides are right.

During December the Pike fishing starts in earnest along with days after Chub and Roach. By the end of December the flatfish in the estuaries get some attention and the year has come full circle.

For me variety is the spice of fishing and I enjoy every moment of it, whether it be by a hurrying Dartmoor stream, a lush Carp pool, a silkily furling chalk stream, wading in storm beach surf or bobbing in the dinghy.

Good fish are just the icing on this already rich cake for there is so much more to enjoy in fishing in South West England than just catching fish!

Prized Predators
from the Exeter Canal

Pete Gregory

For the last thirty years I have travelled and fished the length and the breadth of the UK for many different species, both in freshwater and in the sea. As I grow older and my passion for angling increases as each year passes I find myself chasing an even wider selection of weird and wonderful species. Travelling to various countries within mainland Europe, to Africa and beyond to north and south America. Seemingly though our fondest memories often lie with our experiences as a young lad at grass roots level.

For the majority of my thirty eight years the backbone of my angling apprenticeship was formed in and around Exeter and particularly on the Exeter Ship Canal where I have landed every species of fish present over the years but my first love is, and always will be, predatory fish. And at the top of the food chain, without any doubt, is the freshwater Pike.

In recent years the canal has produced a good number of 20lb plus specimens with the odd one or two weighing over the magical 30lb - every Pike angler's dream fish.

Realistically on every trip I set my sights on catching double figure fish worthy of photographs but the Pike angler must be prepared for lengthy blanks or the odd small Jack. Whatever the size of the fish treat them all with the same level of respect. Make sure you have the correct unhooking tools and make sure you get the fish back in the water quickly and with the minimum of fuss. - remember a Jack today could be a twenty a few years down the road!

Pike can be caught all the year round with lure anglers doing better in the warmer months, but for most of us who fish the canal the Pike season really takes off as the nights begin to draw in and late autumn arrives. With the air and water temperatures plummeting natural baits reign supreme with livebaits and sea deadbaits regularly taking good quality Pike. All accepted and legal methods are allowed on the canal and, with the recent reintroduction of livebaiting, all our options are now open. However please note that livebaiting is permitted only under strict guidelines and anyone found contravening these rules will be severely dealt with.

It is my opinion that the larger Pike will always prefer a deadbait when the water temperature is very cold. Large Pike are generally lazy fish and rely more on scent and scavenging, whereas small Pike like to chase and react well to movement. I have personally caught more than thirty Pike of over 20lb from the canal with most of them falling to seabaits.

So, what makes the Exeter Canal an exceptional Pike fishery and different from your 'traditional' canal? There may be a number of reasons but I think it is mainly that the canal is termed a 'deep water canal', with the average depth varying from 9 to 11 feet, depending on whether you fish the upper canal which extends from the city basin to the double locks (which has the greater depth) or from beyond the double locks to the turf basin. The canal has a rich larder of natural foods that all species of fish take advantage of. Much of this 'food' lives among the weed and aquatic plants that are present throughout the canal for much of the year. The whole ecology of the canal is a well balanced one.

We now generally accept the Pike as a true sporting fish, gone are the days when Pike were mistreated and culled senselessly because of old wives tales and ignorance. Ask anyone who has removed all large Pike from a water of the dire consequences that have followed with explosions in the populations of small fish.

The Exeter Canal is without doubt the jewel in the crown as far as Pike fishing in Devon goes. It is not an easy water but, just occasionally, on those rare red letter days it is possible to catch a dozen or more fish. Half of these could be into double figures with a twenty or two thrown in for good measure. Needless to say you can return the next day and fish from dusk to dawn without as much as a single run! Pike can, and do, travel long distances if disturbed.

I have caught some of my largest Pike in the hours of darkness, particularly during the depths

A fine Mirror Carp.
Simpson Valley

A 29lb plus fish caught on a large deadbait.

of winter when temperatures are well below freezing. This is when heavily scented dead baits outscore any other bait and only last November I caught four fish over a two day period. Two 9 pounders, a double of 16lb 3oz and a 'big un' of 24lb 14oz. I subsequently made four more visits and caught absolutely nothing! As with all forms of fishing it is the memories of the good days past and the promise of those, hopefully, yet to come that keep you going through the 'blanks'.

So what of the future of Pike fishing on the Canal? As any angler knows Pike are at the top of the predatory fish food chain and have no natural enemies from below the waterline and very few from above when fully mature. Paradoxically the only real enemy the Pike has is the Pike angler himself. I am sure no angler would set out to deliberately harm any Pike caught but it does happen.

As I fish or walk the canal banks I observe a lot of anglers having a go for Pike, maybe for the first time, and many have woefully inadequate tackle to deal with a big fish. Suitable sized landing nets, unhooking mats, and the correct unhooking tools should all be part of your equipment. The dentistry of the Pike is truly

awesome and great care must be taken to safely unhook a fish with no damage being done to the fish or the angler! Regardless of the species you fish for you owe it to your quarry to learn all you can of its' natural history to keep it in perfect health and ensure its survival for all anglers to enjoy.

So what is the best way to learn? The best place to start is usually the local angling club, in this case the Exeter and District Angling Association. Information is available in the directory section of this guide and the club secretary will be able to point you in the direction of experienced local anglers who will be glad to give help and advice. You could also join The Pike Anglers Club of Great Britain from where you can be put in touch with the regional branch in Exeter. It is without doubt the best way to learn and trust me when I say your catch rate will improve two fold.

So remember, treat all Pike with respect. Despite their reputation as a fierce predator large Pike are still very vulnerable to deep hooking, bad handling or mistreatment of any kind. Enjoy your fishing and I hope to see you all on the Canal very soon.

*A 6lb Common on crust for new proprietor Julian Harrod.
Luccombe Fishery*

A Golden Opportunity

*by Dr Bruno Broughton - Technical Director,
The Angling Trades Association*

When angling historians consider the start of the 21st century, 2001 will stand out as a special year. Before the spring bulbs had emerged, the country was in the grip of the world's worst outbreak of Foot & Mouth Disease. Fisheries in large swathes of the countryside were shut; tackle retailers were facing bankruptcy; and many believed that angling would be damaged irreparably.

Yet, remarkably, the sport is now in a far healthier position that anyone could have predicted. For example, the major national angling bodies pooled their expertise and shelved their differences to form the National Angling Alliance. Against the expectations of the pundits, the NAA has gone from strength to strength, tackling major issues and campaigning quietly, but effectively, to ensure that angling really did punch its full weight.

Behind-the-scenes contact and co-operation with the Countryside Alliance proved that even where there were deep-seated differences, the maxim of "Jaw, jaw, not war, war" was a sensible course. At the very least, the ongoing dialogue will ensure that anglers of different persuasions will not be duplicating their efforts… something which has marred the sport for decades. Against the odds, anglers flocked back to the banks of rivers and lake; reservoirs and canals; piers and offshore wrecks. Commercial fisheries enjoyed an unexpected boom, starters fishing kits were sold in record numbers, and the Environment Agency (EA) licence sales exceeded the gloomy expectations. More importantly, there was clear evidence that young people were turning back to angling.

Important Research

At the start of 2002 came the news that will shape many forthcoming initiatives to draw more people to angling. The EA revealed the findings of its 'attitudes to angling' research. The headline results are startling: almost 8% of the population is very or quite interested in taking up angling… and if they all did so the angling community would almost double in size!

Thankfully, angling has been well aware of the need to unify, to modernise its structures, and to promote the benefits of the sport to society as a whole and politicians in particular. It is no mere coincidence that interest in the sport is burgeoning and angling is again becoming a trendy pastime for young people. It is the consequence of the persistence, determination and flow of hard-earned cash that the major angling bodies have invested in the future.

Take A Friend Fishing

For example, the Angling Trades Association (ATA) has been the driving force behind the 'Take A Friend Fishing' campaign. For more than a decade the scheme - which has taken several forms - has targeted existing anglers and encouraged them to introduce others to angling. The wisdom of this approach is underlined by the research findings: the most important impediment to participation among non-anglers was found to be the absence of anyone with whom to fish. Not surprisingly, the 'Take A Friend Fishing' campaign, and its offshoot 'Give Angling A Go' will form the theme for the promotion of the sport in the next few years.

For details of how you can help, contact the Angling Trades Association at: Federation House, National Agricultural Centre, Stoneleigh Park, Warks. CV8 2RF.

Professional Coaching

In other sports a raw newcomer would expect to be able to hire the necessary kit and receive expert guidance during his or her first sessions. This guiding principle led to the formation of the Professional Anglers Association (PAA) three years ago. Since then, almost 200 experienced anglers have been taught how to teach others, and these qualified, professional coaches have the skill, training and equipment to help new and inexperienced anglers. The three angling governing bodies have joined the PAA in a new, government-backed coaching scheme… another example of the fruits of angling unity.

As this scheme develops during the year, every qualified coach will have been trained to the same, high standard, received Child

Protection training, be in possession of insurance and First Aid qualifications, and been screened by the Criminal Records Bureau. The move will boost the number of PAA coaches, each of whom will be encouraged to form links with local fisheries, retailers and angling clubs.

Details of the coach nearest to you can be found on the PAA website (www.paauk.com). For more information and for details on how you can become a coach, contact the PAA on Tel: 01952 691515.

National Fishing Week... or Fortnight!

Regular readers of this guide will know already that the week beginning with the August holiday weekend is designated as National Fishing Week (NFW). Such has been the success of the initiative that the 'week' is now a two-week period during which numerous special events will be staged throughout the country. They will include nature trails by the waterside, coaching sessions, angling competitions and angling festivals... amongst others. In 2001 the number of participants and spectators reached a new, all-time high of almost half a million!

Details of what is being planned near you will appear in the national angling press and in regional newspapers. Further information is available from: NFW, Merley House, Merley House Lane, Wimbourne, Dorset BH11 3AA. There is a website link on the website www.fisheries.co.uk

All At Sea

Those who fish at sea have long since realised that their sport is dependant on the quantity and quality of the marine fish that are not exploited by commercial fishing. The failure of the Common Fisheries Policy to protect stocks has led to vigorous campaigning for the rights of anglers to an equitable share of the 'catch'. This unsung but unstinting work - which receives little publicity - shows signs of bearing fruit.

The EU Commissioners are now well aware of the Europe-wide lobby on behalf of recreational sea anglers, and there is optimism that, finally, they will acknowledge that sport-fishing yields financial benefits which far outweighs the value of the commercial catch.

Anyone who cares about sea angling is encouraged to add his or her voice to this groundswell for change by contacting the National Federation of Sea Anglers. Details of what you can contribute are available from the NFSA on Tel: 01364 644643.

Win, Win

These and many other action plans demonstrate why, for all the problems it will encounter, angling is in a strong, healthy state to face the future and expand its number of participants. That possibility should act as a shot in the arm for ailing angling clubs and associations; a spur to existing and would-be fishery owners; an important opportunity for the manufacturing and retail trade; and a vital lifeline for the cash-strapped Environment Agency.

More anglers mean greater investment in the infrastructure of the sport and greater benefits for everyone. The only potential losers? Those people who wanted to take up angling but who failed to do so. It is up to all of us to make sure that they receive the invitation!

The ACA

The ACA fights pollution actively. It's main function is to protect the waters you fish, not only for you, but for the many generations to follow. Over the years the ACA has achieved some remarkable success, but it can't continue without your support.

No other body performs the vital task carried out by the ACA. If your sport has been ruined by pollution we will advise you on the evidence necessary for legal action to be taken and will fight the case on your behalf. The ACA will meet the legal and other costs of the case.

The ACA is the most effective anti-pollution organisation in Britain.

For further details and application forms please contact us at:
Anglers' Conservation Association,
6 Rainbow Street,
Leominster,
Herefordshire HR6 8DQ
Tel: 01568 620447

The business end of a 24lb 9oz Common. Bake Lakes

Book Reviews

Guardians of the Salmon

- Gordon H Bielby

Halsgrove
ISBN 1-84114-139-9
£16.95

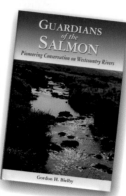

GUARDIANS *of the* **SALMON**
Pioneering Conservation on Westcountry Rivers

Gordon H. Bielby

Not a book about fishing but a fascinating insight into the pretty incredible history of the salmon in westcountry rivers.

I was amazed to find that salmon breeding on a large scale started on the Exe as long ago as 1864 and so it has continued in various forms throughout the westcountry to the present day.

There are also references as early as1669 where salmon were seen in 'great quantity' around Plymouth and on the Exe. Those days are far behind us now but, as detailed in other articles in this guide, the promise has rarely been greater for a return to good runs of salmon throughout the area.

Gordon Bielby spent his entire career on the environmental side of rivers management bodies in the South West and this book reflects on his, and his associates, efforts to thwart the adversaries of the salmon, biological, chemical, geographical and the human kind.

There are many humerous anecdotes relating to the constant battle between the baliffs and the poachers and some of the ludicrous excuses people come up with when caught in possesion of illegally landed fish. The book also has an account of the famous unsolved murder of private bailiff Mr Archibald Reed of Tiverton in July 1887.

There are a few black and white pictures, some showing the awesome catches that were not uncommon, including a famous 61lb fish taken from the Exe nets in March 1924.

Overall this is an entertaining and informative book and gives a valuable insight into the work done over the years by the few to try and maintain the salmon as a sporting quarry for the many.

The Secret Carp - Chris Yates

Merlin Unwin Books - ISBN 1-873674-28-7
£17.99

This is one of those books you should read whether you fish or not. Chris Yates has almost done the impossible and distilled the 'essence' of angling into the 171 pages of The Secret Carp.

It's not about tackle and rigs and bait but about what it is that makes us want to go fishing. Of course everybodies 'essence' will be slightly different and what brings a state of euphoria for one angler may leave another cold.

It's main focus is carp angling but the beautifully descriptive appreciation of his surroundings, the changing weather, the wildlife that accompanies you as you fish will strike a chord with all anglers, whether you are wading in a trout stream, standing in the surf, cruising to a wreck at dawn or, as the author is, nestled in the undergrowth by a perfect carp lake.

Chris has highlighted details that we take for granted, such as smell, and described how we make associations, we can all relate to it, mackeral, lobworms, trout pellets, maggots all evoke a mental picture for anglers - I know you are doing it now!

The book is a sort of real time narration of a fishing session on a carp lake, detailing observations and thoughts as Chris jots them in his notebook, interspersed with other related stories and musings on his own fishing experiences. It's pretty 'wordy' in places for a fishing book but is wonderfully evocative and really explains what makes Chris (and the majority of us) go fishing.

There is also a chapter where Chris gives his opinion on artificially stocked 'holes in the ground' but we have to bear in mind there are not enough secret carp lakes to satisfy the huge commercially driven machine that is modern carp angling.

I can only hint at the pleasures that await within the pages of this book. Buy it and read it, again and again.

THE SECRET CARP
Chris Yates

'Unquestionably the read of the year, indeed of many years. It's a potential classic'
The Times

*Another successful young angler with a 9lb Common Carp.
Meadowside Fishery*

Coombe Water Fishery

CARP - TENCH BREAM - ROACH

3 secluded lakes in beautiful surroundings

Situated just half a mile from Kingsbridge.

IDEAL FOR MATCHES
Top Match Weight 149lb!

No EA Licence required
- Carp to 25lb
- Open dawn to dusk
- Self Catering plus Farmhouse B&B with full en-suite facilities

All enquiries please phone Jonathan & Beni Robinson

TEL: 01548 852038

The South West's Leading Pet and Aquatic Centre

ESCOT AQUATIC CENTRE

Fishery Management
- Coarse fish supply and control
- Pond construction and management
- Pond weed management (including certification to spray)
- Reedbed construction and management
- Aquatic planting
- Associated tree and shrub planting
- Fencing

Twice winners of National Specialist Pet Centre of the Year

Other services include:
- Garden pond and water feature design, construction and landscaping
- Pond filtration, maintenance and cleaning
- Fish health and husbandry
- Garden landscaping and planting

www.escot-devon.co.uk

ESCOT AQUATIC CENTRE

Escot Ottery St Mary Devon EX11 1LU

Telephone (01404) 822188
Fax (01404) 822903
Email: escot@eclipse.co.uk

Coarse

River Doctors
The Cain Consultancy

by Wendy Trevennor.

Remember the Cruikshank cartoon "The March of Bricks and Mortar", deploring the Victorian spread of urbanisation and destruction of the countryside? Yes, you do; it's in all the history books.

Now picture, in a glorious reversal of that image, trout, brooklime and dragonflies in a city centre park. A pipe dream? Not if Simon Cain, the Wiltshire-based "river doctor", has anything to say about it. And he has a whole black bag full of solutions. For just as rural chalk streams damaged by natural or agricultural factors can be healed and brought back to their full glory, so can even the lifeless bottle and supermarket trolley-laden waters of urban waterways be made to bloom again. With the right technical knowledge and a degree of commitment from supporting agencies, habitats can be created and sustained for a wide range of wildlife, and in stretches less than 100 meters in length.

Simon, who specialises in sustainable green engineering and innovative solutions to environmental problems affecting waterways, is currently working on the Rivers Avon and Nadder around their confluence in a Salisbury park where human activity has been one of the most important factors in the breakdown of riparian habitats. The Avon is listed among the top 100 rivers in Europe for biodiversity - out of town, that is. Simon's challenge was to find aesthetically pleasing and environmentally sound ways to extend this into the city centre.

This spring and summer he and his workers will have the joy of seeing "a mosaic" of habitats come to life along rebuilt banks in Salisburys' Queen Elizabeth Gardens, where last year only ducks and bread-throwing strollers could enjoy the river. Over the course of years the river has widened here as banks broke down under the pressure of currents, human feet and water bird activity. This widening caused the river to flow more sluggishly, depriving water life of oxygen and silting up the gravel bed. Trout will not tolerate this, and neither will Ranunculus, a vital indicator of water quality. Also, as the banks continuously errode and fall in, plant life is lost, reducing diversity on the margins.

"A common solution along urban river banks is the use of gabions - metal cages filled with armour stone," said Simon. "Of course this produces a completely sterile environment and plants can't grow in stony ground."

So here's the clever bit. Unpromising looking man made materials, including plastic mesh reinforced with galvanised steel wire, can be used to mend the banks in such a way that they stay mended and look beautiful. "In areas like this one, where there is intense human activity, like children climbing in and out of the water, any natural material would rapidly deconstruct. This solution is sustainable."

A stroll along the two short stretches of river now reveals banks lined with a geo-textile fabric, neat as surgical sutures but with rather more potential for a full return to natural beauty. Some planting of sedges and other marginal species has already taken place, using plants supplied by the British Native Plant Species Centre in Buckinghamshire, and the textured revetments will trap the natural rootstock and seed bank, delivered to the site during the winter floods. This will ensure a full compliment of Avon plants to bind the structure together as they become established.

Mid-stream the water now runs fast and clear over clean gravel, a dream home for Ranunculus, Stone Loach and Bullheads, and a spawning haven for wild trout, and who knows, even salmon may use it. And by use of brushwood mattresses, Simon has created sloping marginal sills where silt and detritus will welcome aquatic worms, snails, midge larvae and brook lampreys, a European protected species. Still further up the margin, this gives way to habitat for water loving land plants such as Purple Loosestrife, Meadowsweet and a variety of sedges and reeds.

"It is interesting, when you put a wild river bank in the middle of a city centre, to see what species turn up and how they adapt to the new habitat." said Simon. "We may have expectations about the colonisers, but there are always

Sue Brittain from Southampton with a scale perfect 12lb 8oz Common.
Avalon

Coarse

Coarse

surprises, as fish and birds follow the insect life. You are never quite sure what you will get."

As summer draws on he expects butterflies: Red Admirals, Peacocks, Fritillaries, in addition to mayflies, stoneflies, caddis and dragonflies.

Wild birds such as blackbirds, robins, wrens, wagtails and snipe should arrive to join the ducks, swans moorhens and coots, and the habitat will be ideal for nesting wildfowl.

"The food chains are highly complex, but basically plants equals insects equals fish equals birds," said Simon.

"All of these works are the result of a careful planning process involving English Nature and the Environment Agency," said Simon. "Although gradients have been built into the banks, their height is unchanged and thus their carrying capacity is undiminished." He added that careful planning is vital to make sure enhancement works don't detract from essential flood defence issues.

"All these works are the result of more than a decade's collaboration with English Nature and the Environment Agency to push forward the knowledge of green engineering and habitat enhancement," explained Simon. He and his work force have received a very positive response from the general public, who have watched the proceedings with great interest every day.

"Councils are beginning to realise the benefit of making their waterways attractive. Attractive surroundings means more tourists and more money going into the local economy. A win-win situation."

The Cain Consultancy - 01980 621088

New "Association of River Trusts"

The Eden Rivers Trust, Tweed Foundation, Westcountry Rivers Trust and Wye Foundation announced on Thursday 4th October 2001 at a meeting and seminar in Derby, the public launch of an "Association of River Trusts" for England and Wales. This development has followed a considerable consultation period including communication with other river and fishery improvement trusts, the Scottish Fishery Trusts and the Environment Agency. The four "founder member" Trusts have all made significant contributions in their own areas to improve the aquatic environment and adjacent river corridor.

The main aim of the Association will be to network, co-ordinate, represent and develop the aims and interests of the member Trusts. Its main activities will be:

a) Exchange information/ best practice (including workshops and publications)
b) Discuss common problems and make appropriate representations to Government, decision makers and opinion formers and other appropriate organisations
c) Provide advice and guidance to its members and help with new start ups and emerging like-minded groups
d) Explore funding opportunities

Arlin Rickard, Director of the Association said, "There is an increasing awareness of the importance of rivers for wildlife and of managing catchments and their ecosystems as environmental service providers. Improving the riverine corridor and surrounding catchment is a complex process involving many diverse organisations. The Association of River Trusts provides an opportunity to influence and develop this in a positive way."

David Clarke, the Head of Fisheries Recreation and Conservation for the Environment Agency said, "The Environment Agency welcomes the formation of the Association of Rivers Trusts and looks forward to working closely with them to improve our rivers."

For further information, please contact Arlin Rickard (ART Director and spokesman) C/o Westcountry Rivers Trust, Fore Street, Lifton, Devon, PL16 OAA
Tel: 01566 784488
Fax: 01566 784404
E.mail: wrt@wrt.org.uk

76

*That's the fish of a lifetime!
Ten year old Ben Jury with a 29lb 4oz Mirror
Carp from the 11 acre lake.
New Forest Water Park*

Coarse fishing in the South Wessex Area

By Steve Carter

The Hampshire Avon

The Hampshire Avon rises in the Vale of Pewsey and, with its tributaries the Bourne and Wylye, drains the chalk of Salisbury plain. The River Nadder, which is joined by the Wylye near Salisbury drains part of the South Wiltshire Downs and (more significantly for anglers) the clays of the Wardour Vale.

The River Ebble and the Ashford Water enter the Avon downstream of Salisbury and Fordingbridge respectively.

Below Fordingbridge a number of New Forest streams enter the Avon. The Avon flows into Christchurch Harbour where it is joined by the River Stour.

The total fall from Pewsey to the sea is 110m, the average gradient downstream of Salisbury is approximately 2m/km. The flow is characterised by a high groundwater component derived from springs rising in the headwaters of the Avon and its major tributaries.

The river and its tributaries are of national and international importance for their wildlife communities. The majority of the river has been designated as a river Site of Special Scientific Interest (SSSI). The river is also a Special Area of Conservation (SAC) under the EU Habitats Directive (Atlantic Salmon are listed as threatened in Annexe II of the EC "Habitats and species" Directive). The catchment is an internationally important area for over wintering waders and wildfowl.

The Hampshire Avon is nationally renowned as one of Britains' premiere coarse fisheries. The name 'Hampshire Avon' distinguishes it from the other seven 'River Avons' found in the UK, while in fact the Hampshire Avon passes through Wiltshire, Hampshire and Dorset.

The Avon is essentially a 'chalk stream', the chalk aquifer ensures an exceptionally high water quality contributing to the species richness and the abundance of aquatic biota, this has proved a highly advantageous situation for coarse fish populations in the Avon, in terms of growth rates.

The chalk influence of the Avon catchment ensures that the river reacts relatively slowly to rainfall compared to the clay dominated Dorset Stour catchment. However once the chalk aquifer reaches critical saturation level during winter, the springs 'break'. The extra groundwater often maintains a high flow and level through the rest of the winter. Without the influence of floodwater from the Nadder, the Avon would run clear for most of the year.

Species of coarse fish to be found in the Avon include barbel, bream, carp, chub, dace, perch, pike, and roach. All of these species reach specimen sizes, in particular barbel, chub, pike and roach. The majority of coarse angling takes place between Salisbury and Christchurch.

The Avon is perhaps best known for its superb roach fishing. Many specimens of 2lb+ are caught every year including several fish over 3lbs. The best roach fishing can be found on the middle and lower reaches of the river. Local roach anglers will often wait until the New Year before targeting specimen roach. By this time the river has flushed out old weed growth and the increased flows will have pushed roach into their winter lies. Notable areas for specimen roach include: Salisbury & DAC and London AA waters around Salisbury; Fordingbridge Rec. (day ticket venue); Christchurch AC stretches (Fordingbridge area and Somerely Estate); Ringwood & DAS (Ibsley and Ringwood area) through to Winkton (day ticket).

Chub fishing has been extremely good over recent years, 2001 was no exception with many fish in the 6lb bracket, several of 7lb+ (up to 7lb10oz) the largest chub reported included fish of 8lb 2oz and 8lb 10oz. Specimen chub are caught throughout the season. Notable areas for chub extend from Salisbury to Hale, but also include the middle to lower reaches: Christchurch AC waters (Somerely Estate, Royalty Fishery); Ringwood & DAS (Ibsley and Ringwood area); Lifelands (day ticket).

*'Little Blackie' (that's the fish) at 32lb 12oz
Newton Abbot Fishing Association*

Barbel captures reported in 2001 included many fish between 10lb+ and 13lb+, most of these fish came from the middle and lower stretches of the Avon. Exceptional specimens reported in 2001 included fish of 16lb 4oz, 15lb1oz, and 14lb 5oz. Barbel are caught throughout the season and are to be found from London AA waters around Salisbury downstream to the Royalty Fishery at Christchurch. Areas of note include: Lifelands, Ringwood, Severalls Fishery, and the Royalty Fishery.

Ross Urquart - 2lb gravel pit Perch

Dace are found throughout the Avon and River Nadder. In 2001 Lifelands and the Severalls Fishery, Ringwood produced 30lb nets of dace during the autumn. The Royalty Fishery at Christchurch offers good all round coarse fishing, with barbel 10lb+, carp 30lb+, chub 6lb+, pike 30lb +, nets of dace, and in 2001 a 200lb haul of bream was reported. The Royalty Fishery is now under the control of Christchurch AC, day tickets are available as usual.

Season tickets, guest tickets and day tickets for various club waters can be obtained from local tackle shops. There are also a number of smaller syndicates that offer limited membership and access to estate waters. Day ticket fisheries can be found at Fordingbridge, Ringwood, Bisterne, Winkton and the Royalty at Christchurch.

The Dorset Stour

The Stour rises on the greensand at St Peter's Pump in Stourhead Gardens and flows 96km to the sea at Christchurch: the fall over its entire course is approximately 230m. The catchment lies predominantly within the county of Dorset with smaller areas falling within Somerset and Wiltshire.

From Stourhead, the river flows south to Gillingham where it is joined by the Shreen and Lodden. The Blackmore Vale to the west and south is drained by the Stour and a dense network of tributaries. Flowing towards Sturminster Newton, the Stour is joined by several clay influenced tributaries. Fewer tributaries join the Stour as it flows through a narrower valley towards Blandford Forum. Downstream of Blandford the landscape opens up again across pasture and arable fields. Towards the coast, the floodplain widens to form extensive level pastures, marsh and mudflats, meeting the Hampshire Avon at Christchurch Harbour.

The clay influence of the Blackmore Vale ensures that the river reacts more quickly to rainfall compared to groundwater dominated chalk streams in the neighbouring Frome and Avon catchments. Rapidly rising levels and coloured water are regular winter features of this river.

The Dorset Stour has often been perceived as being outshone by its near neighbour the Hampshire Avon. However "dyed in the wool" Stour anglers have over the years quietly notched up some very impressive specimen coarse fish catches topped by the British record roach of 4lb 3oz from Corfe Mullen in 1990.

Through the summer months the many relatively slow flowing impounded sections on the Stour are highly productive in terms of aquatic plants and invertebrates supporting a wide diversity of coarse fish species with roach being the most abundant. However, the Stour

81

has traditionally been regarded as a winter fishery, fishing well once the weed has blown out, especially after a flood, when the river is fining off but still carrying a little bit of colour.

Species of coarse fish to be found in the Stour include barbel, bleak, bream, carp, chub, dace, perch, pike, roach and tench. Barbel, chub, pike and roach all reach specimen sizes.

Coarse fishing takes place on the Stour from Gillingham to Christchurch Harbour. The upper reaches from Gillingham to Marnhull are noted for throwing up the occasional big roach of 2lb+. Chub, dace, perch and pike are also present. Most of the club water here is controlled by Gillingham & DAA.

Matt Carter - 31lb 4oz Avon Pike

Towards the later part of 2001 the stretch upstream of Sturminster Newton Mill produced good bags of roach with weights topping 30lb. The waters from Sturminster to Durweston are noted for having produced specimen chub of 6lb+, roach of 3lb+ and pike of 20lb+. Shoals of large bream and the odd large tench are also present. Parts of these stretches are controlled by Sturminster & Hinton AA and Durweston AA; a number of other local clubs also control short sections of fishing within this reach.

The Stour around Blandford has got a good track record for producing roach over 2lb, chub of 5lb+ and pike of 20lb+. Good mixed nets of roach, dace, chub and perch along with bags

of large bream are taken in matches. A bream of 8lb 10oz was reported from the Crown Meadows in 2001. Blandford & DAC control parts of this section, and there is a limited "free stretch" owned by the council at Blandford (Please note: an Environment Agency rod licence is still required to fish here).

Moving downstream to the Wimborne area, some exceptional specimen chub and barbel have been captured here in recent years including chub of 7lb+ and barbel of 14lb+. The last 7 years have seen an increase in the stocks of perch with 2lb+ specimens appearing regularly; specimens of 3lb+ were captured in 2001. Wimborne & DAC, Christchurch AC and Ringwood & DAS control fishing on various sections around Wimborne.

Longham, Manor Farm, Muscliffe and Throop are well known for the specimen coarse fish produced each season including: 10lb+ barbel, 6lb+ chub, 20lb+ pike and 2lb+ roach. At least two barbel of 14lb+ were reported from the lower Stour in 2001, with a 14lb 9oz being the largest. A number of big chub were reported from the middle and lower reaches of the Stour in 2001 including several over 7lb topped by a 7lb14oz specimen. There is limited "free fishing" (an Environment Agency rod licence is still required) on the council owned stretches at Longham and Muscliffe. Most of the club controlled waters in this reach come under either Christchurch AC or Ringwood & DAS.

Apart from numerous 6lb+ chub and double figured barbel reported in 2001, Throop is also noted for its bream shoals with a 100lb haul of bream in 2001, the largest bream reported weighed in at 11lb.

The tidal Stour includes lower Throop downstream to the Harbour. Here some of the best pleasure and match fishing weights of roach and dace can be made in the area.

Throop Fishery is managed by Ringwood & DAS, whilst the tidal section is largely controlled by Christchurch AC. Both clubs issue day tickets; contact local tackle shops for more details.

The River Frome

The River Frome rises on the North Dorset Downs near Evershot, and flows down a gradient of 2.2m/km over approximately 60km to the sea at Poole Harbour. The catchment is predominantly rural and lies entirely within the county of Dorset.

From Evershot the Frome flows south to be joined near Cattistock by the Wraxall Brook, and at Maiden Newton by the River Hooke. Two small streams, the Sydling Water and the Cerne, also join the Frome upstream of Dorchester. Below Dorchester, the Win, South Winterbourne and Tadnoll Brook enter from the south, while the Frome itself meanders in an easterly direction to Poole Harbour.

The Frome downstream of Dorchester has been notified as a river Site of Special Scientific Interest (SSSI). This section supports species rich plant communities, rare and scarce aquatic invertebrates and a range of fish species.

The Frome is similar in character to the Hampshire Avon in the fact that both rise from chalk based aquifers.

The River Frome is primarily a salmonid fishery controlled by private syndicates and large estates, access to coarse fishing on the River Frome is therefore fairly limited. However the range of coarse fish found in the River Frome is unique in that it represents a more natural assemblage of species. This is because the fishery has been managed almost exclusively for salmon and trout.

Coarse fish species found in the Frome include dace, roach, grayling and pike, these species regularly turn up fish of specimen sized proportions. Of the coarse fish, the Frome is most noted for specimen grayling, regularly producing fish over 2lb, with several fish over 3lb reported each season. Specimen grayling exceeding 4lbs have been recorded in the past. The fishery at Wareham is owned by the

Environment Agency. Coarse fishing in the area around the quay allows good bags of roach and dace to be made from autumn onwards. This stretch has in the past produced specimen roach over 3lb.

In 2001 numbers of grayling between 12oz to 2lb and good nets of dace have been caught on various stretches owned by the Wareham & DAS and Dorchester & DAS. Specimen sized grayling are recorded each season at the Pallington Lakes day ticket stretch of the Frome. Christchurch AC lease a stretch of the main river and carrier at Tincleton, an area which contains specimen sized grayling and dace.

Dorchester FC control stretches of the Frome around Dorchester although this is primarily a premier trout fishery. Some of the most notable specimen grayling have been recorded from the main river and its carriers in this area. Small numbers of 2lb+ roach have also been caught here in recent years.

Stillwaters and Canals

There are many stillwaters offering coarse fishing throughout the South Wessex Area, including ponds, lakes, gravel pits and a short section of the Kennet and Avon Canal near Devizes.

Many gravel pits were dug out in the Ringwood area during the 1950s and 1960s. These are now fully matured coarse fisheries offering anglers the opportunity to catch carp of up to 40lb, tench over 10lb, and large bream and roach.

Coarse fish reported from the Ringwood pits in 2001 included: specimen carp (a large number of 20lb fish, several over 30lb and a 42lb 6oz specimen); specimen tench (a large number between 6 and 9lb, several 10lb+, with the largest weighing 12lb1oz); bream to 14lb 4oz; crucian over 3lb; pike over 20lb. Christchurch AC and Ringwood & DAS control most of the lakes and pits around Ringwood.

Most of the angling clubs in the South Wessex area have several lakes and ponds under their control, further information can be found in this guide (see fishing directory) or from local tackle shops. Season tickets, guest tickets and day

A real 'lump' of a Carp weighing 23lb 8oz from Somerley Lakes.
Christchurch Angling Club

Tom Carter - 5lb Avon Bream

Coarse

Go fishing with Wessex Water

Whether you are a keen angler or just enjoy an occasional day out fishing, Wessex Water's reservoirs provide the perfect setting.

Anglers can enjoy their favourite sport at our Somerset fisheries at Clatworthy, Hawkridge and Sutton Bingham. Durleigh Reservoir, just south of Bridgwater, offers coarse anglers a similar opportunity.

Clatworthy:

Season: 20 March - 13 October 2002

Situated in the Brendon Hills on the edge of the Exmoor National Park in west Somerset, Clatworthy Reservoir impounds the head waters of the River Tone.

Anglers can enjoy fishing for rainbow and brown trout from the banks of this 130 acre reservoir or from a boat, which anglers are recommended to book in advance.

Clatworthy offers good top of the water fishing with nymphs or dry flies or at the deep areas with sinking lines and flashing lures.

For further information about fishing at Clatworthy, contact the ranger Dave Pursey on 01984 624658.

Hawkridge:

Season: 20 March - 13 October 2002

This upland reservoir, seven miles west of Bridgwater, nestles in a small valley on the Quantock Hills in an Area of Outstanding Natural Beauty.

The 32 acre reservoir provides fishing facilities for brown or rainbow trout from the bank or a boat, which anglers are recommended to book in advance.

An updated fishing report as well as information on the latest flies, tactics and catch rate can be found in the lodge.

For further details about fishing at Hawkridge, please contact the ranger Gary Howe on 01278 671840

tickets for various club waters can be obtained from local tackle shops. There are also a large number of day ticket fisheries offering a variety of ponds and complexes of lakes, with mixed coarse fish (bream, carp, crucian, perch, pike, roach, and tench).

In the Avon catchment some of the day ticket fisheries include: Hurst Pond, the Longhouse Fishery, New Forest Water Park, Peter's Finger Lake, Walden's Farm, and Witherington Farm. Captures reported in the angling press in 2001 included: Hurst Pond (several large perch to 3lb7oz); Longhouse Fishery (carp bags to 174lb, tench to 6lb12oz, perch 3lb); New Forest Water Park (several carp over 20lb, tench of 7lb, perch 3lb); Shearwater (carp bags of 100lb+, bream bags of 50lb+); Walden's Farm (carp bags 50lb+, perch 3lb, pike 19lb, tench 7lb); Witherington Farm (carp bags 100lb+).

Day ticket fisheries in the Stour catchment include Todber Manor Fishery where captures reported in 2001 included carp bags of over 100lb.

Day ticket fisheries in the Frome catchment include: Luckfield Lake, Pallington Fishery, Radipole Lake, and Warmwell Lakes. Captures reported in 2001included: Luckfield Lake (tench to 7lb 8oz); Pallington Lakes (several carp over 20lb, largest 33lb; and tench to 7lb 8oz); Warmwell Lakes (carp to 31lb 8oz, perch to 3lb14oz).

Coarse

Fabulous 10lb 15oz Barbel from the Bristol Avon at Avoncliffe for Neville Day. Bristol, Bath and Wilts A.A.

Sutton Bingham:

Season from 20 March - 13 October 2002

Situated some four miles south of Yeovil, Sutton Bingham reservoir is a 142 acre lowland fishery, set in the gently rolling hills of the Somerset and Dorset border.

The reservoir offers excellent fly fishing for rainbow and brown trout, either from the bank or a boat. A " wheelie " boat is available for wheelchair users. It is recommended to book boats in advance.

Because Sutton Bingham is a lowland reservoir, the water is not deep and the most popular method of fishing is with a floating line and mainly small lures and nymphs.

For more details about fishing at Sutton Bingham, contact ranger Ivan Tinsley on 01935 872389.

Otterhead Lakes:

Season from 1 April - 30 September 2002

The two lakes at Otterhead once formed part of a landscaped estate. The surroundings have now run wild and provide a beautiful setting for fishing.

It is now a nature reserve managed by the Somerset Wildlife Trust on behalf of Wessex Water.

The lakes are situated on the Blackdown Hills, south of Taunton and one mile north of the village of Churchingford.

For further information contact club secretary Mike Woolen on 01460 65977.

Durleigh:

Open every day except 25 & 26 December and 1 January

One of the oldest in the Wessex Water region, Durleigh reservoir is the only Wessex Water reservoir dedicated to public coarse fishing.

Anglers can fish over 80 acres which provide an abundance of coarse fish for matches or the casual angler.

This lowland reservoir contains carp, roach, bream, perch, tench and specimen size pike.

For further details about fishing or matches, contact the ranger Paul Martin on 01278 424786.

Blashford Lakes

Blashford Lakes are a series of former gravel pits set in the River Avon Valley on the Dorset and Hampshire borders.

Blashford, Spinnaker Lake offers coarse fishing to members of the Christchurch Angling Club during the coarse fishing season.

For further information, contact the club secretary Mr C Harrison, 19 Victoria Gardens, Ringwood, Hampshire BH24 1FD or telephone 07885 761 381.

Tucking Mill:

Season from 16 June 2002 to 14 March 2003

Set in a secluded wood, Tucking Mill is located in the attractive Midford Valley, south of Bath.

Wessex Water offers free coarse fishing for disabled anglers at this small lake which is stocked with roach, chub, tench and large carp.

There are six specially designed wheelchair platforms with space for two wheelchairs each plus further platforms for the more mobile anglers.

Each disabled angler may bring along one able-bodied person who may also fish but has to use the same site.

For more information: General enquiries on fishing, a request for our free brochure on fishing and recreation or season tickets should be made through Wessex Water customer services on 0845 600 4 600.

Alternatively you can view our fishing brochure on-line at:
www.wessexwater.co.uk

Day or evening tickets for fishing and boat hire are available on a self serve basis from the public fisheries at each lodge.

clear commitment

*A truly fabulous specimen Carp.
Stafford Moor*

Coarse Fishing in the Bristol Avon area

by Mike Goodchild

The Bristol Avon flows from its twin sources near Sherston and Tetbury to its confluence with the River Severn at Avonmouth and travels some 117 kilometres in total (72 miles). The river has five major tributaries, the Rivers Marden, Somerset Frome, Chew, Bristol Frome and the By Brook. All provide excellent coarse fishing although the By Brook is mostly controlled by private syndicates so it is not available to the average angler.

Most waters in the area are controlled by local angling clubs and membership must be obtained before fishing. Club membership can usually be purchased from local tackle shops. There are some sections of the river in Malmesbury, Bath, Saltford, Keynsham and Bristol that are considered "free fishing". These sections of the river are mostly owned or controlled by local authorities and not leased to angling clubs. It is important to note that a valid Environment Agency rod licence is also required when fishing any of these waters; licences can be obtained from all post offices as well as from local Environment Agency offices.

Malmesbury, a picturesque old Cotswold market town with its 12th century Abbey as its' focal point, is the uppermost point on the Avon open to the coarse angler. Although fishing is difficult when the water is clear it has produced roach and perch of over 3lb and carp of 20lb plus in the past two seasons.

Neville Day with the kind of Barbel that the Bristol Avon is renowned for.

From Malmesbury the river meanders its way downstream to the market town of Chippenham and has many weirs that provide impounded sections above weirs, with riffle and pool below. Barbel, chub and roach predominate in the faster water giving way to large bream shoals just upstream of Chippenham town. Notable catches include a five hour match record of 140lb of bream. Individual records include a monster pike of over 33lb and the almost unbelievable tench of 12lb 7oz caught by Rick Seal from Cardiff in the river at Christian Malford in November 1998.

Downstream of Chippenham town centre "free fishing" extends from the weir to the bypass road bridge (fishing the right hand bank) and then transfers to the left hand bank downstream to and including Mortimers Wood. This section is some 1.25 miles in length and contains good quality fish. Most notably barbel to 12lb, chub to 4½lb, bream to 7lb, tench to 4lb, perch to 2lb and pike to 18lb.

Further downstream at Lacock, the river passes by this National Trust village, best known for its Abbey and as the home of early photographer Fox-Talbot, and onto Melksham which is dominated by the Avon Tyre factory (now owned by Coopers of America). Match weights vary from 2lb to 12lb on the upper reaches to perhaps 60lb on the lower reaches near Melksham (if the bream are feeding!).

Onward to Staverton, then Bradford on Avon with its tythe barn, old church and antique shops (a must for tourists), Avoncliffe and Limpley Stoke. All have large impoundments above their weirs. Here fish can be a little more difficult to locate but large bream shoals are here to be found and caught. The liberal use of ground bait, an open ended feeder with a hook bait of red maggot, worm or caster usually does the trick. One place not to be missed after a hard day's slog on the river bank is the Cross Guns Public House at Avoncliffe — well known by the locals for its good beer and steaks at a reasonable price. Below Avoncliffe are the Limpley Stoke and Claverton weirs, nestling within a scenic valley, where wooded sides rise in places, some 300 feet above. In these sections where the water runs faster and is quite weedy in the summer months, lie the haunts of very large barbel. The best captured so far, nearly 15½lb weight, is very close to the national rod caught record. Most other species can also be caught with good roach, dace, chub, tench, perch and bream. Also, it is not unusual for the pike angler to capture specimens of 12-20lb with the best reported fish of 26lb caught by Gary Court at Claverton in 1988.

The city of Bath with its Roman Baths and internationally renowned Georgian architecture provides a scenic backdrop to over 2.5 miles of "free fishing". Below Pulteney Weir hot water spills into the river from the Roman Baths, which provides interest for carp of over 20lb. Individual anglers have reported superb roach catches of over 30lb, just upstream of North Parade Bridge and 40lb plus nets of chub, taken on caster at Widcombe. Another hot spot near Windsor Bridge produces large quantities of bream, with individual fish weighing over 7lb in weight. It makes this particular stretch well worth consideration.

The river below Bath becomes slower and boat usage more intense. Newbridge, Saltford and Keynsham provide excellent match stretches where individual weighs vary from 2 to 20lb with roach, chub, bream and eels predominating. There are further "free" sections at the Shallows in Saltford and a small area 200 yards downstream of Keynsham weir on the far side of the roadbridge.

At Hanham the "free fishing" extends on the right hand bank through Conham Park to Netham Weir some 3.5 miles in total. Conham Park has a car park, toilets and facilities for the disabled. Fishing on this stretch is quite good with mixed nets of dace, roach, chub, perch and eels. From Netham to the river's confluence with the River Severn at Avonmouth, the river becomes an estuarine environment with one of the largest tide variations in the world. Near Netham Weir some coarse fish can still be caught together with the occasional mullet and flat fish.

Bristol has numerous attractions, few more inviting, for the angler, than the sight of a large expanse of water. The City docks, also known as the Floating Harbour, is a large area, and situated in the centre of the City. This, together with its connection to the main river, the Feeder Canal, provides a venue with numerous swims for the match and pleasure angler. Permits are available both on the bankside and from tackle shops or the Harbour Masters Office, situated near the restored SS Great Britain. The Docks have an average depth of 15 feet. Roach, dace, bream and perch can be caught in good numbers with carp or chub as a bonus. Most fish are caught using an open ended feeder with a hook bait of maggot, bread, worm or sweetcorn. In the summer months fish tend to feed off the bottom more, float fished baits presented at a depth of 3 to 6 feet can produce good catches.

Most barbel fishing is upstream of Bath, popular venues being Warleigh, Limpley Stoke, Avoncliffe, Lacock, Chippenham, Peckingell, Kellaways and Christian Malford. Any of these venues offer the realistic prospect of a double figure barbel. Legering with large bait such as meat, flavoured paste or lob worm will often bring results, though this approach generally works best when the river is coloured. In hard fished areas or in clear water conditions, try

using particle baits like maggots or sweetcorn, which can be put down with a bait dropper or fished in a feeder. Hemp will usually get fish feeding, but in some areas barbel have become wary of feeding on hemp. Experimenting with different baits and techniques is often the key to catching barbel consistently. Where permitted, fishing large baits after dark is without doubt the best way to target the larger fish. It is best to return barbel to the water as soon as possible, avoiding the use of keepnets. They can become exhausted when caught, particularly in hot weather, and should be supported in the flow until they regain strength to swim away.

The Kennet and Avon Canal, a navigation built to join the rivers Thames and Bristol Avon, was opened in 1810. After years of neglect in the 1950s and 1960s, work started on its restoration. Now some 30 years later and with many millions of pounds spent, the canal is nearly restored to its former glory. In North Wessex, our area commences at Horton just east of Devizes. From Horton it winds its way through Devizes and drops down the spectacular Caen Hill flight of 29 locks to Sells Green, Semington and onwards to Bradford on Avon, Limpley Stoke and Bath where it joins with the River Avon, a distance of approximately 25 miles. The canal will provide the angler with plenty of sport, particularly during the summer months, with favoured swims for large carp in the ponds below Devizes.

Most species can be caught throughout the canal's length with roach, rudd and bream falling to float fished punched bread with small balls of liquidised bread used as an attractant. Tench, crucian carp, perch and eels can be tempted with red worm, maggot or caster used as hook bait. Small amounts of chopped worm or pinkies added to the ground bait keep their interest. Remember to stake your keepnet securely to the bank or it may be carried away by a passing boat. Also please remember that walkers and cyclists are entitled to use the tow path and you must not obstruct them with fishing tackle, rod or pole. *The Waterways Code is available from all Waterways Offices.*

There are more than 100 lakes and ponds in the North Wessex area for the angler to take advantage of. Some are managed by syndicates, others privately owned and available to fish on day tickets. Lakes such as Sevington, a small village on the outskirts of Chippenham, Erlestoke near Devizes, Longleat (a series of lakes in the grounds of Lord Bath's Estate) and Ivy House Lakes at Grittenham in the Wootton Bassett area provide good coarse fishing.

Trout fishing is also catered for with large lakes like the nationally renowned Chew Valley Lake and smaller venues like Mill Farm at Great Cheverell. There are many lakes and ponds run by angling clubs such as Newton Park which are available through Bathampton AA membership. Bristol, Bath and Wiltshire AA has Shackells, Sword and Sabre lakes. Both clubs have other larger facilities, two of which are:

Tockenham Reservoir near Lyneham lies just three miles from M4 intersection 16 via the A3102. This beautiful 12.5 acre lake, surrounded by oak woodland, was created in 1836 to provide water for the Wilts and Berks Canal. Purchased by Bristol, Bath and Wiltshire AA in 1980 it has since been developed into a magnificent fishery stocked with carp to 30lb, tench to 7lb, bream to 8lb, plus roach, perch and crucian carp. All fishing is from platforms, including three purpose built for the wheelchair disabled, and there are good parking facilities.

Bathampton AA's **Hunstrete Lakes** are situated 7 miles west of Bath. They comprise a mature 5 acre lake plus two newly constructed lakes of 3.5 acres. These are set in 21 acres of landscaped grounds and provide picturesque and tranquil surroundings with provision for 120 swims. The main lake contains carp to 28lb, tench to 7lb, pike to 20lb and plenty of other fish to maintain your interest. The new lakes, Bridgepool and Withypool, have been stocked with over £30,000 worth of fish, with carp to 5lb, bream to 4lb, roach to 2lb, plus perch, crucian carp and chub. Car parking and toilets are provided with facilities for the disabled, including 15 purpose built platforms.

Please remember that as an angler you are an ambassador for the sport. It is important to remove all litter and discarded line from your swim and return all fish to the water with the utmost care.

The truly huge 'Smirk' at 50lb.
Newton Abbot Fishing Association

Superb haul of Tench for Chris Turner of Bristol.
Avalon

Sea

Government recognises Sea Anglers

as "stakeholders" of our natural fish stock resources

Malcolm Gilbert

Four key events took place in 2001 that are significant for the salt water sport angling sector. They are, in no particular order:

Foot and mouth disease.
The Common Fisheries Policy Review.
Government's response to the Salmon and Fresh Water Fisheries Review.
The renaming of MAFF to DEFRA.

Foot and Mouth

Whilst no-one can possibly deny this appalling disease turned the lives of many farmers upside-down, the real economic penalties were felt right through rural life and tourism was by far the biggest economic loser. The major component of any rural tourism is recreation and since angling has more participants than any other recreational pursuit, the link between tourism and sport angling is obvious - or should be! The study into Inland and Marine Fisheries in Wales carried out by Nautilus Consultants, (see it under reports at www.nautilus-consultants.co.uk) commissioned by the National Assembly for Wales, was severely critical of those who have responsibility for developing tourism in Wales for not appreciating the link between tourism, angling and healthy fish stocks. Their Welsh study revealed that the economic impact from salt water angling dwarfed that of commercial fishing and yet the policies and management of fish stock resources, upon which all fisheries (commercial and recreational) depend, was dominated by a commercial fishing mindset. They further pointed out that even though the economic impact from recreational sea angling was so significant, it was nevertheless based

on severely depleted fish stocks and if such fish stocks could be restored then the potential for developing the recreational saltwater sport fishing industry is enormous and that coastal tourism interests as stakeholders of fish stock resources really should take an interest.

Although England has had no such similar study, I believe a very similar situation prevails. The provision of fresh water fishing venues that have mushroomed in the West Country over the last quarter of a century demonstrates the appetite for tourism fishing opportunities, but as the availability of coarse fishing opportunities has grown, the quality of salt water angling, for which the West Country was at one time justifiably famous, has been substantially degraded by unsustainable commercial fishing. According to the United Nations Code of Conduct for Responsible Fisheries, fish stock resources are one of 'humanity's natural heritage' and 'recreation' is actually listed in the Code of Conduct as one of the valid and legitimate uses for which fish stocks should be managed. It is imperative that those who have responsibility for tourism with its inherent huge economic impact must insist that tourism interests have a role to play in the policy and management decisions surrounding our natural fish stock resources.

MAFF out - DEFRA in

The Ministry of Agriculture, Fisheries and Food incurred much criticism for being too close to producers. One result of which, was the setting up of the Food Safety Agency and the removal of food safety responsibilities from MAFF. Whether the removal of the words 'agriculture' and 'fisheries' from the now Department of Environment, Food and Rural Affairs, will actually lead to a new cultural mindset, remains to be seen. It is however being increasingly recognised, that commercial fishing has seriously out-punched its weight and is by any criteria a very small part of the UK economy. The entire first-hand sale value of all fish commercially landed in England and Wales is only £200 million. If shellfish and those fin fish that are of no direct interest to recreational sport fishing (eg: hake & monk) are removed from these figures we are left with a value in the order of £100 million only. So in a nutshell, we have an entire management regime within government that has responsibility for managing

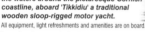

our natural fish stock resources but that does so exclusively from a commercial fishing perspective. Another user stakeholder, recreational sport angling that has far greater socio-economic impacts, and which is equally dependent on the wellbeing of many of the same fish stocks is ignored. Furthermore, this management regime that is so preoccupied with the commercial industry and which is now publicly acknowledged to have failed to look after the actual fish stock resources is paid for by the tax payer! This situation is at best wholly illogical and irrational, and at worst obscene.

Of course, senior civil servants and politicians are well aware, but rarely have the courage to speak out. However, ex-Minister, John Gummer, has done just that and was quoted in the commercial fishing press as saying "I was never able to press for the necessary conservation measures at National and EU level, due to the nations 'emotional attachment' to fishermen. The Industry has too much political clout. The lawn mowing industry employs more people but does not have four ministries, England, N. Ireland, Wales and Scotland." What a pity he did not have the courage to say this when he was Minister!

A shore caught Pollack is returned. Picture by Henry Gilbey

The Common Fisheries Policy Review

The EU Commission published the Green Paper that pulled no punches and spelt out just how appallingly bad European fisheries management has become and how critical it is for all stakeholders to have an input into a new approach to managing fish stock resources. In England, DEFRA saw fit to conduct a full public consultation and many from the recreational sea angling sector stood up to be counted. In fact the overwhelming majority of responses to the government's consultation came from sport angling interests. The result is that in the UK's formal response to the EU Commission, sea anglers are amongst the stakeholders listed under the heading "Stakeholder Involvement and Good Governance".

Under paragraph 15, headed: "Environmentally Friendly Fishing, Including Sea Angling", sea anglers are said to, "have a strong interest in the development of the Common Fisheries Policy and it is acknowledged that sea angling makes a significant contribution to local fishing communities and the policies adopted need to ensure that this is fully taken into account." In view of the weight of opinion from the recreational angling sector to the Government consultation process, some would say that we have been short-changed. However, it is a significant improvement on the recognition that sea angling has achieved historically and the door for sea anglers has now been well and truly unlocked. It is now up to sea anglers to adequately fund the governing bodies of the sport, the Welsh, Scottish and the National Federations of Sea Anglers, so that the salt water sector can develop the competence and professionalism to represent sea angler's opinions effectively.

Salmon & Fresh Water Fisheries Review

As the title of this review suggests, it had little to do with recreational sea angling. However,

Top: A Porbeagle Shark awaits tagging and releasing. Bottom: Wayne Thomas with a Grey Mullet caught from Lynmouth Harbour. Combe Martin Sea Angling Club

let me share the following thoughts with you. In early 1998, MAFF and the Secretary of State for Wales set up a small independent group to review existing policies and legislation throughout England and Wales concerning the management and conservation of salmon, trout, eels and freshwater fish.

This review group submitted its report in early 2000 and throughout the remainder of that year over seven hundred individuals and organisations sent in comments. In 2001 the government published its response and here are some of them:

"The Government states that the Environment Agency should have a statutory duty to enhance the social value of fishing as a widely available and healthy form of recreation and to enhance the contribution fisheries make to the economy, particularly in remote rural areas and in areas with low levels of income."

Furthermore, in Chapter 9 of the Government response, headed "Social Economic and Recreational Importance of Angling", attention is drawn to the England Rural Development programme, which was approved by the European Commission in October 2000 and which recognises the contribution that fresh water fisheries make to the rural economy and the link between angling and tourism is highlighted. Indeed, the Government states that it will encourage Tourist Boards and the Environment Agency to collect data on visiting anglers. It also agrees with the findings of the Review Group, that expanding the demand and opportunities for angling must be part of the Environment Agency's role.

Sea anglers who are unaware of the details of this government response may well be forgiven for finding the contents quite incredible, given that these words come from the same Government that has allowed inshore sea fish stocks to be decimated and has allowed the commercial fishing industry that has decimated conventional species of commercial value to increasingly target species that historically have been regarded as angler's fish, such as flounders and wrasse. There is no doubt that the Government's role for 'recreational angling' is inconsistent and discriminates against the salt water sector.

Ed Schliffke with a nice Bream. Picture by Russ Symons

Finally, let us be clear about one thing. The UK recreational saltwater sport angling sector has a huge amount of work ahead of it if it is going to grasp the opportunity provided by the government's published recognition that we are 'stakeholders'.

Only sea anglers can collectively provide the resources for the work, NO ONE ELSE WILL DO IT FOR US! Unfortunately there is no angling organisation at present with sufficient professional resources to effectively carry out the complex political work in order to raise the profile of the sport of sea angling. If the sector wishes to engage with government, to be involved with policy and management decisions, to bring the Departments of Sport & Tourism into the debate surrounding fish stocks, to confront head on DEFRA's policy of constant acquiescence to the commercial fishing industry etc. then it has to raise the funds to do so. Anglers are renowned for whinging about gill nets, trawling close to shore and lack of fish, and they have every right to express their concerns about such issues BUT now is the time for all sea anglers to 'put up or shut up!'. The sport's English governing body, the NFSA, (visit: www.nfsa.org.uk) has provided the opportunity for anglers to get behind them and to collectively contribute with the introduction of individual membership to taking the sport meaningfully into the 21st century. I desperately hope the participants of this wonderful recreational pursuit are up for it.

Further information on the campaign by sea anglers to bring an end to overfishing can be found at: www.ukbass.com and also at www.anglersnet.co.uk/sacn/

Sea Charters & Clubs

Cornwall

BOSCASTLE
Boscastle Peganina
Contact: Ken Cave, 01288 353565

FALMOUTH
Blue Minstrel
Contact: Lance Peters, 01326 250352
Gamgy Lady
Contact: Roger Buxton, 01326 375458
Leo I
Contact: Ken Dodgson, 01326 312409/315849, Mobile: 07779 376641
Mawnan Angling Club
Contact: Tim Varney, 01326 374135, *Water:* Sea fishing club with boat and shore sections, *Species:* Sea fish, *Charges:* £8 senior, £3 junior. Club meet on 4th Monday of month at Cross Keys, Penryn. New members welcome. Enquiries to Tackle Box, Falmouth or Telephone Tim on number above.
Patrice II
Contact: Michael Tuffery, 01326 313265, Mobile: 07979 335181
Segue
Contact: Rob Searle, 01326 312116, Mobile: 07774 226046, rob@seguecharters.co.uk

HAYLE
San Pablo II
Contact: Dougie Wright, 01209 716970

LOOE
Mystique
Contact: David Bond, 01503 264530, Mobile: 07812030008

MEVAGISSEY
Aquila
Contact: Martin Carrington, 01726 842222

NEWQUAY
Cornish Federation of Sea Anglers
Contact: Mr Ralph Elcox (Hon Sec), 44 Town Farm, Falmouth Road, Redruth, TR15 2XG, 01209 314389, *Water:* Sea Fishing. Shore and boat. Tidal fishing in estuaries, excluding Bass, *Permits:* None required, other than reasonable harbour charges, *Charges:* C.F.S.A. affiliation £41 per annum per club. Personal members £7.50. Family membership (ie husband, wife and children under 16) £10. All memberships inclusive of third party insurance, *Season:* None, *Methods:* Two rods three hooks maximum. No netting.

PADSTOW
Treyarnon Angling Centre
Contact: Ed Schliffke, Treyarnon Bay, St Merryn, Padstow, 01841 521157, Water: Shore Fishing Trips,

REDRUTH
Camborne Angling Association
Contact: Mr Ralph Elcox (Hon Sec), 44 Town Farm, Falmouth Road, Redruth, TR15 2XG, 01209 314389, *Water:* Sea Fishing Association, C.F.S.A. affiliation.

ST IVES
Dolly Pentreath
Contact: Mike Laity, 01736 797269

Devon

BARNSTAPLE
Combe Martin Sea Angling Club
Contact: Wayne Thomas, The Shippen, Loxhore Cott, Nr Barnstaple, EX31 4ST, 01271 850586, waesox@shippen99.freeserve.co.uk, *Charges:* Family £10, Senior £6, Junior £1.

BIDEFORD
Appledore Shipbuilders Angling Club
Contact: M Horrel, 52 Devonshire Park, Bideford, 01237 474614, *Water:* Shore and Boat fishing. Roving monthly competitions. Annual Festive competitions. Founded in 1971, 50 plus members. South West Federation member.New members welcome, *Charges:* £4 Adult. £2 Juniors.
Sanderling
Contact: Randall, Appledore, 01237 479585, Mobile: 07779 443472, *Water:* Estuary fishing. 2 hour trips in 'Sanderling, fully licenced and insured for 12 anglers. £8 per person. Rod and bait supplied if required, *Species:* Bass, Plaice etc.

BRIXHAM
Seaspray III
Contact: Chris Willicott, 01803 851328

CLOVELLY
Jessica Hettie
Contact: Clive Pearson, 01237 431405 (eve), Mobile: 07774 190359, *Water:* Sea Angling trips around Clovelly and Lundy, *Species:* Shark, Pollack, Mackeral, Bass, *Season:* April to September.
Ralph Atkinson Angling Charters
Contact: Ralph, Isis, Irsha Court, Irsha Street, Appledore, EX39 1RN, 01237 475535, Mobile: 07774 164086, *Water:* Inshore and offshore reefs, wrecks and banks and deep sea in the Bristol Channel onboard 'Hooker', *Species:* Tope, Shark, Bass, Pollack, Rays, Congers, Huss, *Permits:* 20 mile day or night licence for up to 8 people. Fully equipped with all safety gear and tackle, *Charges:* Individuals £26. To book boat £160, *Season:* Operating all year. Boat leaves Clovelly 9am each day and returns at 5pm,

DART
African Queen
Contact: Alan Hemsley, Mobile: 07885 246061

DARTMOUTH
Gemini III
Contact: Dave Harrison, 01803 851766, Mobile: 07968 599245
Jennifer Ann of Dart
Contact: Barry Lingham, 01803 834590, Mobile: 07831 400783
Saltwind of Dart
Contact: Lloyd Saunders, 01803 554341
Samuel Irvin
Contact: Ian Noble, Mobile: 07780 970803, samuelirvin@tesco.net
Two Rivers
Contact: Steve Parker, 01803 329414

Sea

Cornish Cream
Surf fishing for Bass
Simon Toms

Bass! The very mention of the word in sea angling circles is enough to make many anglers sit up and take notice. Many regard the bass as the salmon of the sea and, as one our most attractive sea fish, it has an almost fanatical following among those who appreciate the sporting and culinary qualities of this fish. Invariably, shore fishing for bass in Cornwall takes place against a backdrop of spectacular coastal and cliff scenery on clean surf beaches warmed by the Gulf Stream. This provides a challenging and exciting backdrop from which to lure a wild and hard fighting fish.

In the 1960's and 70's, bass were regarded as common and widespread on the Cornish surf beaches with fish caught from open beach venues averaging 4 lb. However, with the advent and unrestricted use of monofilament gill nets and a market value of up to £6 per lb, the species was steadily and remorsefully exploited wherever it existed. In particular, estuaries supporting large stocks of juvenile and adolescent fish, were targeted by commercial netsmen resulting in the eventual decline of the future breeding stock.

As a result, bass stocks declined and the once prolific beaches of Cornwall became a mere shadow of their former glory. However, following the introduction of legally protected bass nursery areas throughout the UK in 1990, the last 6 years has seen a steady increase in the numbers and average size of bass returning to their historic feeding grounds. Fish within the 2-3lb bracket have become common captures with fish of 3-4lb increasingly evident during recent seasons. In addition, there still exists the possibility of capturing larger specimen fish of over 5lb and even the chance of a fish of a lifetime in excess of the magical 10lb barrier.

Venues
Surf fishing for bass invariably means seeking the large sandy bays, beaches and coves located on the North and South Cornish coasts. Although it is fair to say that some beaches attract and hold more bass than others and, in some cases a higher than average size, bass can be found on all surf beaches in Cornwall. Bass will show up on any part of the beach at some point during the tidal cycle and, for consistent success, it is imperative to fish different surf conditions and locations on your favoured beach until a successful pattern begins to emerge. Once learnt, it is very often the case that the same set of specific conditions at a given location will produce bass consistently on that beach for years to come. If time is not available, you can help to increase success by learning how to read the beach for specific features that bass find particularly attractive.

Rocky outcrops associated with scour holes, rivers or streams running across the beach into the sea, seaward facing sandbars and gullies are all favoured locations because these features attract the food favoured by bass. In addition, the size and volume of the surf itself can affect the way in which these features attract fish. Although it has to be a huge surf to drive fish offshore, bass tend to avoid surf that suspends the sand in cloudy plumes or where loose, decaying seaweed hangs in the water. As a general rule, conditions are likely to be perfect on most beaches when holding 2-3 ft of surf and 3 or 4 lines of surf. In terms of the time to fish for bass, they can be caught during both night and day.

However, in the summer months, bathers and surfers can compete for space and at such times it pays to fish either very early or very late in the day. Certainly for consistent success, bass fishing during the hours of darkness is often very productive with the fish venturing very close into the shallows, often into as little as 1 or 2 ft of water. Long casting in the dark is often not necessary for success.

Tackle
Although it is possible to fish the South Cornish surf beaches with light tackle such as a fixed spool, 10-12 lb line, carp rod and 2-3 ounce lead weight, the strong lateral tides that exist on the North Cornish coast surf beaches invariably means that heavier rods are often required. Many purists suggest that the rod should be held at all times. However, many Cornish surf bass are feeding on the "hoof" and take the bait aggressively in surf conditions.

Sea Charters & Clubs

EXMOUTH

Blue Thunder
Contact: Mike Deem, 01626 891181, Mobile: 07860 499120
Restorick III
Contact: Colin Pike, 01363 775316
Smuggler III
Contact: Colin Dukes, 01626 890852, Mobile: 07974 437740
Stuart Line Fishing
Contact: 5 Camperdown Terrace, Exmouth, EX8 1EJ, 01395 275882, Mobile: 07968 586750, info@stuartlinecruises.co.uk, *Water:* Lyme Bay, *Species:* Mackeral, Ling, Pollack, Whiting, Conger Eel, *Permits:* Please phone, *Charges:* Mackeral £5. Deep Sea £10, *Season:* Easter to end of October.
Tamesis
Contact: Nigel Dyke, 01769 580376, Mobile: 07968 182975

ILFRACOMBE

Ilfracombe & District Anglers Association (Sea)
Contact: David Shorney, Victoria Cottage, 8b St Brannocks Road, Ilfracombe, EX34 8EG, 01271 865874, orphaneannie@amserve.net, *Water:* Beaches and rock marks. Founded in October 1929, the oldest club in North Devon, *Species:* Bass, Pollock, Conger, Mullet, Ray, Coalfish, Cod and various other species, *Permits:* From Variety Sports, Broad Street, Ilfracombe, *Charges:* Fees per year: Family £10, Adult £8, OAP £4, Junior £2. 17 competitions per year and an annual fishing festival in July/August, *Season:* January to January.

INSTOW

Adventure
Contact: Royston, 01271 860889, Mobile: 07890 720762

NEWTON ABBOT

National Federation of Sea Anglers
Contact: Head Office, Level 5, Hamlyn House, Mardle Way, Buckfastleigh, TQ11 0NS, 01364 644643, ho@nfsa.org.uk, *Water:* Sea Angling, *Species:* All sea fish, *Permits:* None apply, *Charges:* Individual membership £10 per year. Personal membership £15 per year, *Season:* None applicable.

PADSTOW

Emma Kate
Contact: John Wicks, 01841 533319

PAIGNTON

Charlotte Lousie
Contact: Ashley Lane, Mobile: 07767 622727, ashley@boyrichard.co.uk
Our Joe-I
Contact: Simon Pedley, 01803 551504, simon@ourjoe-l.co.uk
Tuonela
Contact: Peter Bingle, 01803 666350, Mobile: 07715 735842

PLYMOUTH

Plymouth Command Angling Association (Sea)
Contact: Mr Vic Barnett Hon.Sec, 5 Weir Close, Mainstone, Plymouth, PL6 8SD, 01752 708206, victor.barnett@talk21.com, *Water:* Boat & Shore Fishing,

Species: All sea fish, *Permits:* Membership is open to all serving members of HM Forces. Associate membership is also open to ex-serving members of HM Forces, no matter when the time was served, *Charges:* Costs for full membership or associate membership are available on application or enquiry at the above.
Silver Crest
Contact: Silverline Cruises, Derek Smith, 01752 226243
Storm
Contact: Rod Davies, 01752 492232
Tiburon
Contact: Jim O'Donnel, 01752 518811, Mobile: 07855 040015, jim@plymouthcharters.co.uk, Water: Wreck, reef, bank and Shark fishing,. Season: Full day, half day and evening trips.
Tikkidiu
Contact: Fly Fishing Experiences, Mobile: 07812 360764, flyfishingexperiences@breathemail.net
Venture
Contact: Peter Fergus, 01752 709070, Mobile: 0378 494274

SALCOMBE

Anglo Dawn III
Contact: Ted Cooke, 01548 531702
Calypso
Contact: Kevin Oakman, 01548 843784
Lodesman
Contact: Pat Dean, 01548 843319, Mobile: 07836 726676
Phoenix
Contact: Mick Allen, 01548 853987
Tight Lines
Contact: Kevin Rowe, 01548 843818, Mobile: 07980 344604
Tuckers Boat Hire
Contact: Chris Puncher, 01548 842840

TORQUAY

Jubrae
Contact: Geoff and Fred, 01803 213866, Mobile: 07860 200247

WESTCOUNTRY

South West Federation of Sea Anglers
Contact: Colin Davies (chairman), 12 Ilton Way, Kingsbridge, TQ7 1DT, 01548 852706, Mobile: 07971 258327, c.j.d.freelancephowrit@btinternet.com, *Water:* South West coastal waters. The Federation is on www.fishingworld.co.uk

Hampshire

BOURNEMOUTH

Primo S.C
Contact: Advanced Angling, 499 Christchurch Road, Boscombe, Bournemouth, 01202 303402, *Water:* Sea match fishing around the Dorset coast, *Charges:* £10 per year including N.F.S.A. membership

Fishing with a wired grip lead ensures that the fish is hooked the instant it takes the bait. Many of the most successful Cornish surf bass anglers use multiplier reels loaded with 18lb mainline with a 50lb shockleader, 12' beachcasters with a 5 oz breakaway lead weight and a fixed paternoster rig with a 30 lb. trace line ending in a 5/0 hook. Certainly the numbers and size of fish caught by this method has proved effective over the years.

Bait

The choice of bait can vary considerably and, as bass are opportunists, they will take a wide range of food items. For consistency, good quality frozen sandeel, lugworm, Peeler crab, King Ragworm, Squid and Mackerel will all catch fish on a regular basis. However, it is very often worth visiting the local tackle shop to get advice and find out what local anglers are purchasing. On occasions, bass can become pre-occupied with one food item that is locally or seasonally abundant and, at such times the sport can be hectic if the correct bait is selected.

Once you have cast into the surf, reel in any available slack line and tighten the line against the lead weight. If you have done your homework and identified a suitable feeding spot with the correct surf conditions at the right state of the tide, it is then simply a case of waiting for a bite. If bites are not forthcoming after several casts it can very often pay to move along the beach and try another feature. For the dedicated bass angler, patience is most definitely the most important attribute that you can have. Sooner or later your patience will be rewarded with success. Bites can vary considerably from a slight rattle on the rod tip to a rod bending pull or slack line bite. Bass of any size can produce any of these bites so always maintain concentration on the rod tip and strike at any indication that a fish might be mouthing the bait.

For the holiday angler, it is worth visiting the nearest tackle shop to find out what is happening locally. In terms of well known and proven venues on the North Cornish Coast any of the beaches around Newquay including Fistral, Whipsiderry, Watergate Bay, Crantock, Mawgan Porth, are worth trying. In addition, Portreath, Porthtowan, Chapel Porth, Perranporth, Constantine, Harlyn, Polzeath, Trebarwith strand and Tregardoc are all worth

Simon with a nice Cornish Bass

trying. On the South Cornish Coast try Whitsand Bay, Crinnis, Carne, Pendower, Towan, Loe Bar and Praa sands. There are many other small coves and bays around the Cornish coastline and these also offer opportunities to the bass angler. However, always consider safety first and always let someone know where you are fishing and when you are expected to return.

Bass Size limits

Cornwall, unlike many other areas of the United Kingdom, has 2 distinct takeable size limits for bass. The designated estuarine Bass nursery areas have a minimum landing size of 36 cm (14.5 inches) measured from the tip of the snout to the tip of the tail. However, the open coastal areas extending from the outer limits of the estuaries have a size limit of 37 ½ cm (15 inches). However, it is wise to respect a voluntary size limit of 45 cm (18 inches) which roughly equates to a bass of approximately 2 ½ lb. This ensures that a fish has had at least one opportunity to spawn and hopefully sustain the future of your sport.

So, if you want to sample free fishing for hard fighting wild fish in exhilarating surroundings then why not have a try for surf bass in Cornwall. Certainly, the recent increase in bass numbers has encouraged a notable increase in anglers targeting bass. I can guarantee that once you have hooked a big bass in the surf, the thrill and excitement of that experience will stay with you for a lifetime.

Good fishing!

Sea Charters & Clubs

Dorset

BRIDPORT
Channel Warrior
Contact: Chris Reeks, 01460 242678, Mobile: 07785730504

LYME REGIS
Amaretto II
Contact: Steven Sweet, 01297 445949
Blue Turtle
Contact: Douglas Lanfear, 01297 34892, Mobile: 07970 856822
Joint Venture
Contact: Paul Blinman, Mobile: 07720900235
Marie F
Contact: Harry May, 01297 442397, Mobile: 07974 753287
Neptune
Contact: Peter Ward, 01297 443606, Mobile: 07768 570437
Shemara
Contact: Ron Bailey, 01297 443674, Mobile: 07850 180331

POOLE
Aries II
Contact: Duncan Purchase, 01425 278357, Mobile: 07759 736360
Dawn Louise
Contact: Gary Snook, Mobile: 07976 252248
Helena B
Contact: Dave Beck, 01202 579898, Mobile: 07811 817919
Mistress Linda
Contact: Phil Higgins, 01202 741684, Mobile: 07860 794183
Ooker
Contact: Pat Manley, 01202 672849, Mobile: 07860 320818
Our Gemma
Contact: Merve Minns, 01425 274636
True Blue
Contact: Steve Porter, 01202 665482, Mobile: 07967 598669

SWANAGE
Swanage Angling Club
Contact: Swanage Angling Centre, 01929 424989, *Water:* Fishing around Swanage & Purbeck coastal areas, pier fishing at Swanage, close to Chesil beach, *Permits:* Swanage Angling Centre (01929) 424989
Sangina
Contact: Swannage Angling Centre, 01929 424989, *Water:* Deep sea fishing trips. Fully licenced for 12 anglers. Experienced Skipper

WEYMOUTH
Atlanta
Contact: Dave Pitman, 01305 781644, Mobile: 07721 320252
Autumn Dream
Contact: Len Hurdiss, 01305 786723, Mobile: 0766 360961
Bonwey
Contact: Ken Leicester, 01305 821040, Mobile: 07831 506285, bonwey@aol.com
Channel Chieftain III & IV
Contact: Pat Carling, 01305 787155, Mobile: 07976 741821, ppcarlin@aol.com
Flamer
Contact: Colin Penny, 01305 766961, Mobile: 07968 972736

Ladygo-Diver
Contact: David Gibson, 01305 750823
MV Freedom
Contact: Peter, Mobile: 07976 528054, peterfreecat@aol.com, Water: Disabled Angling. Totally wheel chair accessible.
Offshore Rebel
Contact: Paul Whittall, 01305 783739, Mobile: 07860 571615
Out-Rage
Contact: Rod Thompson, 01305 822803, Mobile: 07970 437646
Peace & Pleanty
Contact: Chris Tett, 01305 775775, Mobile: 07885 780019
Top Cat
Contact: Mr Wellington, 01305 823443, Mobile: 07966 133979
Valerie Ann
Contact: Ron Brown, 01305 779217, Mobile: 07976520607

LYMINGTON
Challenger
Contact: Mike Cottingham, 01425 619358, Mobile: 07884 394379
Sundance
Contact: Roger Bayzand, 01590 674652

Isles of Scilly

Falcon Faldork & Firethorn
Contact: David Stedeford, 01720 422866

Somerset

BRISTOL
Bristol Channel Federation of Sea Anglers
Contact: Keith Reed, 27 St Michaels Avenue, Clevedon, BS21 6LL, 01275 872101, Mobile: bcfsa@hotmail.com, *Water:* Bristol Channel, Hartland Point. North Devon to St Davids Head, Dyfed (all tidal waters eastwards), *Species:* All sea fish, both boat and shore records,Yearly update. 52 different species recorded in major (over 1lb) rec.list, 15 different species in minor (under 1lb) rec.list, *Charges:* £22.50 per CLUB per year inclusive of shore activities insurance, *Season:* All year round activities, shore and boat contests, small boat section with inter-club activities, *Methods:* Fishing to specimen sizes, all specimen fish awarded certificate, best of specie annually, plus fish of the month. Team & Individual annual awards.
Clevedon Breakaways Sea Angling Club
Contact: R. Addicott (Sec.), 12 Dampier Road, Ashton, Bristol, BS3 2AT, 0117 9660400, *Water:* Boat Shore and Competitions in the Bristol Channel and South West. Affiliated to B.C.F.S.A. and N.F.S.A, *Species:* All species, *Charges:* Adult £20 plus £2 joining fee. Juniors £6. OAP £6 per year.

BURNHAM-ON-SEA
Kelly's Hero
Contact: Dave Saunders, 01278 785000, Mobile: 07970 642354

WATCHET
Scooby Doo Too
Contact: Stephen Yeandle, 01984 361310/634540

Tuition

Instructors

- the importance of getting it right

*Malcolm Hanson
(Salmon and Trout Association Development Officer)*

During the course of a year we can spend a significant amount of money participating in our sport. Whilst we all experience those glorious red-letter days these are often interspersed with periods of frustration as we struggle to deal with our own ability to perform. This may stem from poor techniques, an inability to handle differing fishing conditions or simply a lack of experience. Despite this, the notion that we should have a lesson or a series of lessons from a angling instructor is alien to many of us.

For almost thirty years the angling governing bodies have been at the forefront of ensuring that a high standard of instruction is available to those wishing to learn to fish or to improve their existing skills. Initially there was the National Anglers Council Instructors Qualification. Following the demise of the NAC, the Salmon and Trout National Instructors Certificate (STANIC) replaced this in 1994. The STANIC qualification has long been recognised as a stepping-stone to becoming an Advanced Professional Game Angling Instructor (APGAI).

The National Federation of Anglers (Coarse Fishing) and the National Federation of Sea Anglers have also seen fit to develop a coaching scheme to ensure that qualified instructors deliver instruction in their own disciplines. These Qualifications have always been a benchmark by which standards can be set. Achieving standards amongst our instructors has always been our major goal. To this end the Governing Bodies in angling, have been working together to review their practices and to develop a common approach to the delivery of instruction.

The Joint Angling Governing Bodies (JAGB) working party was set up two years ago. Fishing is one of the top twenty participation sports in the UK and the aim has been to align the instruction programme with that of other major sports. As a result of their work the Sport of Angling will have its own Instructor Licensing Scheme to be operational by April 2002. Local Authorities are already asking sports coaches/instructors for evidence of qualified status. The JAGB are currently working with water authorities, the leisure and tourist Industry, further education and the stillwater fisheries, through their own professional association, to ensure that only licensed instructors will be able to instruct on their waters.

An Instructor Licence will be renewable every 3 years. Each Instructor will have gained a recognised qualification awarded by their Governing Body. Each instructor will be trained in Child Protection awareness, and more importantly will him/herself be submitted to checks with the Criminal Record Bureau. Instructors will hold a recognised First Aid Certificate and will be required to carry adequate third party insurance. Furthermore they will be committed to ongoing professional development to enhance their own skills.

The JAGB believe that angling instruction should be of the highest professional standard. Instructor's work hard to achieve their qualification, the new scheme will serve to ensure that unlicensed and unqualified instructors cannot work in our industry. Further more, it will serve as a kite mark to assure the public of value for money.

I wish you every success in the coming season; however, if that success eludes you we have over 500 professional instructors in all disciplines of Angling across the UK who will gladly assist.

For further information about Licensed Coaches:
The National Federation of Anglers
(Coarse Fishing)   01283 734735
The National Federation of Sea Anglers
(Sea Fishing)   01364 644643
The Salmon and Trout Association
(Game Anglers)   01672 514219
The Game-angling Instructors Association
                          01342 850740
Other Instructor or Coach Licensing Issues
                          01672 514219

KEY

Name
Contact details
Qualifications
Area covered
Equipment available
Specialities

Game

Coarse

Sea

Roy Buckingham

Arundell Arms, Lifton, Devon PL16 0AA
Tel 01566 784666
Fax 01566 784494
Email: reservations@arundellarms.com
www.arundellarms.com
Full member APGAI. STANIC qualified instructor.
Lifton area of Devon. Based at The Arundell Arms Hotel.
Rods, Reels Flies etc.

Spey casting. Individual tuition and courses. Beginners and refresher courses, including Spey casting.

Alex Henderson

Husk Hill, Frithelstock Stone, Torrington EX38 8JR
Tel 01805 624662. Mobile 07866 305464
Email: aneilhenderson@hotmail.com
www.flyfishing-uk.co.uk
NAC/STANIC Trout & Salmon. Basic and advanced
North Devon
Tackle and Flies.

Fly casting. Spey casting. Double haul. Fly dressing. Children over 12 years only.

Devon & UK Fly Fishing School

Roddy Rae, 6 Hescane Park, Cheriton Bishop EX6 6SP.
Tel 01647 24643. Mobile 077868 34575
Email: roddyrae@btopenworld.com
www.flyfishing-uk.co.uk
STANIC / REFFIS
UK and Worldwide inc. Australia and New Zealand
All tackle available

Single and double Spey casting. Double haul and snake roll casting. Wild Brown Trout, Salmon and Sea Trout. Please Note: Children to be accompanied by an adult.

Derek Aunger

Bake Lakes, Trerulefoot, Saltash PL12 5BW
Mobile 07812 360764 Fax 01503 240819
Email: flyfishingexperiences@breathemail.net
www.flyfishingexperiences.com
STANIC & REFFIS Salmon and Trout. GIA. Fly Dressers' Guild. Assn Stillwater Game Fishery Managers
East Cornwall
Game and Coarse tackle shop. Rod repair service.

Saltwater fly fishing from a sloop rigged boat in the waters off the East Cornish coast.

Peter Keen

c/o Eggesford Country Hotel, Eggesford, Chulmleigh,
Devon EX18 7JZ
Tel 01769 581127 (home). Mobile 07790 914066
Email: relax@eggesfordhotel.co.uk
www.eggesfordhotel.co.uk
REFFIS
Rivers in Devon - especially the Taw.
Rods & reels for hire. Casts and flies for sale.

*Brown Trout, Salmon and Sea Trout. Day and night
fishing. For age 10 and over.*

Nick Hart

Exford View, 1 Chapel St, Exford TA24 7PY
Tel 01643 831101. Mobile 079711 98559
Email: nick@hartflyfishing.demon.co.uk
www.sport-fishing.co.uk
STANIC
Somerset, North Devon, Southern England & overseas.
All equipment including waders.

*All usual disciplines. Guided saltwater fly fishing.
Guided Pike fly fishing. Quick start fishing days.
Children welcome.*

Darren Herbert

Amherst Lodge Fishery
Tel 01297 442773. Mobile 07765 817206
www.amherstlodge.com
STANIC
Devon and Dorset
Tackle, baits, flies and lures.

*Stillwater Trout. River fishing. Saltwater flyfishing,
Fly casting. Distance casting. Saltwater spinning.
Beach and Pier fishing.*

Robert Jones

South Lodge, Courtlands, Exmouth EX8 3NZ
Tel 07020 902090 Mobile 0797 0797 770
Email: robertjones@eclipse.co.uk
FRICS. EA Beginners Licence Agent.
The West Country centred on East Devon and rivers
Otter, Axe, Teign, Exe, Avon and Camel.
All equipment including EA Licence.

*Rivers. Sea Trout by fly at night. Guiding.
For age 10 and over.*

R.E.F.F.I.S

The Register of Experienced Fly Fishing Instructors, Schools and Guides (REFFIS) exists to assure the public of the highest standards. All our members are thoroughly vetted before being accepted onto the Register; teaching and guiding skills are rigorously examined to ensure they match the exacting standards set by REFFIS.

We have members well spread across the UK and Eire and even a few overseas. They offer a superb range of locations: small stillwaters, large reservoirs, lush chalk-streams, mighty Scottish and Irish rivers, wild spate rivers and the lovely lochs of Scotland and Ireland - join up with the friendly network of REFFIS members and sample the lot!

REFFIS members introduce many hundreds of people to the delights of game fishing every season. New recruits, young and old, are essential if the aquatic environment is to be safeguarded for future generations. REFFIS takes this responsibility very seriously and we wholeheartedly support the efforts of organisations such as The Salmon and Trout Association, The Game Conservancy, The Atlantic Salmon Trust and The Wild Trout Trust, all of whom work tirelessly for the benefit of game fish and the healthy environment that is so vital for them and indeed for us. We urge you to go game fishing and to choose an experienced mentor from within the ranks of REFFIS.

Roy Buckland

8 Millington Drive, Trowbridge BA14 9EU
Tel 01225 760465. Mobile 07967 558772
Email: roy@buckland-1.freeserve.co.uk
STANIC Trout.
West Wiltshire and the Chew Valley
Rods, reels, lines etc.

Beginners. Roll casting. Double hauling

The Game-angling Instructors Association

When looking for a game angling instructor one could be forgiven for finding the market place a little confusing. There is STANIC and APGAI; as well as SGAIC (The Scottish Game Anglers Instructors Certificate). However, from January 2002, all of these recognised qualifications in the UK have come together under one umbrella group, The Game-angling Instructors Association (GIA).

GIA, who will be working with the angling governing bodies to develop and ensure the quality of the technical side of game angling instruction, will also be a one stop source for anglers wishing to find an instructor in their area.

With a membership of over 250 registered coaches operating from Caithness to Cornwall as well as Ireland, they will be able to put any anglers looking for instruction into contact with an appropriate tutor. The GIA will be developing their own web site to aid a personal search. In the meantime, GIA can be contacted on 01342 850740.

David Griffiths

Tel 01747 871695
Email: d.griffiths@freenet.co.uk
www.flyfishing-tuition.co.uk
APGAI/STANIC Trout, Salmon, Sea Trout.
Exclusive private lake in Wiltshire. Chalk Streams.
River Shannon, Ireland. River Tweed, Scotland.
Tackle provided by negotiation

Novices and experienced. Hourly and daily rates.
3 or 6 day Salmon fishing courses.
All game fishing casting techniques taught.

David Green

2 Morgans Hill Close, Nailsea, N. Somerset BS48 4NZ
Tel 01275 854725. Mobile 07810 545014
www.shoot-and-fish.com
STANIC
The West Country
Tackle and Clothing

Rivers and Stillwaters. Beginners and advanced

Martin Cottis

3 Hillhouse Road, Downend, Bristol BS16 5RR
Tel 0117 9877285. Mobile 07747 843548
Email: mart_chris@mcottis.freeserve.co.uk
STANIC Trout fishing & casting, fly tying.
England international.
Specialising in Bristol waters but will work anywhere in the country.
Full tackle and flies provided if required.

Top of the water fly fishing, nymph fishing techniques.
Fly fishing for Pike.

Michael Fanner

Spring Cottage, Chapel Hill, West Grimstead,
Salisbury SP5 3SJ
Tel 01722 710615. Mobile 0784 7547 448
Email: mf@thereelthing.co.uk
www.thereelthing.co.uk
APGAI Trout, Sea Trout, Salmon and Fly Dressing.
Devon, Dorset, Wiltshire, Hampshire. Rivers Taw,
Mole, Axe, Test and Wylye
All tackle

Sea Trout, Salmon, Brown Trout, Grayling. Age 18 plus

Mike Gleave

Dresden, 7 Dundry Lane, Dundry, N. Somerset BS40 8JH
Tel 01275 332339 / 01275 472403
www.bristolwater.co.uk
STANIC & REFFIS
Bristol & the South West, Bristol Water Fisheries.
All Tackle, not clothing.

Stillwater techniques. Fly Tying. Guiding from boat and bank at Blagdon and Chew.

Tuition

KEY		
Name		Game
Contact details		
Qualifications		Coarse
Area covered		
Equipment available		Sea
Specialities		

Fly Rod Reviews

I spent a very pleasurable afternoon at Temple Trout near Bodmin, courtesy of Julian Jones where I tried out the following rods.

Orvis T3 865 Mid Flex - £540
Orvis T3 905 Tip Flex - £550

It never ceases to amaze how tackle manufacturers come up with something completely new every year to sell their wares to us anglers. The new T3 range uses a completely new 'Thermoplastic' technology which, without going into too much detail, coats the individual graphite fibres in a protective strengthening sheath. The result being each fibre is tougher and stronger meaning a high modulus graphite can be used to produce a rod of much less weight with improved power.

Presentation and finish is, as always, immaculate. You get an alloy rod tube in green with a screw on gold coloured cap, a cloth rod bag with an embroidered label and even a small cloth to clean your rod.

The rod is finished in a translucent olive green with gold coloured snakes and looks very classy. The reel seat is a fabulous piece of wood and the reel is locked in place by screwing up the stainless steel butt cap which has an engraving of the Orvis logo, beautiful attention to detail.

So how does all that technology translate in use? This is a real rapier of a rod, very 'quick' and precise with a power which belies its 3.5oz

weight. Teamed with the new Rocky Mountain LA Reel and a floating line it's an effortless partnership combining sensitivity and strength - not cheap but the ultimate combination!

Contact Orvis in Exeter on 01392 272599 or Bath on 01225 331471 or browse their full range at www.orvis.co.uk

Peregrine S9. 9'6" #7 - £195

If the Orvis is the rapier then this is the longbow in your armoury. 9'6" of truly hand crafted rod from Roger McCourtney in Bath. The finish is translucent amber with a lined butt ring and snakes throughout, the reel seat being an uplocker with a lovely piece of wood. I always think the reel seat is one of the few places on a rod where the maker can try and be a bit different and it makes a real difference to the overall impression a rod gives. This is a very elegant rod which actually seemed to slow my casting action down, improving it considerably! Loads of grunt with a very 'through' action, an excellent reservoir rod with distance in mind. Sea Trout and Grilse would also be a distinct possibility on this rod which will still respond well to 2lb stockies on your local stillwater. Peregrine offer a complete range and being rod makers you can have pretty well what you want, though this may well be all you will ever need!

Contact Peregrine on 01761 436900.
www.flyfish-peregrine.co.uk

Carbotec 6' #4 - £145

If we have tried the rapier and the longbow this must be the épée. This is about as small as it gets when you are talking fly rods. It's quite weird picking this up after the Peregrine, it is SO light and wispy. Different tools for different jobs though and this is a real tiny trout stream rod. Where I live we have the Inney, Ottery and Kensey among many other trout streams. This is the perfect weapon for their upper reaches where they become very overgrown and being able to steer your backcast through the undergrowth is vital. I thought #4 might be a bit heavy for a 6' rod but, as westcountry based Carbotec explained you have to get the rod loaded. By definition you will use this rod on very small streams which means a relatively short line - therefore you will want the rod to be 'working'

Left to right: Carbotec, Peregrine, Orvis.

Quality Common Carp for Dave Ware.
Spires Lakes

on a shorter line than would be normal. Perfect sense and it works beautifully. Finish is excellent with a lined butt, snakes throughout and a woodgrain uplocking seat, though you can specify your preference when ordering as all rods are built in the the south west. Six ounce trout will be real sport on this.

For more details on this or any other rods in the comprehensive Carbotec range phone Exeter Angling Centre on 01392 435591 or browse the web site at www.carbotec.co.uk

Bruce & Walker 'Derek Aunger' Saltwater Fly Rod. 9' #10/11 - £299

Saltwater fly fishing could well be the next 'big thing' as game anglers, perhaps disenchanted with the sport in the rivers, look elsewhere for their sportfishing kicks. This is a rod designed by a westcountry angler with a wealth of experience in this area and it shows. It's built to get a good length of line out quickly with either a double taper or, preferably, a shooting head. It certainly does that, even in my hands 30 yards with a single haul is certainly possible when using a shooting head. It's unique feature is the additional 'stripper' ring seen in the photo. This seems to reduce resonance in the line and aids casting. It's a four piece so it travels well and the matt black blank is fitted with three lined rings at the butt and chromed snakes with the benefit of strengthened ferrules, all finished immaculately as you would expect from such a reputable rod maker. You won't be investing nearly £300 on something you can only use at sea either, you could certainly use this on the river or reservoir and for a rod with so much poke, capable of dealing with the variety of fish you are likely to encounter in the sea, it can be very delicate, especially in trained hands!

Contact Derek on 07812 360764, Email: flyfishingexperiences@breathemail.net or find more info at www.flyfishingexperiences.com.

Bruce & Walker can be contacted on 01487 813764 and their web site is at www.bruceandwalker.co.uk.

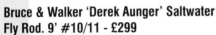

Footnote:

As ever I will reiterate the importance of trying a rod before you buy. It is still a buyers market and with so many companies 'on line' you can buy very easily. Consumables and flies, lines etc can be purchased safely and easily over the web but you can't try a rod 'on line' and, perhaps more importantly, you can't haggle!

All the rods reviewed offer something different and all are excellent examples - go on treat yourself!

Nice Trout, nice tackle, nice venue. Temple Trout.

Mike Heelis with a limit of quality Rainbows from Milemead

Fly Reel Reviews

Snowbee XS Large Arbor Fly Reel - Around £140

This is a brand new product from Plymouth based Snowbee and, at the time of writing, has yet to reach the shelves. It will though and I got a sneak preview at Tavistock's Milemead Fisheries, where I met Director Russell Weston and Product Development Consultant Russell Symons.

This is another reel in the large arbor style which is very fashionable at the moment. This reel is being prototyped and manufactured at British Fly Reels right here in Cornwall and a company with a more proven track record would be hard to find.

It's a good looking reel with a decent capacity, some large arbors compromise capacity which can leave your fly line chafing the reel cage, especially if it's wound unevenly. Its real 'innovation' however, is in the drag system. Fly reels never used to have drag systems at all and many anglers will still use the pressure of their hand to control a running fish but the drag is undeniably useful if you have a fish lunging on a short line and your reel hand is holding a landing net.

The system on this reel was inspired by the 'multi disc' systems commonplace in multiplier reels. Basically you have three metal discs and sandwiched between them two other discs manufactured from 'broflon'. The centre metal disc is locked to the spool and rotates with it, the friction being created from two sides and controlled by a wide diameter 'knob' on the rear of the reel, which goes from nothing to solid within a single turn. The acid test is how it performs when a fish is taking line. Beautifully is the answer, the take up is fantastically smooth and there is no bouncing of the rod tip which happens with most traditional systems where it requires a fair initial degree of tension to get the clutch to slip. This tends to cause line to come off the reel in 'bursts' but with this system the slip is amazingly even and smooth.

The reels are machined from aerospace grade aluminium with all stainless steel internals - no corrosion so equally at home in saltwater. Priced at around £140 it's got some stiff competition from some other famous name reels but I think that drag system, at the moment, is unbeatable.

For further information contact Snowbee on 01752 334933 or visit their web site at www.snowbee.co.uk

Looks like a winner to me!

Orvis 'Rocky Mountain' LA Reel - £57

The price was the first thing I noticed as well! Orvis has relied on the undisputed talents of its Battenkill range for many years now and it has

Snowbee XS

Orvis Rocky Mountain

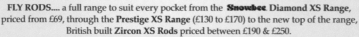

115

become something of a standard in the £150 bracket. The introduction of a brand new reel at £57 suddenly puts a genuine Orvis within the price range of a whole new bracket of budget conscious (that's me) anglers.

It's all alloy, no composites or graphite, and is coloured in a blue/green and grey. It has the usual 'off centre' Orvis drag adjusted by a small detented knob on the back, just like the Battenkill. The only danger with making your reel 'coloured' is the colours may not appeal but it's very tasteful on this model. Yet again it's large arbor but a deeper spool than the Battenkill which gives it a more chunky appearance. In use it's as you would expect from Orvis - flawless and you have their superb guarantee behind it. The sample supplied was loaded with an Orvis Silver Label fly line which also performed perfectly. I can see a lot of fly fisherman being interested in this, at less than half the price of a Battenkill or similar competitors reel you are going to see a lot of these around!

Orvis Battenkill

Orvis Battenkill III LA - £150

We covered this reel last year and it's a beauty. In my opinion the best looking reel around and with a proven history. Beautifully presented and a long time favourite of many fly fishermen.

Contact Orvis in Exeter on 01392 272599 or Bath on 01225 331471 or browse their full range at www.orvis.co.uk

Accessories

Gerber Fisherman - approx £84.99

This Gerber represents the very best in terms of materials and construction and being 100% stainless steel means it will survive saltwater use as well. Tools are: needle nose pliers (one handed opening), wire cutters, shot splitter, shot crimper, carbide file for hook sharpening, scissors, medium and small screwdriver, phillips screwdriver, bottle opener, serrated blade awl, lanyard ring and, of course, a very sharp knife!

The fisherman comes with a nylon sheath you can attach to your belt and it's one of those 'how did I manage before' tools. Not cheap but you'll only ever need to buy one.

Phone 08707 280696 for stockists or find Gerber on the web at www.gerberblades.com

'TW' Matchman Rod Carrier - £7.95

This is a very basic bit of kit but it really does the job at an excellent price. It's not competing with a lot of the holdalls around with loads of sections and pockets, it's purely a rod carrier, with one outside pocket with straps for banksticks etc. and a shoulder strap.

It's called the matchman but I could see fly fishermen and sea fishermen who carry a couple of rods finding it very useful. Against the trend for green and 'cammo' colours it's finished in bright yellow - you won't lose it.

Contact TW Tackle Direct on 01271 862363 or at www.tackledirect.co.uk

The Editor returns a 13lb February Carp taken on crust. Avallon Lodges.

120

Wayne Thomas pictured with a double figure autumn Salmon about to be safely returned to the river Taw.
Combe Martin Sea Angling Club

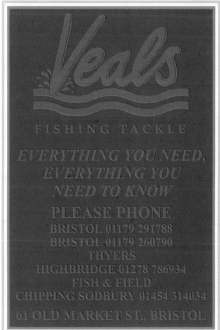
Tackle

Advice for Anglers

Lifesavers, The Royal Life Saving Society UK, is a national charity and the governing body for lifesaving and lifeguarding in the UK. Each year, its volunteers train approximately 250,000 people in water safety, rescue techniques and life support, including 95 per cent of all pool and beach lifeguards.

With the start of the new Open Season for anglers, Lifesavers, The Royal Life Saving Society UK, Britain's leading lifesaving and lifeguarding organisation, would like to offer safety tips for all would-be fishermen.

• Keep your carbon fibre poles away from overhead electricity cables. The carbon attracts electricity and a number of anglers have been fatally shocked by the arc from the cables to the long pole
• When in a boat, standing up to reel-in or cast-off often alters the balance of the craft. Several anglers have drowned from this unexpected occurrence
• Look out for undercut river banks. When standing on the edge the bank may well give way underneath you, giving you wet feet and a big surprise
• When wading, remember rivers can alter the profile and path during winter high water levels. Where you felt safe last season may not be as you last found it
• Especially with the recent extreme weather that we have been experiencing, sea anglers must be ready for the surprise big wave that can wash you off your perch
• Always wear a life jacket. Modern ones cost around £50 and are unobtrusive. This is a small price to pay for a good safety device
• And remember, alcohol, angling and water don't mix. Keep the alcohol for the dry nights at your club room, where the only water is that added to the whisky

Di Standley, Chief Executive of Lifesavers, comments: "Every year anglers die while taking part in their hobby - in 2000 15 anglers died from drowning. Don't let yourself be one of them. The majority of our advice is really common sense, but that's the most important thing for all anglers to remember, think logically and always play safe."

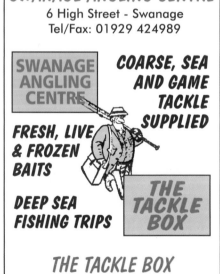

Where to Stay

The following section details some of the increasing number of locations throughout the westcountry offering holidays with a fishing theme. Most have their own lakes, many with residents only fishing. Advertisers in other sections of the guide mat also offer accommodation. Foor a complete listing please use the index Don't forget to mention us when you phone them!

'Kez' with an eight pounder from Avallon Lodges

Everything for the Whole Family

South West Tourism

The west country is one of the most popular areas in Britain for taking a short break or long. From superb lakes and idyllic rivers to fast waters and slow meandering streams, estuaries, coves, inlets and the open sea, the west country has everything for all the family.

The region starts at the river Thames, beginning as a small trickle at Thameshead in Gloucestershire and extends to the peaceful Isles of Scilly, emerald islands in turquoise seas. Unique views from Lands End can be seen at the most westerly point of England where from the dramatic cliffs different seabirds show off their aeronautical displays. In the north of the region, sand-stoned Cotswold villages provide a wonderful holiday destination whatever the season while the Royal Forest of Dean, the first designated National Forest Park in England offers hours of uninterrupted walking over miles of nature trails. The West Country region also extends to the south coast of Dorset where Regency towns such as Lyme Regis and Sidmouth sit in grandeur, overlooking sandy and shingle beaches with many coastal paths to wander.

This fantastic region of contrasts includes Wiltshire, land of the chalk white horse, magical stone circles and open landscapes less than an hour from London; Rolling sub tropical Dorset, bordered by the sea and almost wholly an Area of Outstanding Natural Beauty filled with wonderful views; Bristol and Bath, individual, exciting and vibrant cities with centuries of culture, stimulating nightlife and excellent shopping; Somerset, a mix of heather covered Exmoor, the level plains of Sedgemoor and wonderful family coastal resorts, brimming with beautiful landscapes and renowned for cider and superb cheeses; Devon with it's fine countryside and two coastlines, The south coast, warm and relaxing ideal for families, and the north coast with views across to the Island of Lundy marine reserve.

Further along the more Victorian atmosphere of Lynton and Lymouth present a different age of holiday taking; And the wide open spaces of Dartmoor and Bodmin, each one revealed with its own ever changing characteristics through famous authors such as Jane Austen and Sir Arthur Conan Doyle; Rugged Cornwall, Atlantic facing, wind swept and bounded by the sea, is home also to the awe inspiring and award winning Eden Project which will make any journey to the end of England worthwhile. And don't miss a visit to the fantastic fish markets at Brixham and Looe or Rick Stein's Seafood Restaurant in Padstow.

The West Country cities are some of the most beautiful to be found anywhere and cathedrals spires grace attractive cities like Salisbury, Truro, Exeter or Wells the smallest city in England, while the 2000 year old city of Bath, designated as a World Heritage Site boasts the famous Roman Spa and the sweeping splendour of the Georgian Crescent.

Maritime history features particularly strongly in the West Country and Plymouth, home to the National Marine Aquarium, is where the Pilgrim

One of the Rogers brothers with a Carp. Nanteague

Fathers, Charles Darwin and Captain Scott of the Antarctic all sailed from. Gloucester is home to Gloucester Docks, a museum of waterway life on the canals and rivers of the region and in Bristol, the largest city in the West Country, you will find the ss.Great Britain and the award winning science centre, @ Bristol, a fascinating attraction for adults and children.

Wherever you go in the West Country you will see some of the most wonderful scenery and spectacular coastline that England has to offer. Try walking part of the 982 kilometre South West Coast Path from where the sea is never far away. The path is one of many in the west country that allow visitors to experience sandy beaches, dramatic cliffs, secluded coves and estuaries, or picturesque fishing villages and some of the larger and more livelier resorts, each with plenty to do.

Inland, meander through picture postcard villages with thatched cottages and village greens, or call in on stately homes with their landscaped gardens - colourful whatever the season, friendly pubs in riverside settings, prehistoric heritage sites, intriguing caves, historic monuments, and of course the wide open spaces of the National Parks, Exmoor and Dartmoor.

If that doesn't give you a taste for more, try the local food and drink - ciders, real ales, gin from Plymouth and locally produced wines, the best of beef, lamb and fish, clotted cream for that delicious cream tea, Cornish pasties, Star Gazey pie, the Bath bun, the Dorset knob... all this plus excellent accommodation, the perfect answer to a perfect holiday.

For more information on west country accommodation, be it in a farm or cottage, historic house, seaside apartments or holiday flats, bed and breakfast or self catering, visit www.westcountrynow.com which also has information on events, attractions and destinations in the region or, for more information on water events and water activities in the region visit www.sailsouthwest.com

Girl power! The winners of a junior competition at Spires Lakes - The Tithecott sisters and the Mansfield sisters.

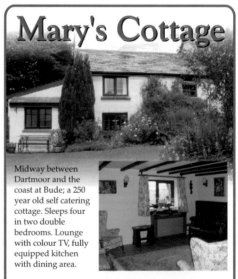

Alf with his best to date, an 8lb Common. Avallon

*Colin Lewis with a 9lb 10oz Brownie caught
during the 2001 Vranch House Charity Challenge.
Bake Lakes*

Luke with a nice Pollack.

Head over heels™ with
South West farms

The benefits of fishing related breaks on Westcountry farm holidays

Cartwheel is the leading farm tourism organisation for a wide variety of farm holidays in the South West, which include a specific activity. Cartwheel has an extensive range of farms with fishing on site, much of which is free to the guest or visitor.

Coarse fishing, sea fishing and private river fishing are available on many Bed & Breakfast, Self Catering and Camping & Caravanning Cartwheel farms, throughout Cornwall, Devon and Somerset.

Cartwheel farms cater for all age groups, offering plenty of opportunity for contact with animals, exploring the countryside, or simply relaxing amongst peaceful surroundings. This makes them an excellent choice for a short break at any time of the year.

Discover the beauty of the countryside by bicycle. Many farms have paths and lanes to cycle on away from the crowds, and provide secure cycle storage. You could jump into a hot tub, sauna or swimming pool afterwards to relax.

Why not explore on foot and get even closer to the wildlife? Farm trails and walks give the visitor a pleasant, unhurried way to discover nature at its best. Hold your breath and watch a barn owl feed her young. Pick mushrooms, blackberries, wild strawberries - or enjoy a picnic. You may be able to take your dog along for company.

Cartwheel farms are the best places to sample the range of delicious, locally produced food the Westcountry has to offer. It is no secret that farmers wives are truly superb cooks and will take great effort and time to source local produce for your meals! Imagine the taste of fresh crabs from the quay at Newlyn, apple juice from the orchards in Devon, Cornish Yarg cheese from Liskeard & Penryn, thick clotted cream from Devon and Cornwall, Cornish new potatoes, Somerset cider and tender beef and lamb from our farms to your plate.

Horse and pony rides, for absolute beginners and the very experienced are also featured. Try the new cross country course in Cornwall - two and a half miles of clifftop riding with stunning views. Some farms even accommodate horses, so you can treat them to a holiday, too!

Alternatively, try your hand at woodturning, study the sky at night with an astronomy weekend, or brush up on your creative skills with an art break. With over 220 quality farms to choose from, there really is something for everyone, so no need to seek out foreign shores for that something different this year - a Cartwheel farm is right on your doorstep.

For a FREE Cartwheel brochure please call 0870 241 1098, or visit www.cartwheel.org.uk

Beautiful 5lb Tench from Somerley Lakes.
Christchurch Angling Club

Float Tubing with The South West Lakes Trust.

Where to Stay

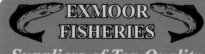

*Paul Blake with a cracking 7lb 3oz Bream
from the River Exe.
Combe Martin Sea Angling Club*

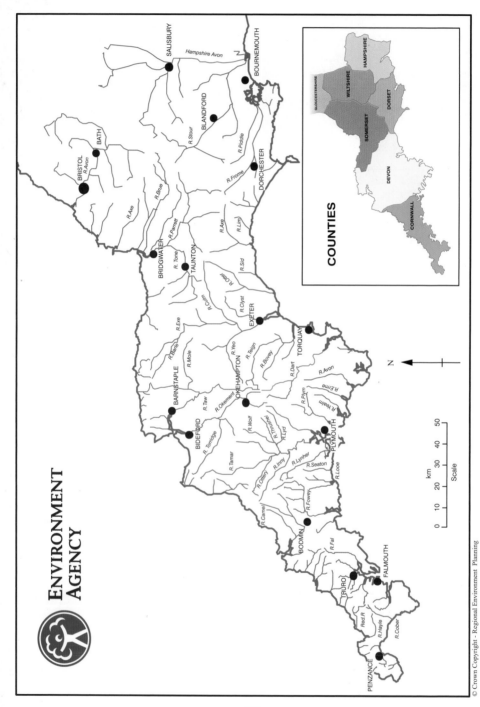

ENVIRONMENT AGENCY

COUNTIES

GLOUCESTERSHIRE
HAMPSHIRE
WILTSHIRE
DORSET
SOMERSET
DEVON
CORNWALL

N

Scale

km

0   10   20   30   40   50

© Crown Copyright - Regional Environment Planning

SALISBURY
Hampshire Avon
BOURNEMOUTH
BLANDFORD
R.Stour
R.Piddle
BATH
R.Avon
BRISTOL
DORCHESTER
R.Frome
R.Blue
R.Axe
R.Parrett
R.Axe
R.Lim
BRIDGWATER
R.Tone
TAUNTON
R.Culm
R.Sid
R.Otter
R.Clyst
EXETER
R.Exe
TORQUAY
R.Yeo
R.Teign
R.Bovey
R.Barle
R.Mole
OKEHAMPTON
R.Dart
BARNSTAPLE
R.Taw
R.Okement
R.Avon
R.Erme
R.Yealm
R.Plym
R.Wolf
R.Thrushel
BIDEFORD
R.Torridge
R.Lyd
PLYMOUTH
R.Tamar
R.Inny
R.Lynher
R.Seaton
R.Looe
R.Ottery
R.Camel
R.Fowey
BODMIN
R.Fal
FALMOUTH
TRURO
Red.R
R.Hayle
R.Cober
PENZANCE

138

The Directory

The Directory is divided into counties.
Each county is sub divided and colour coded:

River Fishing	Stillwater Coarse	Stillwater Trout

Many associations offer both game and coarse fishing on many different

Each county section starts with river fishing and includes a short descri
ributaries followed by entries offering fishing on that river. This section
hame (see map opposite).

The Stillwater Coarse and Stillwater Trout sections are sorted under the

Entries in the Directory highlighted in blue are advertisers and more
available elsewhere in the guide via the advertisers index. These entries
ocation on the inside back cover.

www.gethook

Every entry in this Directory and the sea fishing Directory also appears on our web sit
www.gethooked.co.uk (unless we have been requested not to do so by the owner)

The 'Fish Finder' on the web site enables you to do a text based search of all the entrie
earch by species, town, county, name, post code or any combination.

ADD YOUR FISHERY!
f you wish to add your fishery or club to the Directory you can use the form on the we
Email info@gethooked.co.uk, fax to 01271 860064 or post to Diamond Publications,
Bideford, Devon EX39 4YN.
THERE IS NO CHARGE FOR INCLUSION IN THIS DIRECTORY OR THE WEB SITE DIRE

CORNWALL River Fishing

CAMEL

The Camel rises on the north west edge of Bodmin Moor and flows past Camelford to its estuary at Wadebridge. The run of Salmon tends to be late with some of the best fishing in November and December. Sea Trout in summer. Also moorland Brown Trout fishing.

River Camel Fisheries Association
Contact: E.D.T. Jackson, Butterwell, Nr Nanstallon, Bodmin, PL30 5LQ, 01208 831515, *Water:* The association represents all major riparian owners and fishing clubs on the river Camel and agrees fish limits, conservation policy and enhancement projects in co-operation with the Environment Agency.
Angling 2000 (Camel)
Contact: Simon Evans, Westcountry Rivers Trust, Fore Street, Lifton, PL16 0AA, 01566 784488, wrt@wrt.org.uk, *Water:* New beats on the De Lank. Flexible permits fishing for Trout, *Species:* Trout, *Permits:* From the above, *Charges:* £5 per day, *Season:* 1 April to 30 September.
Bodmin Anglers Association (Camel)
Contact: R. Burrows, 26 Meadow Place, Bodmin, 01208 75513, ivanl@breathe.com, *Water:* 11.5 Miles on River Camel, 0.25 miles on River Fowey, *Species:* Salmon, Sea Trout, *Permits:* Roger Lashbrook at Stan Mays Store, Bodmin. D.Odgers, Gwendreath, Dunmere, Bodmin, *Charges:* 1st May - end November £15 per day or £40 per week. Juniors half price. Membership details from Secretary, *Methods:* Fly, Worm, Spinner.

Butterwell
Contact: Tyson & Janet Jackson, Butterwell, Nr Nanstallon, Bodmin, PL30 5LQ, 01208 831515, tyson@butterwell.u-net.com, *Water:* 1.5 miles River Camel, *Species:* Sea Trout (to 10lb 2oz) & Salmon (to 18lb), *Permits:* On site, *Charges:* £18/day, Max. 5 rods/day priority given to residents of Butterwell guest house, *Season:* 1st May - 30th August, night fly fishing only for Sea trout. 1st September - 15th December for Salmon, *Methods:* Any method for Salmon after 1st September.
Fenwick Trout Fishery (River Camel)
Contact: David & Shirley Thomas, Old Coach Road, Dunmere, Bodmin, PL31 2RD, 01208 78296, *Water:* 570 yards on the river Camel. See also entry under stillwater trout, *Species:* Sea Trout and Salmon, *Permits:* On site. EA licence required, *Charges:* Please phone for details, *Season:* As current EA Byelaws, *Methods:* Fly fishing from bank only
Wadebridge & Dist. Angling Association
Contact: Mr Stan Spry (Hon. Sec.), 'Bos an dowr', 23 Treforest Road, Wadebridge, PL27 7HE, 01208 813494, 07970 751578, bosandowr@yahoo.co.uk, *Water:* 10 miles River Camel, 1 mile River Allen, *Species:* Salmon to 27lb, Sea trout to 7lb, *Permits:* Day / Week permits, Bait Bunker, Polmorla Road, Wadebridge 01208 816403. Padstow Angling Centre, The Drang, Padstow PL28 8BL. 01841 532762, *Charges:* Day £25, Week £100, *Season:* Visitor permits end 31st September, although 4 tickets per week (no day tickets) are available until the end of November - must be pre-booked, *Methods:* No maggots permitted. Fly and spinning, natural baits on some beats.

FAL

Fal River Association
Contact: Mr. Tom Mutton, 01872 273858, *Water:* Association protecting the interests of the River Fal,

FOWEY

Rises near the highest point of Bodmin Moor from which it flows south, then turns to the west, and finally south again through Lostwithiel to its long estuary. A late Salmon river. Also good Sea Trout fishing and some Trout fishing.

Fowey River Association
Contact: Chris Marwood (sec), Withy Cottage, Huish Champflower, Taunton, TA4 2EN, 01398 371384, *Water:* An association of representatives of angling clubs and riparian owners on the Fowey whose aim is to secure and maintain the well being of the river and its ecology. It exists largely as a pressure group and negotiating body on behalf of its members, *Permits:* No fishing permits sold through the Association. For membership details please contact the secretary at the above address, *Methods:* E.A. Byelaws apply; catch restrictions: Salmon 1/day, 2/week, 5/season; Sea Trout 4/day, all Sea Trout to be returned in September
Bodmin Anglers Association (Fowey)
Water: See entry under Camel. 0.25 miles River Fowey
Lanhydrock Angling Association
Contact: Brian Muelaner, The National Trust, Regional Office, Lanhydrock, Bodmin, PL30 4DE, 01208 265211, *Water:* 2 miles on River Fowey, *Species:* Sea trout, Salmon, *Permits:* Available from the above telephone number, *Charges:* £15 Daily, £30 Weekly (maximum 6 tickets daily), *Season:* 1st April - 30th September, Sea Trout 31st August, *Methods:* Artificial bait only
Liskeard & District Angling Club (Fowey)
Contact: Bill Eliot (Hon Sec), 64 Portbyhan Road, West Looe, PL13 2QN, 01503 264173, *Water:* 23 Miles of Rivers Fowey, Lynher, Inny, Seaton River, West Looe River; Map of waters with day/week tickets, *Species:* Salmon to 20lb (typically 7-12.5lb) & Sea Trout to 10lb (typically 2.5-4lb), *Permits:* Visitor tickets available until 30 November for winter Salmon. Tremar Tropicals Shop, Liskeard. Lashbrooks Tackle Shop, Bodmin. East Looe Chandlers, The Quay, East Looe. Shillamill lakes, Lanreath. The Tackle shop, Fore Street, Liskeard, *Charges:* Adult: £15/day, £50/week, Membership £55. Joining fee £10. Membership limited to 250 adults, *Season:* River Fowey 1st April - 15th December; Sea

Trout season closes end September, *Methods:* Spinning, Fly Fishing or Bait. Artificials only on some beats. No groundbait, no maggots.

Lostwithiel Fishing Association
Contact: Roger Lashbrook, Rogers Tackle Shop, 1st Floor, Stan Mays Store, Higher Bore Street, Bodmin, PL31 1JZ, 01208 78006, *Water:* 2 miles water, Both banks, River Fowey, *Species:* Salmon, Sea trout, Brown Trout, *Permits:* Rogers Tackle Shop, Bodmin, *Charges:* Season tickets only: £55, *Season:* 1st April - 15th December, *Methods:* All baits

Newbridge Angling Association
Contact: Mr. D Maskell, Jefferys, 5 Fore Street, Lostwithiel, PL22 0BP, 01208 872245, *Water:* 1.5 miles single bank on River Fowey, *Species:* Trout & Salmon, *Permits:* Members only - no day tickets. For membership details please contact Mr. Maskell.

Wainsford Fishery (Fowey)
Contact: Paul Elliot, Wainsford Fishery, Twowatersfoot, Liskeard, PL14 6HT, 01208 821432, *Water:* Two miles on the Fowey. See also entry under Stillwater Trout, Liskeard, *Species:* Salmon to 16lb, Sea Trout to 10lb, *Permits:* On site, *Charges:* £15 per day, *Season:* Salmon 1 April to 15 December. Trout 1 April to 30 September, *Methods:* Fowey River Association limits apply.

LOOE
The twin rivers, East and West Looe, have their sources near Liskeard and join shortly before reaching the sea at Looe. Although small, there is a run of Sea Trout, and Brown Trout throughout.

LYNHER
Rises on Bodmin Moor and joins the Tamar estuary opposite Plymouth. Brown Trout and runs of Salmon and Sea Trout.

River Lynher Fisheries Association
Contact: Arthur White (hon.secretary), River Lynher Fisheries Association, 14 Wadham Road, Liskeard, PL14 3BD, 01579 345428, efsa@talk21.com, *Water:* Consultative body for the river Lynher. Membership comprises riparian owners, angling clubs, lessees of fishing rights, individual anglers and others interested in the Lynher valley environment, *Species:* Salmon, Sea Trout, Trout, *Charges:* £5 annual membership,

Liskeard & District Angling Club (Lynher)
Contact: Bill Eliot, 64 Portbyhan Rd, West Looe, PL13 2QN, 01503 264173, *Water:* 23 miles of Rivers Fowey, Lynher, Inny, Seaton, West Looe; Map of waters with day/week tickets, *Species:* Salmon to 16lb & Sea Trout to 6lb (some very big ones April/May), *Permits:* Tremar Tropicals Shop, Liskeard. Lashbrooks Tackle Shop, Bodmin. East Looe Chandlers, The Quay, East Looe. Shillamill lakes, Lanreath. The Tackle shop, Fore Street, Liskeard, *Charges:* Adult: £15/day, £50/week, Membership £55. Joining fee £10. Membership limited to 250 adults, *Season:* River Lynher & Inny; 1st March - 14th October; Sea Trout season closes end September, *Methods:* Spinning, Fly Fishing or Bait. No groundbait, no maggots.

Woodcocks Club
Contact: Michael Charleston, The Gift House, Buckland Monachorum, Yelverton, PL20 7NA, 01822 853293, mwcharl@aol.com, *Water:* Two miles of the lower and middle Lynher, *Species:* Salmon, Sea trout and Brown trout, *Permits:* Very limited number of annual permits for which there is a waiting list. No short term permits, *Season:* March 1st to October 14th, *Methods:* Fly only for Sea trout and brown trout except in spates. Return of Salmon (catch and release) is encouraged

MENALHYL
Small stream starting near St. Columb Major and entering the sea north of Newquay. Brown Trout fishing.

St. Mawgan Angling Association
Contact: Mr. T. Trevenna, Lanvean House, St. Mawgan, Newquay, TR8 4EY, 01637 860316, *Water:* Stretch around Mawgan Porth, *Species:* Trout, Brown Trout, *Charges:* Limited day tickets from The Merrymoor, Mawgan Porth. Club membership restricted to those in parish of St. Mawgan, *Season:* April 1st - end September, *Methods:* See details on site

SEATON
Short stream to the east of Looe with fishing for Brown Trout.

Liskeard & District Angling Club (Seaton & West Looe)
Contact: Bill Eliot (Hon Sec), 64 Portbyhan Road, West Looe, PL13 2QN, 01503 264173, *Water:* Seaton River, West Looe River; Map of waters with day/week tickets, *Species:* Good small water Sea Trout, *Permits:* Visitor tickets available until 30 November for winter Salmon.Tremar Tropicals Shop, Liskeard. Lashbrooks Tackle Shop, Bodmin. East Looe Chandlers, The Quay, East Looe. Shillamill lakes, Lanreath. The Tackle shop, Fore Street, Liskeard, *Charges:* Adult: £15/day, £50/week, Membership £55. Joining fee £10. Membership limited to 250 adults, *Season:* River Fowey 1st April - 15th December; Sea Trout season closes end September, *Methods:* Spinning, Fly Fishing or Bait. Artificials only on some beats. No groundbait, no maggots.

TAMAR
The Tamar rises near the north coast, and for most of its course forms the boundary between Devon and Cornwall. It is always a lowland stream flowing through farmland and this fact is reflected in the size of its Trout which have a larger average size than the acid moorland streams. Around Launceston, the Tamar is joined by five tributaries - Ottery, Carey, Wolf, Thrushel and Lyd - which offer good Trout fishing, as does the Inny which enters a few miles downstream. There is a good run of Salmon and Sea Trout, the latter being particularly numerous on the Lyd. There are also Grayling in places.

Angling 2000 (Tamar)
Contact: Simon Evans, Westcountry Rivers Trust, Fore Street, Lifton, PL16 0AA, 01566 784488, wrt@wrt.org.uk, *Water:* More than 20 beats on the Tamar, Taw and Torridge. Flexible permits fishing for Trout, Salmon, Sea Trout and Grayling.More than 6 beats on the Inny, Tamar and Lyd new for 2002, *Species:* Salmon, Sea Trout, Trout and Grayling, *Permits:* From the above, *Charges:* £5 to £10 per day depending on beat, *Season:* 15 March to 14 October. Grayling fishing to 30 November on selected beats.

Bude Angling Association
Contact: Mr L. Bannister, 2 Creathorn Road, Bude, EX23 8NT, 01288 353986, *Water:* 3 miles on the upper reaches of the River Tamar, *Species:* Brown Trout (Wild), *Permits:* Bude Angling Supplies, Queen Street, Bude. Turner Tackle, 19 Fore Street, Holsworthy Devon, *Charges:* £3 day, Week tickets available - £12, *Season:* March 15th - Sept 30th, *Methods:* Fly only.

Dutson Tamar Fishery
Contact: Mr Broad, Lower Dutson Farm, Launceston, PL15 9SP, 01566 773147 or 01566 776456, *Water:* Half a mile on the river Tamar at Launceston, *Species:* Brown trout, Salmon and occasional Sea trout, *Permits:* Homeleigh Angling and Garden Centre, Dutson, Launceston. Tel: 01566 773147, *Charges:* £5 per day, *Season:* 1st March - 14th October, Salmon as current EA Byelaws, *Methods:* See current EA Byelaws.

Launceston Anglers Association
Contact: Colin Hookway, 7 Grenville Park, Yelverton, PL20 6DQ, 01822 855053, *Water:* 6 miles on River Tamar and Carey, 7 miles River Inny, *Species:* Brown Trout, Sea Trout, Salmon, *Permits:* The Fishmonger, 16 Southgate Place, Launceston, *Charges:* Salmon & Sea Trout; Day £15, Week £40. Brown Trout: Day £7.50, Week £25, Juniors £2 a day. Day tickets valid for 24 hours from time of purchase. Annual membership from £50, *Season:* From 1st March to 14th October, *Methods:* Brown trout - fly only, Salmon & Sea Trout - any method subject to byelaws.

CORNWALL
Stillwater
Coarse

BODMIN
East Rose Farm
Contact: Veronica Stansfield, East Rose Farm, St. Breward, Bodmin Moor, PL30 4NL, 01208 850674, eastrose@globalnet.co.uk, *Water:* Complex of four lakes with 22 permanent pegs (two specially constructed for disabled). 3 acres of water, *Species:* Mixed fishing in two largest lakes: Tench / Roach / Rudd and Crucian. Lower lake has Carp to 8lb. Deep Pool - Carp to 20lb & Tench to 3lb. *Permits:* Day tickets available from Farmhouse at East Rose, *Charges:* Day tickets: £4 adults, £2.75 OAP's, Disabled & under 16's. Reduced rate evening tickets, *Season:* No closed season, No night fishing, *Methods:* No keepnets unless by prior arrangement. No barbless hooks. No boilies

Lakeview Coarse Fishery
Contact: Don, Old Coach Road, Lanivet, Bodmin, PL30 5JJ, 01208 831808, *Mobile:* 07733 345456, admin@lakeview-country-club.co.uk, *Water:* 3 lakes, 4 acres in total, *Species:* 13 in total inc. Carp to 20lb, Tench to 6lb, Bream to 5lb & Roach to 5lb 3oz, Perch 4lb 9oz, *Permits:* On site Tackle Shop & Main Reception, *Charges:* £4.50/day/Adult, £3 Junior-O.A.P-Disabled. Season ticket available, *Season:* Open all year, *Methods:* No boilies or night fishing

BUDE
Bude Canal Angling Association
Contact: Mr Dick Turner, 2 Pathfields, Bude, EX23 8DW, 01288 353162, *Water:* Bude Canal (1.25 miles), *Species:* Mirror, Common, Crucian Carp, Bream, Tench, Roach, Rudd, Perch, Eels, Gudgeon, Dace, *Permits:* On the bank, *Charges:* Seniors day £4, Seniors week £18, Juniors & O.A.Ps day £2, Juniors & O.A.Ps week £10, *Season:* Closed season April 1st May 31st inc, *Methods:* Micro barb or barbless hooks only, Strictly one rod only, No camping or any equipment deemed to be associated with camping.

Houndapitt Farm
Contact: Mr Heard, Houndapitt Farm, Sandymouth, Bude, EX23 9HW, 01288 355455, *Mobile:* 07968 171255, tony@houndapitt.co.uk, *Water:* Small lake, *Species:* Golden Tench to 1.5lb. Rudd to 1.5lb. Various Carp to 9lb, *Permits:* From Sandymouth Bay Holiday Park, *Charges:* £2.50 per day, *Methods:* Barbless hooks.

South West Lakes Angling Association
Contact: Roy Retallick, 21 Alstone Road, Tiverton, EX16 4LH, 01884 256721, r.retallick@btinternet.com, *Water:* All 14 South West Lakes Trust fisheries plus 1 exclusive member only water at Lower Tamar, *Species:* All coarse fish - Carp 35lb, Pike +20lb, Bream +8lb, Tench +7lb, Roach 2lb, Perch 3lb 7oz, Eel 4lb, *Permits:* Please contact Roy Retallick, *Charges:* £8 per year membership, £7 junior, OAP and disabled. Entitles 10% discount on day and season tickets to fish any South West Lakes Trust Coarse Waters, *Season:* Open all year, *Methods:* As South West Lakes Trust rules displayed on site

Upper Tamar Lake

Contact: South West Lakes Trust, 01837 871565, info@swlakestrust.org.uk, *Water:* Ranger Tel 01288 321262, *Species:* Carp to 28lb. 50lb plus bags of Bream and 30lb plus bags of Rudd. Regular competitions, *Permits:* See South West Lakes Trust coarse advert. Self service permit hut on site, *Charges:* Full day £4.50, Concession £3.50, 24 Hour £8.50, Season Day £80, Season Concession £60, Season Child (under 16) £35, Season Day & Night £120, Additional Fisheries £20 each. This venue can be booked for competitions, *Season:* Open all year 24 hours a day, *Methods:* No child under 14 years may fish unless accompanied by an adult over 18 years. No child under 16 may fish overnight unless accompanied by an adult over 18 years, and then only with permission of parent or legal guardian (letter to this effect must be produced)

Water Front Fishing Lake

Contact: Water Front Fishing, The Lower Wharf Centre, Bude, EX23 8LG, 01288 359606, simon@waterfrontfishing.freeserve.co.uk, *Water:* One acre lake, *Species:* Carp (mixed species), Rudd, Roach and Eels, *Permits:* Day tickets from the above, *Charges:* £4.50 per day, *Season:* Open all year, dawn to dusk, *Methods:* Barbless hooks only. No keepnets, Groundbait restrictions on request.

DELABOLE

Ferndale

Contact: Steve Davey, Rockhead, Delabole, PL33 9BU, 01840 212091, ferndale@agriplus.net, *Water:* Three half acre lakes set in a sheltered valley 3 miles off the North Cornwall coast, *Species:* Roach, Rudd, Bream and Carp, *Charges:* Adults £3.50 per day. OAP's and juniors £2.50 per day. After 5pm £2.50. Extra rod £1 per day, *Season:* Open all year from dawn to dusk.

FALMOUTH

Argal

Contact: South West Lakes Trust, 01837 871565, info@swlakestrust.org.uk, *Water:* Ranger 01579 342366, *Species:* Carp to 30lb plus, Bream, Tench, Pike to over 30lb, and Eels, *Permits:* Self service unit at Argal Car Park. See South West Lakes Trust coarse advert, *Charges:* Full day £4.50, Concession £3.50, 24 Hour £8.50, Season Day £80, Season Concession £60, Season Child (under 16) £35, Season Day & Night £120, Additional Fisheries £20 each, *Season:* Open all year 24 hours a day, *Methods:* No child under 14 years may fish unless accompanied by an adult over 18 years. No child under 16 may fish overnight unless accompanied by an adult over 18 years, and then only with permission of parent or legal guardian (letter to this effect must be produced).

HAYLE

Marazion Angling Club

Contact: Mr Andrew Bradford, 7 Chy Kensa Close, Hayle, 01736 757330, *Water:* St. Erth Fishery (3 acres), Bills Pool (2.5 acres), Wheal Grey (4 acres), River Hayle (600yd upstream from St. Erth Church), *Species:* Carp, Bream, Tench, Roach, Rudd, Perch, Golden Orfe, Golden Rudd, Gudgeon, Trout, Flounders & Eels; Wheal Grey reputed to hold Cornwall's biggest Carp (+30lb), *Permits:* Available in local shops: Newtown Angling Centre, Praa Sands. Tims Tackle, St. Ives. Atlantic Tackle, Helston. County Angler, Camborne. Post Office, St. Erth plus many more outlets (Please phone for more details) - Permits MUST be obtained prior to fishing, *Charges:* Day £4.50, Conc. £3.50, Week £18, Full membership £40, Assoc. membership £28 (must reside outside Cornwall), Night fishing £60, *Season:* Open all year dawn till dusk; Night fishing by appointment only; Matches held regularly throughout the year, *Methods:* Barbless hooks, full rules & byelaws displayed at lake side (best baits: maggot, worm, pellet, sweetcorn, meat, boilies, nuts)

Sharkey's Pit

Contact: Dave Burn, Strawberry Lane, Joppa, Hayle, 01736 763721, *Water:* 2 lakes approx 2.5 acres, *Species:* Common, Crucian, Mirror and Ghost Carp, Tench, Golden Orfe, Roach, Rudd, Gudgeon & Eels, *Season:* Open all year.

HELSTON

Middle Boswin Farm

Contact: Jonno, Middle Boswin Farm, Porkellis, Helston, TR13 0HR, 01209 860420, middleboswin@lineone.net, *Water:* 1 acre lake; New Carp Lake and match lake pending, *Species:* Roach 2lb, Rudd 1.5lb, Bream 4lb, Tench 3lb, Perch 2lb, Hybrid (Roach/Bream) 2.5lb plus single figure Mirror and Common Carp, *Permits:* Day tickets available at farm, *Charges:* Adult £4, concessions £3, Second rod £1 extra, *Season:* Winter; Dawn to Dusk, Summer 7am - 9 pm, *Methods:* Barbless hooks only, No fixed legers, No cereal groundbait, hemp or nuts, no trout pellets. No keepnets or carpsacks.

LAUNCESTON

Dutson Water

Contact: Mr Broad, Lower Dutson Farm, Launceston, PL15 9SP, 01566 773147 or 01566 776456, francis.broad@btclick.com, *Water:* 0.75 acre lake, *Species:* Carp, Tench to 6lb 2oz, Bream to 5lb 2oz, Rudd, Perch to 3lb 4oz etc, *Permits:* Available on farm and Homeleigh Garden and Angling Centre, Dutson. Tel: 01566 773147, *Charges:* Day ticket £5. Night fishing by arrangment, *Season:* Open all year, *Methods:* No Groundbait, Barbless hooks only.

Elmfield Farm Coarse Fishery

Contact: Mr J Elmer, Elmfield Farm, Canworthy Water, Launceston, PL15 8UD, 01566 781243, *Water:* 2 acre & 1.25 acre lake, *Species:* Carp to 24lb, Tench to 6lb, Roach to 3lb, Perch to 3.5lb, Bream, Orfe to 1lb, Chub to 3lb & Koi, also Barbel, *Charges:* £5 - 2 Rods, £4 Children/OAP's, *Season:* Open all year, *Methods:* No keepnets, ground bait in feeders only, barbless hooks, no boilies

Hidden Valley Coarse Fishing Lakes

Contact: Mr. P. Jones, Tredidon, Nr Kennards House, Launceston, PL15 8SJ, 01566 86463, hiddenvalley@tredidon.freeserve.co.uk, *Water:* 2 acre & 0.75 acre lake, *Species:* Common, Mirror, Crucian & Ghost Carp to 22lb, Tench to 6lb, Roach, Bream & Rudd, *Permits:* Day tickets from Hidden Valley reception, *Charges:* Adults £5 for 2 rods, Child/ OAP £4 for 2 rods, *Season:* Open all year, 6am to dusk, *Methods:* Barbless hooks only. No groundbait.

St. Leonards Coarse Fishing Lake
Contact: Andy Reeve, St. Leonards Equitation Centre, Polson, Launceston, PL15 9QR, 01566 775543, *Mobile:* 07860 431225, paintballpolson@totaleyes.co.uk, *Water:* 0.75 Acre lake, *Species:* Tench, Crucian, Leather, Mirror and Common Carp, *Permits:* From House, *Charges:* £4 per rod per day, *Season:* Open all year, *Methods:* Barbless hooks only.

LISKEARD
Badham Farm
Contact: Joyce and Robert Brown, St Keyne, Liskeard, PL14 4RW, 01579 343572, *Water:* 0.75 acre lake, *Species:* Carp 15lb, Roach 2.5lb, Tench 3lb and Rudd 2lb, *Permits:* On site, *Charges:* £4/rod/day, *Season:* Open all year dawn to dusk, *Methods:* Barbless hooks; No boilies; No keepnets; Landing nets must be used; No groundbait

LOOE
Shillamill Lakes & Lodges
Contact: Shillamill Lakes, Lanreath, Looe, PL13 2PE, 01503 220886, *Water:* 3 Lakes totalling approx 5 acres, *Species:* Main specimen lake: Common, Mirror and Leather Carp. Second lake: Common, Mirror and Ghost, Roach, Perch. Third: Common and Mirror, Golden Rudd, Golden Orfe, Perch, Tench, Roach & Crucian, *Charges:* Private fishing for residents and season ticket holders only, *Methods:* Fishery requirements on applications.

NEWQUAY
Goonhavern
Contact: S.Arthur, Oak Ridge Farm, Bodmin Road, Goonhavern, TR4 9QG, 01872 575052, *Water:* 2 acres, *Species:* Carp, Tench, Rudd, Roach, Perch, *Permits:* On the bank, *Charges:* £3 Adults. £2 children, OAP's, *Season:* Open all year, *Methods:* Barbless hooks, No Carp keepnets.
Gwinear Pools
Contact: Simon & Jo Waterhouse, Gwinear Farm, Cubert, Newquay, TR8 5JX, 01637 830165, *Water:* 3 acre mixed lake, 60 peg match lake, *Species:* Carp, Roach, Bream, Perch, Rudd, Tench, *Charges:* Day tickets from farm and self service kiosk: £5 adult. £3 OAP's & Juniors. Evening £3 & £2, *Season:* No Close season, *Methods:* Barbless hooks. No keepnets

Oakside Fishery & Fish Farm
Contact: Brian & Sandra Hiscock, 89 Pydar Close, Newquay, TR7 3BT, 01637 871275, *Water:* 3 Acre Lake, *Species:* Carp to 20lb, Tench 6lb, Rudd, Bream 8lb, Perch, Roach 2lb, Crucians 2lb, *Permits:* Pay Kiosk, checked by bailiff, *Charges:* Adult £4 (Two rods), Junior, O.A.P.'s, Disabled £3 (Two Rods), *Season:* All year round, *Methods:* Barbless hooks, No tiger nuts or peanuts and no Carp in keepnets.
Penvose Farm Holidays
Contact: Jonathan Bennett, St. Mawgan, Nr. Newquay, TR8 4AE, 01637860277 or 860432, *Water:* 2.5 acres of water set in a beautiful valley; this year extending to 3.5 acres in total, *Species:* Carp (Common 15-16lb, Mirror 16-17lb, Ghost 19.5-20lb), Tench (Green 3-4lb, Golden 1/2lb) Bream 4-5lb, Crucians 1.5lb, Rudd 1.5lb, Roach 1lb, *Charges:* Adults £4. under 14 £3, *Season:* No closed season, fishing dawn till dusk, *Methods:* Anglers must hold a valid licence; All nets to be dipped in solution tanks, no keepnets except for matches, landing nets must be used; Ground bait up to 2kg max.; Barbless hooks only
Porth
Contact: South West Lakes Trust, 01837 871565, info@swlakestrust.org.uk, *Water:* Ranger Tel 01637 877959, *Species:* Bags of 130lb plus have been caught. Best Bream 9lb 2oz, Tench 9lb 12oz. Rudd to 3lb. Roach to 1lb 4oz plus. Mixed bags of Roach, Rudd, Skimmers to 60lb. Regular competitions, *Permits:* Self service at Porth car park .See South West Lakes Trust coarse advert, *Charges:* Full day £4.50, Concession £3.50, 24 Hour £8.50, Season Day £80, Season Concession £60, Season Child (under 16) £35, Season Day & Night £120, Additional Fisheries £20 each. This venue can be booked for competitions, *Season:* Open all year 24 hours a day, *Methods:* No child under 14 years may fish unless accompanied by an adult over 18 years. No child under 16 may fish overnight unless accompanied by an adult over 18 years, and then only with permission of parent or legal guardian (letter to this effect must be produced)

Trebellan Park
Contact: Trebellan Park, Cubert, Newquay, TR8 5PY, 01637 830522, *Water:* 3 Lakes totalling 2.5 acres, *Species:* Carp, Roach, Rudd, Tench, *Permits: Charges:* Day tickets £3.50 /1 rod, £5 /2 rods, *Season:* No close season, 7am to dusk, *Methods:* Barbless hooks only, No keepnets, No ground bait, no boilies
Trethiggey Farm Pond
Contact: Mr Eustice, Trethiggey Farm, Quintral Downs, Newquay, 01637 874665, *Water:* Small quarter acre farm pond, *Species:* Carp, Rudd, Tench, Roach, Bream, *Permits:* On site, *Charges:* £3 per person, max two rods per person. £1.50 juniors and OAP, *Season:* Open all year dawn to dusk. Please telephone before travelling in the winter months, *Methods:* Barbless hooks, no carp in keepnets, no boilies.
White Acres Country Park
Contact: Tackle Shop, Newquay, TR8 4LW, 0845 458 0065, . *Water:* 14 Lakes totalling approx 25 acres, *Species:* Wide range of almost all species (no Pike or Zander), *Permits:* Available from fishing Lodge, *Charges:* please call for info, *Season:* Fishery open all year round, *Methods:* 'The Method' is banned, Barbless hooks only, Some keepnet restrictions, No peas, nuts, or beans.

PENZANCE
Boscathnoe
Contact: South West Lakes Trust, 01837 871565, info@swlakestrust.org.uk, *Water:* Ranger 01579 342366, *Species:* Common Mirror and Crucian carp with fish into the 20lb range. Roach, Tench, Rudd and Bream also stocked, *Permits:* See South West Lakes Trust coarse advert, *Charges:* Full day £4.50, Concession £3.50, 24 Hour £8.50, Season Day £80, Season Concession £60, Season Child (under 16) £35, Season Day & Night £120, Additional Fisheries £20 each, *Season:* Open all year 24 hours a day, *Methods:* No child under 14 years may fish unless accompanied by an adult over 18 years. No child under 16 may fish overnight unless accompanied by an adult over 18 years, and then only with permission of parent or legal guardian (letter to this effect must be produced).

Choone Farm Fishery
Contact: Mr V.B. Care, Choone Farm, St. Buryan, Penzance, 01736 810220, *Water:* 2 lakes, *Species:* Carp, Tench, Perch, Rudd, *Charges:* 1 rod - £3.50/ person, 2 rods - £4.50, *Season:* Please telephone before travelling, *Methods:* Barbless hooks only, no carp in keepnets.

Tindeen Fishery
Contact: J. Laity, Bostrase, Millpool, Goldsithney, Penzance, TR20 9JG, 01736 763486, *Water:* 3 lakes approx 1 acre each, *Species:* Carp, Roach, Rudd, Gudgeon, Perch, Tench, Trout, *Charges:* Adults £3, Juniors under 14 £2, Extra rod £1 each, *Season:* All year, night fishing by arrangement, *Methods:* Barbless hooks to be used.

SALTASH

Bake Fishing Lakes (Coarse)
Contact: Tony Lister, Bake, Trerule Foot, Saltash, 01752 849027, *Mobile:* 07798 585836, tony.lister@bakelakes.co.uk, *Water:* 7 lakes adding up to over 15 acres, Coarse and Trout, *Species:* Mirror 21lb, Common 24lb 9oz, Ghost 24lb, Crucian Carp, Tench 4lb 2oz, Bream 8lb 4oz, Roach, Rudd, *Permits:* At Bake Lakes, *Charges:* £6.50 per day Specimen Lake, £5 per day Small fish lakes. 2 rods per person, reduced rates for pensioners and juniors subject to change, *Season:* 8am - Dusk. Earlier by appointment, open all year, *Methods:* Barbless hooks, No nuts. No keepnets specimen fish. Landing mats. All nets to be dipped before fishing.

Bush Lakes
Contact: J Renfree, Bush Farm, Saltash, PL12 6QY, 01752 842148, *Water:* 3 Lakes from half to 1 acre, *Species:* Carp to 30lb, Tench to 3.5lb, Rudd to 1.5lb, Roach to 1.5lb, Bream, Perch to 4.5lb, *Charges:* £5 per person, two rods max, *Season:* Open all year, *Methods:* Barbless hooks, landing mat, no nets for big carp.

ST AUSTELL

Glenleigh Farm Fishery
Contact: Mr & Mrs A Tregunna, Glenleigh Farm, Sticker, St Austell, PL26 7JB, 01726 73154, *Mobile:* 07813 490004, fishglenleigh@btinternet.com, *Water:* One acre lake, *Species:* Carp (Common, Ghost, Mirror, Leather), Tench, Rudd, Roach, Eels, Gudgeon, Perch, *Permits:* Tickets from lakeside, permits from Sticker post office, *Charges:* £4.50 day, £3.50 child /OAP. £2.50 evening, £1.50 child /OAP. 12 month membership available, *Season:* Open all year dawn to dusk, *Methods:* Barbless hooks. No keepnets for Carp or any fish over 6lb. No nuts, peas or beans. Max 2 rods per person. Mats to be used

Roche (St Austell) Angling Club
Contact: Mr K. Pyke - Membership Secretary, 41 Roman Drive, Bodmin, PL31 1EN, 01208 79578, Kelvinpyke@aol.com, *Water:* 6 fresh water lakes in St Austell area, *Species:* Roach, Perch, Rudd, Tench, Eels, Carp, Pike & Bream, *Permits:* Fishing restricted to Members and their guests only. Membership applications available from membership secretary direct, *Charges:* Full Annual membership £30, concessionary £10 plus initial joining fee. Membership to Game and Sea sections only at reduced rates, *Season:* Open all year, *Methods:* As specified in club byelaws

Sunnyview Lake
Contact: Philip Gale, 01726 890715, *Water:* Half acre lake, *Species:* Roach, Rudd, Tench, Perch & Carp, *Permits:* Limited day tickets available by prior booking only - please phone number above, *Charges:* £4 /day /person (maximum 4) Sole hire £16 per day, *Season:* All year, dawn to dusk, *Methods:*

ST COLUMB

Meadowside Fishery
Contact: Mr. Terry Price, Meadowside Farm, Winnards Perch, St. Columb, TR9 6DH, 01637 880544, *Mobile:* 07811 757223, info@meadowsidefisheries.co.uk, *Water:* 2 lakes. one mixed coarse fishery, one carp lake, *Species:* Carp 15lb, Roach 2lb, Perch 3lb, Rudd 1lb, Tench 5lb, Bream 6lb, *Permits:* Block permit on site from EA, *Charges:* £3.50/ 1rod, concessions & juniors £2.50/1 rod, £1/extra rod, max. 2 rods, *Season:* No close season, 7.30am to dusk daily all year round, *Methods:* Barbless hooks, no keepnets, unhooking mats.

Retallack Waters
Contact: Retallack Waters, Winnards Perch, Nr St Columb Major, (01637) 881160 / 880057, *Water:* 6.5 acre main lake, separate match canal, *Species:* Common, Mirror and Ghost Carp, Pike, Bream, Tench, Roach and Rudd, *Permits:* Night fishing only available to season ticket holders. Please enquire for details, *Charges:* Canal: £5 adults, £4 children/OAPs. Main specimen lake: £6 adult, £5 children/OAP's, *Season:* Open all year, *Methods:* Barbless hooks only. Unhooking mats and specimen landing net required on specimen lake. Dogs allowed by prior arrangement, please phone first.

ST IVES

Bussow
Contact: South West Lakes Trust, 01837 871565, info@swlakestrust.org.uk, *Water:* Ranger Tel 01579 342366, *Species:* Rudd to 1.5lb. Roach, Bream and Carp, *Permits:* See South West Lakes Trust coarse advert, *Charges:* Full day £4.50, Concession £3.50, 24 Hour £8.50, Season Day £80, Season Concession £60, Season Child (under 16) £35, Season Day & Night £120, Additional Fisheries £20 each, *Season:* Open all year 24 hours a day, *Methods:* No child under 14 years may fish unless accompanied by an adult over 18 years. No child under 16 may fish overnight unless accompanied by an adult over 18 years, and then only with permission of parent or legal guardian (letter to this effect must be produced)

Nance Lakes

Contact: Mr or Mrs Ellis, Nance Lakes, Trevarrack, Lelant, St Ives, TR26 3EZ, 01736 740348, *Water:* Three lakes, various sizes, *Species:* Carp, Roach and Bream, *Permits:* No EA Licence required. Permits at site, *Charges:* £5 per day (evening tickets available), *Season:* Open all year 8am to 5pm, *Methods:* Barbless hooks, no keepnets unless competition.

St. Ives Freshwater Angling Society

Contact: Dr. Charles Franklin, Chy-An-Meor, Westward Road, St. Ives, TR26 1JX, 01736 798251, *Water:* 1.5 acre spring-fed lake with depths from 6 to 24 feet, situated in farmland, 5 miles from St.Ives, *Species:* Bream, Carp, Tench, Roach, Rudd, Perch, Gudgeon, and Eels, *Permits:* 1) Symons Fishing Tackle, Market Place, St Ives. 2) Mr. K. Roberts, Woonsmith Farm, Nancledra, Nr. Penzance. 3) Newtown Angling Centre, Newtown, Germoe, Penzance. Location maps available with permits, *Charges:* Adults: Day £4, Weekly £12. Juniors (under 16): Day £2.50, Weekly £8, *Season:* Open all year. No night Fishing, *Methods:* Barbless hooks only. No fish over 3 lb to be retained in a keepnet. All nets to be dipped in disinfectant tank before use. Good baits are maggots, casters, sweetcorn and trout pellets

TORPOINT

Crafthole

Contact: South West Lakes Trust, 01837 871565, . info@swlakestrust.org.uk, *Species:* Carp and Tench. Quality Carp up to 30lb, *Permits:* See South West Lakes Trust coarse advert, *Charges:* Full day £5 (limited availability from agent), Season Day £150, Concession £135.Family £250 (Husband, wife and up to 2 children under 16). Additional Fisheries £20 each, *Season:* Open all year 1hr before sunrise to 1hr after sunset, *Methods:* No child under 14 years may fish unless accompanied by an adult over 18 years. No child under 16 may fish overnight unless accompanied by an adult over 18 years, and then only with permission of parent or legal guardian (letter to this effect must be produced)

Millbrook

Contact: Mark or Rebecca Blake, Treganhawke Cottage, Millbrook, PL10 1JH, 01752 823210, *Water:* 1 Acre water in sheltered, wooded valley, *Species:* Perch, Tench, Carp, Crucians, Roach, Rudd, Bream., *Permits:* Self service at water in old phone box, correct money needed., *Charges:* £5 per day, £3 after 5 p.m.-evening, *Season:* Open all year, *Methods:* Barbless hooks, Landing net. Night fishing by arrangement.

TRURO

Mellonwatts Mill Coarse Fishery

Contact: Pensagillas Farm, Grampound, Truro, 01872 530808, pensagillas@farming.co.uk, *Water:* 2 Acre lake, *Species:* Carp to 25lb, Common & Mirror, Roach, Tench, Golden Rudd, *Charges:* Day ticket £5, Evening £3, *Season:* Open all year. Night fishing by arrangement only, *Methods:*

Rosewater Lakes

Contact: Mike & Andy Waters, Hendravossan Farm, Rose, Truro, 01872 571598, *Mobile:* 07977 666025, *Water:* 1.5 Acre lake, *Species:* Carp, Tench, Roach, Chubb, Bream, *Permits:* At hut on lakeside, *Charges:* Day £4, u16/OAP £3, Evening from 5pm £2, *Season:* Open all year from dawn till dusk, *Methods:* Barbless hooks only

Threemilestone Angling Club

Contact: Mrs T. Bailey, 9 Sampson Way, Threemilestone, Truro, TR3 6DR, 01872 272578, khaux@aol.com, *Water:* Langarth Pools (2 Pools), *Species:* Carp, Tench, Roach, Rudd, Bream, Perch, Goldfish, *Permits:* At lakeside, *Charges:* Seniors £4, Juniors £3, *Season:* All season, No night fishing, *Methods:* Barbless hooks only, No Peanuts etc.

Tory Farm Angling

Contact: Andy Ayres, Tory Farm, Ponsanooth, Truro, TR3 7HN, 01209 861272, ayres_uk@yahoo.co.uk, *Water:* 2.5 acre lake, *Species:* Mirror, Common, Wild and Ghost Carp to over 20lb. Crucian to 1.5lb. Tench to 3lb. Rudd to 2lb, *Charges:* £6 per day, daylight hours only, *Season:* Open all year, *Methods:* Barbless hooks only, no keepnets, unhooking mats to be used.

CORNWALL
Stillwater
Trout

BODMIN

Colliford Lake

Contact: South West Lakes Trust, 01837 871565, info@swlakestrust.org.uk, *Water:* Ranger Tel 01579 342366, *Species:* Brown Trout, *Permits:* Colliford Tavern, *Charges:* Full day £9.25, Season £120, Reduced day £7.25, Season £90, Child/Wheelchair £2, Season £30, *Season:* Opens 15 March 2001 - 12th October, *Methods:* Catch & Release operates. Barbless hooks only.

Fenwick Trout Fishery

Contact: David & Shirley Thomas, Old Coach Road, Dunmere, Bodmin, PL31 2RD, 01208 78296, *Water:* 2 acre lake plus river fishing. See also entry under Camel, *Species:* Rainbow 1.5lb - 12lb, Browns to 10lb plus, *Charges:* £20/Full day (4 fish, 8hrs), £13/Half day (2 fish, 4hrs), *Season:* All year, *Methods:* Fly fishing only

Temple Trout Fishery

Contact: Mr Julian Jones, Temple Trout Fishery, Temple Road, Temple, Bodmin, PL30 4HW, 01208 821730, *Mobile:* 07787 704966, jj@templetroutfishery.freeserve.co.uk, *Water:* 2.7 Acre lake. Plus new 4.5 acre 'any method' lake, *Species:* Rainbows (15lb 5oz) & Brown trout (16lb 6oz), *Permits:* Available at fishery Tel: 01208-821730, *Charges:* Club membership £7 (2001 price) entitles members to 10% discount on tickets, to fish club events and to purchase a season ticket at £112.50 for 25 Trout - full day £21.50, 5 fish - 3/4 day £19, 4 fish - 1/2 day £15, 3 fish - evening £11, 2 fish - child under 16 & disabled £11, 2 fish all day, extra fish £5.75. Single fish on new lake £5.75, *Season:* Open all year round from 9 a.m to dusk, in winter open 4 days a week Wednesday, Thursday Saturday and Sundays or by appointment, *Methods:* Fly fishing on 2.7 acre lake. Any legal method on one bank of 4.5 acre lake and a sporting ticket available on 4.5 acre lake.

BOSCASTLE

Venn Down Lakes
Contact: Ted & Sue Bowen, Trebowen, Trevalga, Boscastle, 01840 250018, *Water:* 2 pools, 3 acres, *Species:* Rainbow Trout, *Charges:* Ticket to fish £5, plus fish at £1.85/lb. Junior ticket £3 - 1 fish, *Season:* Open all year except Xmas day, *Methods:* Max hook size 10, single fly only.

CAMELFORD

Crowdy
Contact: South West Lakes Trust, 01837 871565, info@swlakestrust.org.uk, *Species:* Brown Trout, *Charges:* Free to holders of a valid Environment Agency Licence, *Season:* 15 March - 12 October, *Methods:* Angling by spinning, fly or bait.

HAYLE

Tree Meadow Trout Fishery
Contact: John Hodge, Tree Meadow, Peverell Road, Fraddam, Hayle, 01736 850899/850583, *Water:* Two lakes. 4 acres in total. Sedge lake to 8lb, Willow lake to 20lb plus, *Species:* Rainbow and Brown trout, *Charges:* Contact for details, *Season:* Open all year dawn to 1 hour after dusk, *Methods:* Catch and release after fish limit. Max hook size 10.

LAUNCESTON

Rose Park Fishery
Contact: Rose Park Fishery, Trezibbett, Altarnun, Nr Launceston, PL15 7RF, 01566 86278, *Water:* Two lakes, *Species:* Rainbow 13lb, Wild Browns 2.5lb. Stocked Brown Trout 9lb 5oz, *Permits:* From the fishery, *Charges:* 1st fish £4 + £1.65/lb. Thereafter each fish £1.65/lb.Please note £4 charge applies only to first fish. All browns £2.05/lb, *Season:* Open all year, *Methods:* Fly fishing. No catch and release.

LISKEARD

Siblyback
Contact: South West Lakes Trust, 01837 871565, info@swlakestrust.org.uk, *Water:* Premier Rainbow Fishery - Boat & Bank (boats may be booked in advance: 01579 342366). Rod average 2001: 3.3 fish per rod day, *Permits:* Self Service Kiosk at Watersports Centre, *Charges:* Full day £16.25, Season £385. Reduced day £13, Season £290, Child/Wheelchair £3, Season £90. Evening Monday - Friday £13. Season Permits can be used on any Premier Fishery only. Boats £10 per day inc. 2 fish extra to bag limits, *Season:* Opens 23 March 2002 - 31st October, *Methods:* Fly fishing only. No child under 14 years may fish unless accompanied by an adult over 18 years

Wainsford Fishery (Trout Lake)
Contact: Paul Elliot, Wainsford Fishery, Twowatersfoot, Liskeard, PL14 6HT, 01208 821432, *Water:* Three lakes. See also entry under River fishing - Fowey, *Species:* Brown Trout to 5.5lb. Rainbows to 12.5lb, *Permits:* On site, *Charges:* £15 per day, *Season:* Open all year.

PENZANCE

Drift Reservoir
Contact: T.B.Shorland (Bailiff), Drift Ways, Drift Reservoir, Penzance, TR19 6AB, 01736 363869, *Water:* 65 acre reservoir, *Species:* Stock Rainbows (3 per day, 9 weekly) Wild Browns. Browns (3 per day, 9 weekly), *Permits:* At Bailiff's house on reservoir (also Environment Agency licences available), *Charges:* £120 season 9 rainbows per week 3 brownies per day, £25 weekly 9 rainbows per week 3 brownies per day, £10 day 3 rainbows per day 3 brownies per day, £7 evening 2 rainbows per evening 2 brownies per evening (after 4pm), *Season:* 1st April - 12th October Brown trout, 1st April - 31st October Rainbows, *Methods:* No static with boobies, any other traditional fly or lures.

REDRUTH

Stithians
Contact: South West Lakes Trust, 01837 871565, info@swlakestrust.org.uk, *Water:* Ranger Tel 01579 342366, *Species:* Intermediate Rainbow & Brown Trout Fishery. Trout to 6lb. 2001 rod average 2.7 fish per rod day, *Permits:* Stithians Watersports Centre (01209 860301), Sandy's Tackle, Redruth (01209 214877), *Charges:* Full day £11, Season £190, Reduced day £10, Season £170, Child/Wheelchair £2, Season £40. Boats £10/day, *Season:* Opens 15 March - 12th October, *Methods:* Fly fishing only. Catch and release - barbless hooks.

SALTASH

Bake Fishing Lakes (Trout)
Contact: Tony Lister, Bake, Trerule Foot, Saltash, 01752 849027, *Mobile:* 07798 585836, tony.lister@bakelakes.co.uk, *Water:* 7 Lakes adding up to 14 plus acres, Coarse and Trout. Troutmaster Water, *Species:* Rainbow 13lb 8oz, Brown Trout 10lb, *Permits:* At Bake lakes, *Charges:* Sporting ticket £10 per day. Catch only £5 plus £5 - 1 fish, £14 - 2 fish, £18 - 3 fish, £22 - 4 fish, specimen to 15lb. £12 - 2 fish to £20 - 5 fish, Dunes, *Season:* 8am - Dusk, earlier by appointment, *Methods:* Catch and release on 1 lake. Barbless or debarbed hooks when releasing.

ST AUSTELL

Innis Fly Fishery
Contact: Mrs Pam Winch, Innis Fly Fishery and Inn, Innis Moor, Penwithick, St. Austell, PL26 8YH, 01726 851162, innis@tiscali.co.uk, *Water:* 15 Acres (3 Lakes), Stream fed enclosed water, *Species:* Rainbow trout, *Permits:* As above, *Charges:* Full day £20 (5 Fish), half day £10.50 (2 Fish), Catch and release £12, *Season:* All year, 8.00 a.m. to dusk, *Methods:* Barbless hooks when catch & release, no static fishing.

TRURO

Gwarnick Mill Fishery
Contact: Sue Dawkins, Gwarnick Mill, St. Allen, Truro, TR4 9QU, 01872 540487, *Water:* 1.5 Acre spring and river fed lake, *Species:* Rainbow Trout to 10lb, *Charges:* 4 Fish £18, 3 Fish £15, 2 Fish £11., *Season:* Open all year, *Methods:* Barbless Hook preferred.

Ventontrissick Trout Farm
Contact: Gerald Wright, St. Allen, Truro, TR4 9DG, 01872 540497, *Mobile:* 07762 781200, *Water:* Half acre, *Species:* Rainbow Trout 1.25lb - 10lb, *Charges:* £5.50 per day rod ticket, £1.60 per lb fish killed, First two fish to be killed, thereafter release optional. £10 sporting ticket, *Season:* 8.00am till 1hr after sunset 10 p.m, *Methods:* Fly only, Barbless if releasing.

DEVON River Fishing

South West Rivers Association
Contact: Michael Charleston (secretary), The Gift House, Buckland Monachorum, Yelverton, PL20 7NA, 01822 853293, mwcharl@aol.com, *Water:* South West Rivers Association is the regional organisation of the river associations of Devon and Cornwall and is a consultative and campaigning body for the protection and improvement of south west rivers, their fish stocks and ecology.

AVON
South Devon stream not to be confused with Hampshire Avon or Bristol Avon. Rises on Dartmoor and enters sea at Bigbury. Brown Trout, Sea Trout and Salmon.

Avon Fishing Association
Contact: Mr J.E. Coombes, 19 Stella Road, Preston, Paignton, TQ3 1BH, 01803 523139, *Water:* 14.5 miles on the river Avon, *Species:* Salmon, Sea Trout and Brown Trout, *Permits:* From the above. No day tickets, *Charges:* £45 weekly, £65 fortnightly, £70 monthly. Plus a £2 donation to the N.A.S.T, *Season:* 15th March to 30th September. 30th November for Salmon only, *Methods:* Fly only except spinning below Silveridge Weir 1st October - 30th November.

Newhouse Fishery (River Avon)
Contact: Adrian Cook, Newhouse Farm, Moreleigh, Totnes, 01548 821426, *Water:* 0.25 mile on the river Avon, *Species:* Brown Trout, Sea Trout and Salmon, *Permits:* On site, *Charges:* £10 Brown Trout, £25 Salmon, *Season:* As current EA byelaws, *Methods:* As current EA byelaws

AXE & TRIBUTARIES
This quiet meandering stream rises in the hills of west Dorset, runs along the boundary with Somerset before flowing past Axminster to the sea at Seaton. The Axe is a fertile river with good Trout fishing and a run of Salmon and Sea Trout. The two main tributaries, the Coly and Yarty, are also Trout streams and the Yarty has a good run of Sea Trout.

Axmouth
Contact: Harbour Services, Harbour Road, Seaton, 01297 22727, *Water:* Axmouth from lower end Pool below Coly-Axe confluence to Axmouth Bridge, *Species:* Mullet, Bass, Sea Trout, *Permits:* Harbour Services. Seaton, *Charges:* £2.50 Day Adult, £1 Child. £12.50 week Adult, £5 Child, *Methods:* Fishing from East Bank of Estuary Only.

Stillwaters (Axe)
info@land-own.demon.co.uk, *Water:* One sea trout rod on River Axe also 1 acre lake see entry under stillwater trout Honiton.

BRAY
Nick Hart Fly Fishing (Bray)
Contact: Nick Hart, Exford View, 1 Chapel Street, Exford, Minehead, TA24 7PY, 01643 831101, *Mobile:* 0797 1198559, nick@hartflyfishing.demon.co.uk, *Water:* 1 mile on Bray (see also entries under Devon River Fishing - Torridge and Exe), *Species:* Brown Trout to 1lb, Sea Trout to 5lb, *Permits:* From Nick Hart Fly Fishing, *Charges:* £12 per day Brown Trout and Sea Trout (night fishing allowed), *Season:* 15 March - 31 September, *Methods:* Fly only, Catch & Release of Trout preferred.

CLAW
Tetcott Angling Club (Claw)
Contact: Mr & Mrs J Miller, The Old Coach House, Tetcott, Holsworthy, EX22 6QZ, 01409 271300, *Water:* Approx half a mile of the river Claw, *Species:* Brown Trout, *Permits:* No day tickets - private club, *Season:* 16th March to 30th September. Daylight hours only, *Methods:* Artificial lures, fly, spinning, worm.

COLY
Higher Cownhayne Farm
Contact: Mrs Pady, Higher Cownhayne Farm, Cownhayne Lane, Colyton, EX24 6HD, 01297 552267, *Water:* Fishing on River Coly, *Species:* Brown & Sea Trout, *Charges:* On application, *Methods:* Fly fishing, no netting

DART & TRIBUTARIES
Deep in the vastnesses of lonely Dartmoor rise the East and West Dart. Between their separate sources and Dartmeet, where they join, these two streams and their tributaries are mainly owned by the Duchy of Cornwall and provide many miles of Salmon, Sea Trout and Trout fishing for visitors. The scenery is on the grand scale and the sense of freedom enjoyed when you know that you can fish away over miles and miles of river is seldom realised on this crowded island. This is a moorland fishery - swift flowing, boulder strewn, usually crystal clear.
Below Dartmeet the river rushes through a spectacular wooded valley before breaking out of the moor near Buckfastleigh and flowing on to its estuary at Totnes. Although there are Brown Trout throughout the river, these middle and lower reaches are primarily Salmon and Sea Trout waters.

Buckfastleigh
Contact: South West Lakes Trust, Higher Coombepark, Lewdown, Okehampton, EX20 4QT, 01837 871565, info@swlakestrust.org.uk, *Water:* 1/4 mile on River Dart. Austins Bridge to Nursery Pool, *Species:* Salmon & Sea Trout, *Permits:* From South West Lakes Trust at above address, *Charges:* Season - £80. Limit of 16 rods, *Season:* 1st February - 30th September.

Dart Angling Association
Contact: D.H. Pakes, Holly How, Plymouth Road, South Brent, TQ10 9HA, 01364 73640, *Water:* 9 miles on river Dart. (3.9 miles of main river open to visitors plus the tidal Totnes weir pool), *Species:* Salmon, Sea Trout, Brown Trout, *Permits:* All permits - Sea Trout Inn, Staverton Tel: 01803 762274, *Charges:* Membership details from secretary. Totnes weir pool £20 per day (only 1 day Salmon, 1 night Sea Trout ticket available). Buckfast (Austin's Bridge) - Littlehempston (left bank) only 2 per day (unless resident at the Sea Trout Inn), *Season:* Salmon 1st February - 30th September. Sea/Brown Trout 15th March - 30th September, *Methods:* Fly (some stretches fly only), spinning, prawn (below Staverton) see club regulations i.e. conservation measures in force.

Duchy Of Cornwall
Contact: Duchy Of Cornwall Office, Duchy Hotel, Princetown, Yelverton, PL20 6QF, 01822 890205, csturmer@duchyofcornwall.gov.uk, *Water:* East & West Dart Rivers and its tributaries down to Dartmeet, *Species:* Salmon and Trout, *Permits:* Charles Bingham Fishing Ltd, West Down, Warrens Cross, Whitchurch, Tavistock. The Old Post Office, Poundsgate, Newton Abbot. Two Bridges Hotel, Two Bridges, Princetown, Yelverton. The Post Office, Postbridge, Yelverton. Princetown Post Office, Princetown, Yelverton. Prince Hall Hotel, Two Bridges, Princetown, Yelverton. The Arundell Arms, Lifton. James Bowden & Sons, The Square, Chagford. Badger's Holt Ltd, Dartmeet, Princetown. Exeter Angling Centre, Smythen Street, Exeter. The Forest Inn Hexworthy, Poundsgate, Yelverton. Peter Collings, Huccaby's News, 33 Fore St, Buckfastleigh, *Charges:* Salmon Season: £125, Week £70, Day £20. Trout Season: £55, Week £15, Day £4, *Season:* Salmon: 1st February to 30th September. Trout: 15th March to 30th September, *Methods:* Fly only. Additional information on permit

Hatchlands Trout Farm
Contact: Malcolm Davies, Greyshoot Lane, Rattery, South Brent, TQ10 9LL, 01364 73500, *Water:* 600 yards, both banks of the river Harbourne (tributary of the Dart), *Species:* Brown Trout, *Charges:* On application, *Season:* See current EA byelaws, *Methods:* Barbless hooks only

Prince Hall Hotel
Contact: Mr Adam Southwell, Nr. Two Bridges, Dartmoor, PL20 6SA, 01822 890403, gamefish@princehall.co.uk, *Water:* Access to all Duchy water, *Species:* Wild Brown Trout 1.5lb, Sea Trout 6lb, Salmon 11lb, *Permits:* Duchy. EA Licences on sale 7 days a week at the hotel, *Charges:* Trout £5 per day. Salmon £22. Trout week £16. Salmon week £75, *Season:* March - September, *Methods:* Fly only

Two Bridges Hotel
Contact: Two Bridges Hotel, Two Bridges, Dartmoor, PL20 6SW, 01822 890581, twobridges@warm-welcome-hotels.co.uk, *Water:* Stretch of 600yds double bank fishing, *Species:* Trout & Salmon, *Permits:* At hotel reception, *Charges:* See Duchy permit, *Season:* E.A. Byelaws apply.

DEER

Tetcott Angling Club (Deer)
Contact: Mr & Mrs J Miller, The Old Coach House, Tetcott, Holsworthy, EX22 6QZ, 01409 271300, *Water:* Approx one mile of the river Deer, *Species:* Brown Trout, *Permits:* No day tickets - private club, *Season:* 16th March to 30th September. Daylight hours only, *Methods:* Artificial lures, fly, spinning, worm.

ERME

A small Devon stream rising on Dartmoor and flowing south through Ivybridge to the sea. The Erme is probably best known for its Sea Trout, but there is also a run of Salmon and Brown Trout are present throughout its length.

EXE & TRIBUTARIES

The Exe rises high on Exmoor and flows through open moorland until it plunges into a steep wooded valley near Winsford. By the time Tiverton is reached the valley has widened and from here to the sea the Exe meanders through a broad pastoral vale until it flows into the estuary near Exeter and finally into the sea between Exmouth and Dawlish Warren. It is the longest river in the south west.
Throughout most of its length the Exe is a good Trout stream, the fast flowing, rocky upper reaches abounding in fish of modest average size, which

increases as the river becomes larger and slower in its middle and lower reaches, where fish approaching a pound feature regularly in the daily catch. The Exe has a good run of Salmon and some fishing can be obtained on hotel waters in the middle reaches. In the deep slow waters around Exeter there is a variety of coarse fish, as there is in the Exeter Ship Canal which parallels the river from Exeter to the estuary at Topsham. In an area noted for its Sea Trout streams, the Exe is unusual in that it has no appreciable run of Sea Trout, but it does have some Grayling, a species not often found in the south west. The two main tributaries - the Barle and the Culm - could not be more different in character. The Barle is a swift upland stream which rises high on Exmoor not far from the source of the Exe, and runs a parallel course, first through open moor and then through a picturesque wooded valley, before joining the parent river near Dulverton. It has good Trout fishing throughout and Salmon fishing on the lower reaches.
The Culm issues from the Blackdown Hills and in its upper reaches is a typical dry fly Trout stream, with good hatches of fly and free-rising fish. From Cullompton until it joins the Exe, the Culm becomes a coarse fishery, with the Dace in particular of good average size.

River Exe & Tributaries Association
Contact: Ian Cook, 01392 254573, *Water:* Association to protect and enhance the natural Trout & Salmon fisheries of the River Exe, *Permits:* No day tickets to fish available.

Bellbrook Valley Trout Fishery (River)
Contact: Mike Pusey, Bellbrook Farm, Oakford, Tiverton, EX16 9EX, 01398 351292, mike_pusey@notes.interliant.com, *Water:* Approx 1 mile on Iron Mill Stream, *Species:* Wild Brown Trout, *Charges:* £10 per day, *Season:* March 15th to September 30th, *Methods:* Fly only.

Bridge House Hotel
Contact: Brian Smith, Bridge House Hotel, Bampton, EX16 9NF, 01398 331298, *Water:* 1 Mile on River Exe, *Species:* Salmon, Trout and Grayling; (2000 Season: 12lb Salmon, 3lb Brown Trout), *Permits:* As above, *Charges:* Salmon £20 per day, Trout £10 per day, *Season:* March 15th - Sept 30th, *Methods:* Fly, occasional spinner

Devon & UK Fly Fishing School (Exe)
Contact: Mr Roddy Rae, 6 Hescane Park, Cheriton Bishop, EX6 6SP, 01647 24643, *Mobile:* 07786 834575, roddy.rae@btopenworld.com, *Water:* 3.5 miles of prime fishing on the river Exe divided into 3 beats, 4 rods per beat per day. Also 1 mile of river Taw and access to rivers Yeo, Creedy, Mole and Torridge, *Species:* Salmon, Brown Trout & Grayling on the Exe, *Permits:* Daily weekly and occasional season lets, *Charges:* Exe - £35 day, *Season:* Exe: 14th February - 30th September for Salmon. Brown Trout 15th March - 30th September, *Methods:* Fly & Spinner on Exe. All other waters fly only.

Environment Agency - Exe and Creedy
Contact: 01392 444000, *Water:* 3 Miles; 4 sections between Cowley Bridge and Countess Wear Bridge, *Species:* Salmon, *Permits:* Season and Day permits - Exeter Angling Centre, Smythen Street, Off City Arcade, Fore Street, Exeter. (Tel: 01392 436404). Day permits - Topp Tackle, 63 Station Road, Taunton; The Environment Agency, Manley House, Exeter Tel: 01392 444000, *Charges:* Season (Limited) £40, Day £4, *Season:* 1st June - 30th September, *Methods:* No worm or maggot. No bait fishing before June 16th. Catch and release of all Salmon prior to June 16th.

Exe Duck's Marsh
Contact: Exeter City Council, River & Canal Manager, Civic Centre, Exeter, EX1 1RP, 01392 274306, *Water:* River Exe, left bank 1 mile downstream Salmon pool weir, *Species:* Salmon (trout), *Permits:* River & Canal Office, Canal Basin, Haven Rd, Exeter, EX2 8DU, *Charges:* Day tickets only: £5.70, *Season:* 14/2 - 30/9; no night fishing, *Methods:* Voluntary restrictions & E.A.byelaw controls; only artificial fly & lures and all fish returned before June 16

Exeter & District Angling Association (River Creedy)
Contact: Terry Reed (Hon. Sec.), PO Box 194, Exeter, EX2 7WG, *Mobile:* 07970 483913, exeteranglingassociation@yahoo.co.uk, *Water:* Cowley Bridge; just a short walk from the Exe, *Species:* Roach, Dace, Gudgeon., *Permits:* Exeter Angling Centre, Smythen Street (Off Market Street Exeter). Bridge Cafe, Bridge Road, Exeter. Exmouth Tackle & Sport, The Strand, Exmouth. Tackle Trader, Wharf Road, Newton Abbot. Exe Valley Angling, West Exe South, Tiverton, *Charges:* £25 adults, £2 for Juniors (annual). Day and week tickets depending on water, ask at agent, *Season:* Different on each water. Details in association handbook or from agents, *Methods:* Different restrictions on each water. Details in association handbook.

(River Culm)
Water: Stoke Canon, Paddleford Pool, Killerton and Beare Gate; Smaller faster flowing river, *Species:* Superb catches of Chub, Roach and Dace possible throughout. An excellent, yet relatively easy Pike water, *Permits:* Exeter Angling Centre, Smythen Street (Off Market Street Exeter). Bridge Cafe, Bridge Road, Exeter. Exmouth Tackle & Sport, The Strand, Exmouth. Tackle Trader, Wharf Road, Newton Abbot. Exe Valley Angling, West Exe South, Tiverton, *Charges:* £25 adults, £2 for Juniors (annual). Day and week tickets depending on water, ask at agent, *Season:* Different on each water. Details in association handbook or from agents, *Methods:* Different restrictions on each water. Details in association handbook.

(River Exe)
Water: Tidal stretch of Exe at Countess Wear; big catches of Mullet, Dace and Bream. Non tidal stretch at Weirfield; big bags of Bream and Carp from 15 to 20lb. Shillhay runs nearly through the City centre; can produce big bags of Bream and Roach. Exwick is a faster flowing section adjacent to St David's railway section; good nets of quality Roach and Dace, fishes well in the autumn. Cowley Bridge is a relatively under fished stretch; good nets of Roach and Dace along the whole length. Oakhay Barton; fewer fish but good size and high quality fish, *Species:* Roach, Dace, Bream, Chub, Perch, Carp, Mullet, *Permits:* Exeter Angling Centre, Smythen

Street (Off Market Street Exeter). Bridge Cafe, Bridge Road, Exeter. Exmouth Tackle & Sport, The Strand, Exmouth. Tackle Trader, Wharf Road, Newton Abbot. Exe Valley Angling, West Exe South, Tiverton, *Charges:* £25 adults, £2 for Juniors (annual). Day and week tickets depending on water, ask at agent, *Season:* Different on each water. Details in association handbook or from agents, *Methods:* Different restrictions on each water. Details in association handbook.

River Exe (Exeter)
Contact: Exeter City Council, River & Canal Manager, Civic Centre, Exeter, EX1 1RP, 01392 274306, *Water:* River Exe, 10 beats between Head Wear & Countess Wear, *Species:* Salmon, *Permits:* Annual, available by post with payment and photograph, *Charges:* £56, limited permits, *Season:* 14th Febuary - 30th September, *Methods:* Voluntary restrictions apply, only artificial fly & lures and all fish returned before June 16th

Tiverton & District Angling Club (River Culm)
Contact: John Smallwood, Exe Valley Angling, 19 Westexe South, Tiverton, EX16 5DQ, 01884 242275, *Water:* 0.75 miles river Culm at Stoke Cannon. Various stretches on several rivers in Somerset. See also entry under stillwater coarse, *Species:* Roach, Dace, Chub, Perch, Pike and Eels. Salmon and Trout in season, *Permits:* Please ring Exe Valley for details. Also available from: Exeter Angling Centre, Enterprise Angling Taunton, Topp Tackle Taunton, Country Sports - Cullompton & Minnows Caravan Park - beside Grand Western Canal, *Charges:* Senior: Day £4, Annual £20. Conc: Day £2.50, Annual £8, *Season:* Coarse: closed 15 March to 16 June. Trout: open from 15 March to 30 September. Salmon: open 14 February to 30 September, *Methods:* Canal Methods: Any. Restrictions: Fish from permanent pegs, No night fishing, No cars on bank, No digging of banks or excessive clearance of vegatation. Lakeside Methods: Any. Restrictions: No night fishing, No boilies, Trout pellets or nuts, One rod only, Fishing from permanent pegs, No dogs, Nets to be dipped. Ring Exe Valley Angling for full details

Tiverton Fly Fishing Association
Contact: Exe Valley Angling, 19 Westexe South, Tiverton, EX16 5DQ, 01884 242275, *Water:* 3.5 Miles on River Exe, *Species:* Trout & Grayling, *Permits:* Exe Valley Angling 01884-242275, *Charges:* Senior £15, Conc. £4, Guests £5, *Season:* 15th March - 30th September, *Methods:* Fly only

LYN
Chalk Water, Weir Water, Oare Water, Badgeworthy Water - these are the streams that tumble down from the romantic Doone Country of Exmoor and join to form the East Lyn, which cascades through the spectacular wooded ravine of the National Trust's Watersmeet Estate. The main river has good runs of Salmon and Sea Trout, and wild Brown Trout teem on the Lyn and the tributary streams.

Cloud Farm Fishing
Contact: Cloud Farm, Oare, Lynton, 01598 741278, holiday@doonevalley.co.uk, *Water:* Badgeworthy Water, tributary of the Lyn - 0.75 miles single bank fishing, *Species:* Salmon and Brown Trout, *Charges:* From £5 per day.

Environment Agency - Watersmeet and Glenthorne
Contact: 01392 444000, *Water:* The fishery is in two parts: The Watersmeet Fishery, leased by the Agency from the National Trust - Tors Road, Lynmouth to Woodside Bridge, right bank only; Woodside Bridge to Watersmeet both banks; upstream of the Watersmeet right bank only to Rockford.
The Glenthorne Fishery - right bank only upstream of Rockford to 300 yards downstream of Brendon Road Bridge. Half a mile of Trout fishing is available on the Hoaroak Water between Hillsford Bridge and Watersmeet; this is specifically for children, who only require a Trout rod licence when fishing this particular stretch if they are aged 12 years or over. WARNING: Anglers are advised that parts of the river are exceptionally steep and rocky and can be dangerous. River Lyn information line - 01398 371119, *Species:* Salmon, Sea Trout, Brown Trout, *Permits:* Mr & Mrs Rigby, Brendon House Hotel, Brendon. Tourist Information Centre, Town Hall, Lynton; Mrs J. Fennell, Variety Sports, 23 Broad Street, Ilfracombe; Mrs Topp,

Topp Tackle, 63 Station Road, Taunton. Porlock Visitor Centre, West End, High Street, Porlock. Rockford Inn, Brendon, Lynmouth, N.Devon, *Charges:* Salmon & Sea Trout, season withdrawn for conservation reasons, week £35, day £13.50, evening (8 pm to 2 am) £4; Brown Trout, season £27.50, week £10, day £3. Bag Limits: 2 salmon, 6 sea trout, 8 brown trout, *Season:* 1st March - 30th September; Sea Trout & Trout 15th March - 30th September. Fishing permitted 8 am to sunset, except from 1st June - 30th September when fishing by traditional fly fishing methods is permitted until 2 am between Tors Road & Rockford, *Methods:* Brown Trout, fly only. Salmon, no shrimp or prawn. Artificial fly or lure only before 16th June. Catch and release of all salmon prior to 16th June. No weight may be used whilst fly fishing. The weight used for worm fishing and spinning must be lead free and not weigh more than 0.5 ounce and must be attached at least 18 inches from the hook.

Southernwood Farm
Contact: John Ralph, Southernwood Farm, Brendon, EX35 6NU, 01598 741174, southernwoodfarm@totalise.co.uk, *Water:* 900 metres on the East Lyn river, *Species:* Salmon, Sea Trout and Brown Trout, *Permits:* Day and Weekly, *Charges:* Day tickets at £12 per day for Salmon and Sea Trout. £5 per day for Brown Trout. Weekly tickets at £35 and £18, *Season:* June 16 to October 31, *Methods:* Any within Environment Agency restrictions.

OTTER
The Otter springs to life in the Blackdown Hills and flows through a broad fertile valley to join the sea near the little resort of Budleigh Salterton. This is primarily a Brown Trout stream noted for its dry fly fishing for Trout of good average weight. There is also some Sea Trout fishing in the lower reaches.

River Otter Association
Contact: Alan Knight (sec), 01404 42318, *Water:* Comprises riparian owners, anglers and conservationists concerned with the preservation of the total ecology of the river Otter.

Clinton Devon Estates
Water: 3.4 mile single bank fishing on the River Otter from Clamour Bridge (footpath below Otterton) to White Bridge near Budleigh Salterton, *Species:* Brown Trout, *Charges:* Free to EA rod licence holders, *Season:* 1st April to 30th September.

Deer Park Hotel
Contact: Reception, Deer Park Hotel, Weston, Nr Honiton, EX14 3PG, 01404 41266, admin@deerparkcountryhotel.com, *Water:* 6 miles on River Otter, *Species:* Brown Trout, *Permits:* From reception desk at hotel, *Charges:* £30 per day. Season permits available. Prices on application, *Season:* 15th March - 30th September, *Methods:* Dry Fly only.

PLYM
A short stream rising on Dartmoor and running into Plymouth Sound. Trout fishing on the Plym and its tributary the Meavy, with some Sea Trout on the lower reaches and a late run of Salmon.

Plymouth & Dist Freshwater Angling Assoc. (Plym)
Contact: Mr D.L.Owen, 39 Burnett Road, Crownhill, Plymouth, PL6 5BH, 01752 705033, douglas@burnettrd.freeserve.co.uk, *Water:* 1 Mile on River Plym, 1.5 miles on River Tavy, *Species:* Salmon, Sea Trout, Brown Trout, *Permits:* Snowbee, Drakes Court, Langage Business Park, Plymouth. D.K.Sports/Osborne and Cragg, 37 Bretonside, Plymouth, *Charges:* £10 a day Monday to Friday up to 30th September incl.; £15 a day Monday to Friday from 1st October to 30th November. To join the association, contact secretary. Annual subscription is about £95, *Season:* Plym: April - 15th December; Tavy: March - 14th October, *Methods:* Artificial baits only

Plymouth Command Angling Association (River)
Contact: Mr Vic Barnett Hon.Sec, 5 Weir Close, Mainstone, Plymouth, PL6 8SD, 01752 708206, victor.barnett@talk21.com, *Water:* Fishing rights on the Plym, Tavy and Walkham plus a small private pond near Ivybridge. Access to rivers for serving members only, *Species:* Salmon, Sea Trout and Trout, *Permits:* Membership is open to all serving members of HM Forces. Associate membership is also open to ex-serving members of HM Forces, no matter when the time was served, *Charges:* Costs for full membership or associate membership are available on application or enquiry at the above contact, *Season:* Plym, Tavy and Walkham as per Environment Agency Byelaws.

Tavy, Walkham & Plym Fishing Club (Plym)
Contact: John Soul, Trevenevow, Crapstone Road, Yelverton, PL20 6BT, 01822 854923, johnsoul@globalnet.co.uk, *Water:* See entry under Tavy, *Species:* Salmon, Sea Trout and Brown Trout, *Permits:* From: DK Sports, Barbican, Plymouth. Moorland Garage, Yelverton. Tavistock Trout Fishery, Mount Tavy, Tavistock, *Charges:* Season Tickets: Salmon £110. Sea Trout £110. Brown Trout £45. Day Tickets available, *Season:* As E.A. byelaws. No day tickets after 30 September, *Methods:* No worm, prawn or shrimp fishing. Complete rules are issued with permit. Full returns must be made to the club secretary as a condition of purchase.

TAMAR

The Tamar rises near the north coast, and for most of its course forms the boundary between Devon and Cornwall. It is always a lowland stream flowing through farmland and this fact is reflected in the size of its Trout which have a larger average size than the acid moorland streams. Around Launceston, the Tamar is joined by five tributaries - Ottery, Carey, Wolf, Thrushel and Lyd - which offer good Trout fishing, as does the Inny which enters a few miles downstream. There is a good run of Salmon and Sea Trout, the latter being particularly numerous on the Lyd. There are also Grayling in places.

Arundell Arms
Contact: Mrs Anne Voss-Bark, Lifton, PL16 0AA, 01566 784666, reservations@arundellarms.com, *Water:* 20 miles of private fishing on Rivers Tamar, Lyd, Carey, Thrushel, Wolf and Ottery. Also 3 acre private lake stocked with Rainbow and Brown Trout, *Species:* Rivers: Salmon, Sea Trout and Brown Trout. Lake: Rainbow & Brown Trout, *Permits:* Arundell Arms, *Charges:* Trout £19. Salmon & Sea Trout £19 to £25. Lake £22, *Season:* Salmon March 1st to October 14th. Trout and Sea Trout March 15th to September 30th. Lake open all year, *Methods:* Fly and spinner for Salmon (1 fish limit per day after June 16 then catch and release). Fly only for Trout and Sea Trout.

Endsleigh Fishing Club
Contact: M.D.S. Healy, Endsleigh House Hotel, Milton Abbot, Tavistock, PL19 0PQ, 0207 6101982, mdsh@ukonline.co.uk, *Water:* River Tamar, *Species:* Salmon maximum 23lb & Sea trout maximum 9lb, *Permits:* EA licences sold at the hotel, *Charges:* Per rod per full day all species, £20 March - April; £25 May to June 15th inclusive; £34 June16th to August 31st; £54 September - October. £12 5pm-midnight April-August Sea Trout only, *Season:* Endsleigh House Hotel opens March 28th, fishing ends October 19th. River Tamar season runs 1st March to 14th October, *Methods:* Fly. Spinning only under certain conditions.

TAVY

This noted Salmon and sea Trout river rises deep in Dartmoor and flows its swift rocky course through Tavistock to its estuary, which joins that of the Tamar to the north of Plymouth. The main tributary is the Walkham, which also rises on Dartmoor and provides good moorland Trout fishing.

Plymouth & Dist Freshwater Angling Assoc (Tavy)
Contact: Mr D.L. Owen, 39 Burnett Road, Crownhill, Plymouth, PL6 5BH, 01752 705033, douglas@burnettrd.freeserve.co.uk, *Water:* River Tavy above Tavistock, *Species:* Salmon, Sea Trout and Brown Trout, *Charges:* Tavy fishing is available to members of the association. Contact the secretary for membership details. See entry under River Plym, *Season:* 1st March to 14th October, *Methods:* Artificial baits only.

Tavy, Walkham & Plym Fishing Club (Tavy)
Contact: John Soul, Trevenevow, Crapstone Road, Yelverton, PL20 6BT, 01822 854923, johnsoul@globalnet.co.uk, *Water:* Rivers Tavy, Walkham, Plym, Meavy, *Species:* Brown Trout, Salmon, Sea Trout, *Permits:* Only through D.K.Sports, Barbican, Plymouth. Moorland Garage, Yelverton. Tavistock Trout Fishery, Tavistock, *Charges:* Season Trout £45, Season Salmon / Sea trout £110, plus other permits. Please phone above No. for details, *Season:* See Environment Agency season dates. Please note, no day tickets after 30th September, *Methods:* No worm, prawn, shrimp on Club permit waters. Please note club rules on back of permit including the dates by which accurate returns must be made as a condition of taking a permit.

TAW

Like the neighbouring Torridge, the Taw is a Salmon and Sea Trout stream with several hotel waters, offering the visiting angler the opportunities to fish on many miles of river. The Taw quickly leaves Dartmoor after rising close to Okehampton and flows through the rolling farmland of north Devon to its estuary at Barnstaple. Its main tributary, the Mole, also has good Salmon and Sea Trout fishing, and the Mole's own main tributary, the Bray, is a good little Trout stream.

Angling 2000 (Taw)
Contact: Simon Evans, Westcountry Rivers Trust, Fore Street, Lifton, PL16 0AA, 01566 784488, wrt@wrt.org.uk, *Water:* Four beats on the Bray, Mole and Little Dart. Flexible permits fishing for Trout, Sea Trout and occasional Salmon. New beats for 2002, *Species:* Trout, Sea Trout and occasional Salmon, *Permits:* From the above, *Charges:* £5 to £10 per day, *Season:* 1 March to 30 September.

Barnstaple & District Angling Association (River)
Contact: S.R. Tomms (Secretary), Barnstaple & District Angling Association, Upcott Farm, Brayford, EX32 7QA, 01598 710857, *Water:* Approx 3 miles on the river Taw plus a stretch on the river Yeo. See also under Stillwater coarse, Barnstaple, *Species:* Salmon, Sea Trout, Brown Trout, Rainbows, *Permits:* No day tickets. Fishing by membership only, *Charges:* Membership £27.50, Juniors £10, *Season:* Current EA byelaws apply, *Methods:* Current EA byelaws apply.

Crediton Fly Fishing Club (Taw)
info@fly-fishing-club.co.uk, *Water:* See entry under Yeo. 1.5 miles River Taw.

Devon & UK Fly Fishing School (Taw)
Contact: Mr Roddy Rae, 6 Hescane Park, Cheriton Bishop, EX6 6SP, 01647 24643, *Mobile:* 07786 834575, roddy.rae@btopenworld.com, *Water:* 1 mile of river Taw also 3.5 miles of prime fishing on the river Exe divided into 3 beats, 4 rods per beat per day and access to rivers Yeo, Creedy, Mole and Torridge, *Species:* Salmon, Sea Trout & Brown Trout on River Taw., *Permits:* Daily weekly and occasional season lets, *Charges:* Taw - £30 per day, *Season:* Exe: 14th February - 30th September for Salmon. Brown Trout 15th March - 30th September, *Methods:* Fly & Spinner on Exe. All other waters fly only.

Eggesford Country Hotel
Contact: Mr J Pitts, Eggesford, Chulmleigh, EX18 7JZ, 01769 580345, relax@eggesfordhotel.co.uk, *Water:* Fishing on Rivers Taw & Little Dart, *Species:* Prime Salmon, Sea Trout & Brown Trout, *Charges:* Prime Salmon & Sea Trout £30/day (24 hrs), Brown Trout £20/day. Salmon, Trout and Sea Trout full week permit (7 days) £100, *Season:* 1st March - 30th September, *Methods:* Spinning March only. Rest of season fly only.

Highbullen Hotel
Contact: Chris Taylor, Chittlehamholt, Umberleigh, EX37 9HD, 01769 540561, info@highbullen.co.uk, *Water:* 3 miles River Mole & over 2 miles River Taw, *Species:* Salmon 24.5lb (2000), Sea Trout 12lb (1998) & Brown Trout 2lb (1998), *Permits:* From Higbullen Hotel, *Charges:* Brown Trout £15per rod day. Salmon and Sea Trout from £25 per rod to £40 per day, *Season:* Salmon 1st March - 30th September, Brown and Sea Trout 15th March - 30th September, *Methods:* Spinner March. Fly March - September. Local byelaw, August and September all Salmon over 70cm have to be returned

Nick Hart Fly Fishing (Taw)
Contact: Nick Hart, Exford View, 1 Chapel Street, Exford, Minehead, TA24 7PY, 01643 831101, *Mobile:* 0797 1198559, nick@hartflyfishing.demon.co.uk, *Water:* 1 mile on Taw (see also entries under Torridge and Exe), *Species:* Salmon (to double figures), Sea Trout (excellent numbers), *Permits:* From Nick Hart Fly Fishing, *Charges:* £25 per day, 2 rods available, *Season:* 1 March - 31 September, *Methods:* Fly only.

Rising Sun Inn
Contact: Heather Manktelow, Rising Sun Inn, Umberleigh, near Barnstaple, EX37 9DU, 01769 560447, risingsuninn@btinternet.com, *Water:* Access arranged (for residents only) to approx 6 miles of Taw fishing, *Species:* Sea Trout 11.5lb, Brown Trout, Salmon 23lb (18lb Salmon Aug. 2000). A quiet 2001 but 2002 shows a lot of promise!, *Permits:* Post Office, Umberleigh for licence, *Charges:* £35 to £45, *Season:* Salmon 1st March - 30th Sept, Sea/Brown Trout 15th March - 30th Sept, *Methods:* As per E.A. rules

Taw Fishing Club
Contact: Mr J.D.V. Michie, Wheel Barton, Broadwood Kelly, Winkleigh, EX19 8ED, 01837 83435, *Water:* 3.25 miles on River Taw between Brushford and Hawkridge bridges, *Species:* Brown Trout, Sea Trout and Salmon, *Permits:* Fishing by membership of club only, *Charges:* £60 season, *Season:* 15 March to 30 September, *Methods:* Fly only, barbless encouraged.

Tremayne Water
Contact: J.G. Smith, 020 89958109, gilbert.smith@virgin.net, *Water:* 1.5 miles single + double bank fishing on the upper Taw and Little Dart, *Species:* Salmon, Sea Trout, *Charges:* Limited season rods only, *Season:* EA Byelaws apply, *Methods:* EA Byelaws apply.

TEIGN

The Teign has two sources high up on Dartmoor which form the North and South Teign but the two branches of the Teign quickly leave the moor to join west of Chagford while still very small streams. Between Chagford and Steps Bridge the river runs through a dramatic wooded gorge which is at its most spectacular at Fingle Bridge, a popular beauty spot. All along the Teign the Spring fisherman is greeted by myriads of daffodils, which are at their most numerous around Clifford Bridge. The upper Teign offers good fishing for wild Trout and Sea Trout, with Salmon fishing in suitable conditions from April to the end of the season. Much of the upper river is controlled by the Upper Teign Fishing Association. From just south of the Moretonhampstead - Exeter road to the estuary at Newton Abbot. the Teign is mostly controlled by the Lower Teign Fishing Association. This water has plenty of Brown Trout but is essentially a Sea Trout and Salmon fishery.

River Teign Riparian Owners Association
Contact: Mr. W.J.C. Watts, Park House, 18 Courtenhay Park, Newton Abbot, TQ12 4PS, 01626 332345, cwatts@wbb.co.uk, *Water:* Riparian Owners Association representing interest of owners of fishing waters on River Teign, *Permits:* No day tickets available through the association

Lower Teign Fishing Association
Contact: Mr R Waters, 121 Topsham Road, Exeter, EX20 4RE, 01392 251928, *Water:* 14 miles River Teign, *Species:* Salmon, Sea Trout, *Permits:* 3 Beats with 3 tickets on each (beat 3 not available until 1st May), *Charges:* £15 per day (24 hour period - night-time Sea Trout fishing). Beat 3 - September £25 per day. Available from Tackle Trader, Newton Abbot, *Season:* 1st Febuary - 30th September, *Methods:* Spinning, fly (fly only at night), No worming or maggots.

Mill End Hotel
Contact: Sandy Park, Chagford, TQ13 8JN, 01647433106, millendhotel@talk21.com, *Water:* 3 miles plus access to a further 8 miles, *Species:* Brown Trout, Salmon and Sea Trout, *Charges:* £5 per day.

Upper Teign Fishing Association.
Contact: Roddy Rae, 6 Hescane Park, Cheriton Bishop, EX6 6SP, 01647 24643, roddy.rae@virgin.net, *Water:* Approx 8 miles on upper Teign, *Species:* Brown Trout to 1lb 4oz, Sea Trout to 8lb & Salmon to 18lb, *Permits:* From: The Anglers Rest, Drewsteignton. Drewsteignton Post Office. Bowdens, Chagford. Drum Sports, Newton Abbot. Mill End Hotel, Sandy Park, Chagford. Clifford Bridge Caravan Park. Braileys Field Centre, Exeter. Exeter Angling Centre. Orvis, Exeter tel: 01392 272599. All anglers must be in possession of a current Environment Agency licence, *Charges:* Ordinary Member - Annual Subscription £150 Full season for Salmon, Sea Trout & Brown Trout. Trout Member - Annual subscription £52.50 Full season for Brown Trout. Temporary Members' Tickets - Salmon & Sea Trout £15 per day (6 ticket limit per day from Anglers Rest plus 4 ticket limit -Salmon and Sea Trout from Drewsteignton Post Office). Sea Trout £7 per day (4 ticket limit per day from Bowdens, Chagford). Membership Enquiries to Secretary. Brown Trout Adult season £40, juvenile (under 16) £15. Week £17.50. juvenile £7. Day £5. juvenile £2.50, *Season:* Brown Trout: March 15th - September 30th. Sea Trout: March 15th - September 30th. Salmon: February 1st - September 30th.

TORRIDGE

Throughout its length the Torridge flows through the rolling farmland of north Devon. It rises close to the coast near the Cornish border and swings in a great arc before flowing into the estuary that it shares with the Taw. The middle and lower reaches are best known for their Salmon and Sea Trout, but can offer surprisingly good Trout fishing. The upper reaches offer good small-stream Trout fishing, as does the main tributary, the Okement, which is formed by two branches that rise on Dartmoor to the south of Okehampton.

Torridge Fishery Association
Contact: Charles Inniss, Beeches, East Street, Sheepwash, Beaworthy, EX21 5NL, 01409 231237, charles.inniss@btopenworld.com, *Water:* An association of riparian owners on the Torridge whose aim is to secure and maintain the well being of the river and its ecology.Several day permits available, please phone for details, *Species:* Salmon to 15lb. Sea Trout to 8lb. Brown Trout to 1lb, *Permits:* Half Moon Inn, Sheepwash, Beaworthy, Devon 01409 231376. Group P. Norton-Smith, Little Warham, Beaford, Winkleigh, Devon 01805 603317, *Charges:* Salmon and Sea Trout from £15 to £20 daily. Brown Trout from £5 to £10 daily, *Season:* March 1st to September 30th, *Methods:* Fly Only.

Angling 2000 (Torridge)
Contact: Simon Evans, Westcountry Rivers Trust, Fore Street, Lifton, PL16 0AA, 01566 784488, wrt@wrt.org.uk, *Water:* Beats on the Walden, Lew, Okement & Torridge. Flexible permits fishing for Trout, Salmon and Sea Trout, *Permits:* From the above, *Charges:* £5 to £12.50 per day, *Season:* 1 March to 30 September.

Clinton Arms
Contact: Wendy, Clinton Arms, Frithelstock, Torrington, EX38 8JH, 01805 623279, clintonarms@yahoo.co.uk, *Water:* Approx half mile of double bank on River Torridge (left hand bank only last 200yds), *Species:* Brown trout, Sea trout, Salmon, *Permits:* The Clinton Arms on 01805 623279, *Charges:* £15/day/rod.

Half Moon Inn
Contact: Charles Innis, Half Moon Inn, Sheepwash, Beaworthy, EX21 5NE, (01409)231376, lee@halfmoon.demon.co.uk, *Water:* 12 miles river Torridge, 3x 2 acre lake, *Species:* River: Sea, Brown & Wild Brown Trout, Salmon; Lakes: Rainbow Trout 2-3lb, *Permits:* Day tickets for residents & non-residents, *Charges:* Sea Trout & Salmon: £17.50, Brown Trout: 3-fish £10, Lakes: 2-fish £10, 4-fish £15, *Season:* Mid-march - 30th September, *Methods:* Dry & Wet Fly only, Spinning in March

Little Warham Fishery
Contact: Group Captain P. Norton-Smith, Little Warham House, Beaford, Winkleigh, EX19 8AB, 01805 603317, *Water:* 2 Miles of River Torridge, *Species:* Salmon, Sea Trout, Brown Trout, *Permits:* As above, *Charges:* £20/day/rod, all species, *Season:* March 1st - September 30th, *Methods:* Fly only

Mill Leat - River Torridge
Contact: Mr Birkett, Thornbury, Holsworthy, EX22 7AY, 01409 261426, cottages@mill-leat.fsnet.co.uk, *Water:* Half mile of single bank on the Waldon (tributary of the Torridge), *Species:* Brown Trout & Coarse fish, *Charges:* £5 to fish the river, *Season:* EA Byelaws apply, *Methods:* EA Byelaws apply

South Hay Fishery (Torridge)
Water: See entry under stillwater trout, Beaworthy. 2 miles on Torridge.

YEALM

Upper Yealm Fishery
Contact: Snowbee U.K. Ltd, Drakes Court, Langage Business Park, Plymouth, PL7 5JY, 01752 334933, flyfish@snowbee.co.uk, *Water:* 1 Mile both banks River Yealm, *Species:* Sea Trout, Brown Trout (Stocked), Salmon, *Permits:* Snowbee U.K. Ltd, *Charges:* Full membership £100, Half rod £50, Day ticket (All species) £10, *Season:* Brown Trout & Sea Trout 15th March - 30th Sept, Salmon 1st April - 15th December, *Methods:* Fly Fishing & Spinning.

YEO

Crediton Fly Fishing Club (Yeo)
Contact: David Pope, 21 Creedy Road, Crediton, EX17 1EW, 01363 773557, info@fly-fishing-club.co.uk, *Water:* 5 miles Rivers Yeo & Creedy, 1.5 miles River Taw, *Species:* Brown Trout, Sea Trout & Salmon, *Permits:* 01363-773557, *Charges:* Weekly (5 days) £20, Season £65, Juniors £5. Two day weekend (Sat-Sun) £20, *Season:* Environment Agency Season, *Methods:* Fly only.

DEVON Stillwater Coarse

BAMPTON

Four Ponds
Contact: Mr Valentine, Bowdens Lane, Shillingford, Bampton, EX16 9BU, 01398 331169, *Water:* 2 ponds totalling approx 1.5 acres, *Species:* Carp to 20lb, Roach, Rudd, Tench to 5lb, Perch to 4lb, *Permits:* At pond, *Charges:* £4/day, *Season:* Open all year, 6am to dusk, *Methods:* Barbless hooks only, all children under 12 must be accompanied by an adult, no keepnets

BARNSTAPLE

Barnstaple & District A. A. (Coarse Ponds)
Contact: S.R. Tomms (Secretary), Barnstaple & District Angling Association, Upcott Farm, Brayford, EX32 7QA, 01598 710857, *Water:* 5 mixed coarse fishing ponds in the Barnstaple area ranging from 0.5 acres to 2 acres, *Species:* Roach, Rudd, Carp, Perch, Bream, Tench and Eels, *Permits:* Members only. Details from the secretary, *Charges:* £27.50 per year adult. Children (18 and under) £10 per year, *Season:* All year, dawn to dusk, *Methods:* Full rules in the membership book. Barbless hooks only.

Little Comfort Farm
Contact: Little Comfort Farm, Braunton, EX33 2NJ, 01271 812414, jackie.milson@btclick.com, *Water:* 1 acre approx, *Species:* Carp, Rudd, Roach, Bream, Orfe, *Permits:* Lakeside, *Charges:* £5 all day, £4 half day, £3 evening, *Season:* Open all year dawn to dusk, *Methods:* Barbless hooks, no keepnets

Riverton House & Lakes
Contact: Dave Shepherd or Sue Bryant, Riverton House & Lakes, Swimbridge, Barnstaple, EX32 0QX, 01271 830009, fishing@riverton.fsnet.co.uk, *Water:* Two 2 acre lakes, *Species:* Carp to 25lb, Bream, Tench, Roach, Perch, Chub, Rudd & Eels, *Permits:* Agent for Environment Agency rod licences, *Charges:* Adult day £5, Junior £3, Match bookings £4 (min 10 pegs). Specials: 'Dads and Lads' (one adult & one junior) £7. Family ticket (2 adults and 2 juniors) £12. Half day ticket available. Night fishing by appointment, *Season:* Open all year, *Methods:* Barbless hooks, care and consideration.

BEAWORTHY

Anglers Eldorado
Contact: Zyg, The Gables, Winsford, Halwill, Beaworthy, EX21 5XT, 01409 221559, info@anglers-paradise.co.uk, *Water:* Four lakes from 1 acre to 4 acres, *Species:* Carp to 25lb, Grass Carp to 18lb, Wels Catfish to 20lb, Golden Tench to 5lb, Golden Orfe to 6lb, Blue orfe to 2lb, Golden Rudd to 2lb, Koi to 10lb, *Permits:* Also from Halwill Newsagents, *Charges:* £4 per day per rod, £3 Juniors & O.A.Ps. £2 excess if fishing without permit, *Season:* All year, 8am-9pm or dusk (Which ever is earlier), *Methods:* Barbless hooks, No keepnets or sacks

Anglers Shangrila
Contact: Mr Zyg Gregorek, The Gables, Winsford, Halwill, Beaworthy, EX21 5XT, 01409 221559, *Water:* Three match only lakes, 240 pegs, *Species:* Carp, Golden Tench, Golden Orfe. Top weights of 100lbs possible, *Permits:* From Zyg only, *Charges:* You book the whole lake charges depend on how many people, *Methods:* Barbless hooks

BIDEFORD

Bideford & District Angling Club
Contact: Mr B. Ackland, Honestone Street, Bideford, 01237 478846, *Water:* Bideford based club with coarse, game & sea sections; fishing throughout South West, *Permits:* Membership form from club, open 7pm-11pm, *Charges:* £5 per annum, concessions for juniors/OAPs.

Fosfelle Country House Hotel (Coarse)
Contact: Hartland, Bideford, 01237 441273, *Water:* Approx half acre pond, *Species:* Carp, Tench, Roach, Rudd, *Charges:* £5 per day, *Season:* Open all year, *Methods:* Displayed on site.

Jennetts
Contact: South West Lakes Trust, 01837 871565, info@swlakestrust.org.uk, *Water:* Ranger Tel 01288 321262, *Species:* Commons to 22lb, Mirrors to 23lb. Quality bags of smaller Carp, Roach and Tench to pole and float, *Permits:* See South West Lakes Trust coarse advert, *Charges:* Full day £4.50, Concession £3.50, 24 Hour £8.50, Season Day £80, Season Concession £60, Season Child (under 16) £35, Season Day & Night £120, Additional Fisheries £20 each, *Season:* Open all year 6.30am to 10pm. Please note that there is no access to the car park outside these times, *Methods:* No child under 14 years may fish unless accompanied by an adult over 18 years. No child under 16 may fish overnight unless accompanied by an adult over 18 years, and then only with permission of parent or legal guardian (letter to this effect must be produced)

Little Weach Fishery
Contact: 1 Weach Cottage, Westleigh, Bideford, EX39 4NG, 01237 479303, *Water:* 2 Lakes totalling approx 1 acre, *Species:* Crucian, Common, Mirror and Koi Carp to 16lb, Tench 7lb, Roach 1.5lb, Rudd, Bream, Goldfish 1lb, *Charges:* £4 per day, £2 Children. Under 12's must be accompanied by an adult, *Season:* Open all year dawn to dusk, *Methods:* No keepnets or boilies.

Melbury

Contact: South West Lakes Trust, 01837 871565, info@swlakestrust.org.uk, *Water:* Ranger Tel 01288 321262, *Species:* Best Mirror 27.5lb. Good mixed bags of Roach, Rudd and Bream to pole, float and feeder, *Permits:* See South West Lakes Trust coarse advert. Limited season permits from South West Lakes Trust, *Charges:* Full day £4.50, Concession £3.50, Season Child (u.16) £35, Season Day & Night £120, Additional Fisheries £20 each, *Season:* Open all year from 6.30am to 10pm, *Methods:* No child under 14 years may fish unless accompanied by an adult over 18 years. No child under 16 may fish overnight unless accompanied by an adult over 18 years, and then only with permission of parent or legal guardian (letter to this effect must be produced).

Torridge Angling Club

Contact: A.J. Kelly (secretary), 40 Ridgeway Drive, Westward Ho!, *Mobile:* 07779 193085, *Water:* Coarse match fishing at local waters. Quarterly meetings. New members welcome. Please contact the secretary, *Charges:* £5 per year. Concessions for juniors.

BOVEY TRACEY

Bradley Pond

Contact: Newton Abbot Fishing Association, newtonfishing@yahoo.com, *Water:* See entry under Newton Abbot Fishing Association. Full members only. 4 acre former clay pit, *Species:* Popular match and carp venue with Roach to 2lb, Perch to 3lb 9oz, Tench, Skimmers, Carp to 28lb and large Trout.

BUCKFASTLEIGH

Nurston Farm Fishery

Contact: Mabin Family, Nurston Farm, Dean Prior, Buckfastleigh, TQ11 0NA, 01364 642285, *Water:* 2.5 acre lake & 3 miles river Dart, *Species:* Roach to 2.5lb, Tench to 5lb, Rudd to 1lb, Bream to 4lb, Carp (different species) to 15lb, *Charges:* Dawn till dusk £5 / u14s £3 / 4pm till dusk £3, *Methods:* Barbless hooks, no keepnets, no boilies / match bookings

CHUDLEIGH

Trenchford

Contact: South West Lakes Trust, 01837 871565, info@swlakestrust.org.uk, *Water:* Ranger Tel 01647 277587, *Species:* Pike up to 30lb, *Permits:* Self service kiosk at Kennick Reservoir, *Charges:* Full day £4.50, Concession £3.50, 24 Hour £8.50, Season Day £80, Season Concession £60, Season Child (under 16) £35, Season Day & Night £120, Additional Fisheries £20 each. Full day boat + fishing £8.50 (boats must be booked 48 hrs in advance), *Season:* Open all year 24 hrs/day, *Methods:* No child under 14 years may fish unless accompanied by an adult over 18 years. No child under 16 may fish overnight unless accompanied by an adult over 18 years, and then only with permission of parent or legal guardian (letter to this effect must be produced)

COMBE MARTIN

Newberry Farm Coarse Fishing

Contact: Mr.& Mrs. Greenaway, Newberry Farm, Woodlands, Combe Martin, EX34 0AT, 01271 882334, *Water:* 2 acre lake, *Species:* Carp & Green Tench to 4kg (8lb), Roach, Rudd & Perch, *Permits:* From above address, *Charges:* £5/day, max 2 rods; evening or half day tickets also available, *Season:* Open Easter till end October (please book in advance to fish Nov.-March), *Methods:* Barbless hooks and non lead weights only, No ground bait or keepnets.

CREDITON

Creedy Lakes

Contact: Sandra Turner, Longbarn, Crediton, EX17 4AB, 01363 772684, info@creedylakes.com, *Water:* 4.5 acre & 1/2 acre spring fed lakes, *Species:* Common to 30lb 12oz, Mirror to 25lb 6oz. Koi Carp plus Tench, *Charges:* Day ticket £5 (up to 2 rods). £6 (3 rods). Evening ticket £2.50 (up to 2 rods). £3 (3 rods), *Season:* March through to end December, *Methods:* Barbless Hooks, Minimum line 8lbs, No keepnets or nut baits. No poles or beachcasters. Unhooking mats and 'Klinik' antiseptic compulsory. No night fishing.

Lower Hollacombe Fishery

Contact: Mr. C. Guppy, Lower Hollacombe, Crediton, EX17 5BW, 01363 84331, *Water:* Approximately 1 acre, *Species:* Common Carp, Koi Carp, Rudd, Tench, Mirror Carp, Crucian Carp, Roach, Perch, *Permits:* At bank side, *Charges:* £5 per day. £3 per day under 14. £2.50 evenings. under 16 must be accompanied by adult, *Season:* All year round, *Methods:* Barbless hooks, no boilies or nut baits.

Oldborough Fishing Retreat

Contact: Wendy Wilshaw, Oldborough Fishing Retreat, Morchard Bishop, Crediton, EX17 6SQ, 01363 877437, wendywilshaw@eclipse.co.uk, *Water:* 2 acres of lakes, *Species:* Mirror, Leather and Common Carp, Tench, Roach, Rudd, Perch and Eels, *Permits:* By prior arrangement, *Charges:* £4 per day. £3 juniors, *Season:* Open all year, *Methods:* Barbless hooks only. No keepnets. No Boilies. No night fishing.

Salmonhutch Coarse Fishery

Contact: Mr Mortimer, Uton, Crediton, EX17 3QL, 01363 772749, *Water:* Three 1 acre spring fed lakes, *Species:* Mirror to 26lb 1oz and Common Carp to 20lb 12oz, Tench to 5lb, Rudd, *Permits:* On Site, *Charges:* Day fishing 7am to 10pm, from £4 for Adults. Night fishing 9pm to 7am, from £4 (prior booking required) Evening fishing from £2.50, *Season:* All Year, *Methods:* Barbless hooks, no long shank bent hooks, no permanently fixed lead rigs. Minimum 8lb line for carp, 4lb for general fishing. No carp in keepnets. Full rules from the fishery

Shobrooke Lake

Contact: Clare Shelley, Shobrooke Park, Crediton, EX17 1DG, Tel: 01363 775153, fish@shobrookepark.com, *Water:* 9 acre lake in superb parkland setting, *Species:* Tench, Carp, Mirror, Rudd, Perch, Roach, *Permits:* Not from above address - Ladd's Sport Shop, Exeter Rd, Crediton 01363-772666 or Crediton Angling Centre, 109 High Street, Crediton 01363-772775, *Charges:* Adult: £5/day, £10/week, £75/year; u.16/Student-Pensioner: £2.50/day, £5/week, £35/year, *Methods:* Fishing by rod or line from bank only; no night fishing; no keepnets

156

CULLOMPTON

Coombelands Coarse Fishery
Contact: Mr & Mrs Berry, Higher Coombelands, Bunneford Cross, Knowle, Cullompton, EX15 1PT, 01884 32320, rosemary@billingsmoor.fsnet.co.uk, *Water:* 4 Lakes totalling approx 3 acres + 3 lakes in 1 acre, *Species:* 1 Carp lake, Mixed coarse fishing ponds, *Permits:* Higher Coombelands, *Charges:* From £3.50 - £5.50 /day, Evening and season tickets available, *Season:* Open all year, *Methods:* Barbless hooks only. No keep nets. No boilies, Night fishing with prior permission only, No dogs.

Exeter & District A.A. (Kia Ora)
Contact: Terry Reed (Hon. Sec.), PO Box 194, Exeter, EX2 7WG, *Mobile:* 07970 483913, exeteranglingassociation@yahoo.co.uk, *Water:* A new, recently built Association water. Currently in the process of being stocked. Opening early 2002, *Permits:* Exeter Angling Centre, Smythen Street (Off Market Street Exeter). Bridge Cafe, Bridge Road, Exeter. Exmouth Tackle & Sport, The Strand, Exmouth. Tackle Trader, Wharf Road, Newton Abbot. Exe Valley Angling, West Exe South, Tiverton, *Charges:* £25 adults, £2 for Juniors (annual). Day and week tickets depending on water, ask at agent, *Season:* Different on each water. Details in association handbook or from agents, *Methods:* Different restrictions on each water. Details in association handbook.

Goodiford Mill Fishery (Coarse Lakes)
Contact: David Wheeler, Goodiford Mill, Kentisbeare, Cullompton, EX15 2AS, 01884 266233, paul@culmvalley.fsnet.co.uk, *Water:* 7 acres, *Species:* Carp: Common, Mirror, Crucian, Leather and Ghost, *Charges:* £5 per day ticket. £3.50 junior and OAP. Children under 14 must be accompanied by an adult, *Season:* All year, *Methods:* Full rules on application. No keepnets except in approved matches.

Millhayes Fishery
Contact: Mr Tony Howe, Millhayes, Kentisbeare, Cullompton, EX15 2AF, 01884 266412, *Water:* 2 Acre spring fed lake, 0.5 acre Tench lake, *Species:* Carp 20lb, Tench, Roach, Rudd, *Charges:* £5 Adults, £3 Under 16, £3 Evenings, *Season:* 1st March - 31st December, *Methods:* Barbless hooks only, No boilies, No night fishing, No carp over 1lb in nets, Nets to be dipped, No dogs

Newcourt Ponds
Contact: Andy Hitt, Newcourt Barton, Langford, Cullompton, EX15 1SE, 01884 277326, *Water:* Four lakes totalling 1.5 acres, *Species:* Carp, Tench, Bream, Golden Orfe, Rudd, Golden Tench, *Permits:* Collected on bank, *Charges:* Adults £3 two rods. under 16 £2 one rod. Extra rods £1, *Season:* Open all year dawn to dusk. No night fishing, *Methods:* No Boilies. Barbless Hooks. No Carp over 2lb in nets

Padbrook Park
Contact: Richard Chard, Padbrook Park, Cullompton, EX15 1RU, 01884 38286, *Water:* 3 acre lake, *Species:* Many Carp up to 20lb, *Charges:* £4 Day. £2.50 half day, *Methods:* No keepnets.

Pound Farm
Contact: Mrs A.M.Davey, Butterleigh, Cullompton, EX15 1PH, 01884 855208, *Water:* Small spring fed pond, *Species:* Mirror, Common Carp, Roach, Tench, Perch, Rudd, *Charges:* £3 per rod per day, £1.50 children, *Season:* All year, *Methods:* Barbless hooks only. No Boilies.

South Farm Holiday Cottages
Contact: Mrs. Susan Chapman, Blackborough, Blackdown Hills, Cullompton, EX15 2JE, (01823)681078, chapmans@southfarm.co.uk, *Water:* 4 lakes (1/3-2/3 acre each), *Species:* Carp, Roach, Chub, *Charges:* £5/day, *Season:* All year, *Methods:* Barbless hooks, restricted use of keepnets, no boilies, net dip

Upton Lakes
Contact: Richard Down, Upton Farm, Cullompton, EX15 1RA, *Mobile:* 07968 029022, richdown11@hotmail.com, *Water:* 1.5 acres and 1.25 acre match lake (day tickets available), *Species:* Carp 23lb 3oz, Bream 9lb 12oz, Tench 6lb, Perch 3lb, Roach & Rudd +/- 1lb plus Crucian Carp, *Charges:* From April 2002 - £4 adults, £3 juniors, up to 3 rods; season tickets £75 adults, £45 juniors. Season tickets run on a 364 day basis, *Season:* Dawn until dusk, No night fishing, *Methods:* Barbless hooks, No boilies, No peanuts

DARTMOUTH

Old Mill
Contact: South West Lakes Trust, 01837 871565, info@swlakestrust.org.uk, *Species:* Carp to over 20lb, Roach to 2lb. Tench and Bream, *Permits:* See South West Lakes Trust coarse advert, *Charges:* Season Child (u.16) £35, Season Day & Night £150, Concession £135. Family (husband, wife & up to 2 children u.16) £250. Additional Fisheries £20 each, *Season:* Open all year 24 hours a day, *Methods:* No child under 14 years may fish unless accompanied by an adult over 18 years. No child under 16 may fish overnight unless accompanied by an adult over 18 years, and then only with permission of parent or legal guardian (letter to this effect must be produced).

DAWLISH

Ashcombe Fishery
Contact: Ashcombe Adventure Centre Ltd, Ashcombe, Near Dawlish, EX7 0QD, 01626 866766, info@ashcombeadventure.co.uk, *Water:* 3 Lakes approx 3 acres, *Species:* Carp 18lb, Tench 4lb, Roach 2lb, *Permits:* Day tickets/permits available from lakes (fishing inspector), *Charges:* Adults £4.50, Juniors / OAP's £3.50, *Season:* Open all year, *Methods:* Barbless Hooks, No large Carp to be kept in keepnets, No boilies

EXETER

Broadclyst Pond
Contact: Jarvis Hayes, Broadclyst, Exeter, EX5 3AD, 01392 461268, jarvishayes@netscapeonline.co.uk, *Water:* One half acre lake, *Species:* Carp to 20lb plus.Tench 3.5lb, Perch 1.5lb, Rudd 12oz, *Permits:* On site - contact for details, *Charges:* £4 per day, *Season:* Open all year, *Methods:* No keepnets, barbless hooks only.

Bussells Farm
Contact: Rob or Diane Downey, Bussells Farm, Huxham, Exeter, EX5 4EN, 01392 841238, *Water:* Three lakes covering 2.5 acres, *Species:* Carp to 20lb, Bream to 7lb, Tench to 7lb. Roach, *Charges:* £5 per day, *Season:* Open all year, *Methods:* Barbless hooks only. No night fishing.

Darts Farm Fishing Lakes
Contact: James Dart, Darts Farm, Clyst St George, Topsham, Nr Exeter, EX3 0QH, 01392 878200, julie@dartsfarm.co.uk, *Water:* 3 acres lakes, *Species:* Carp max 27lb, Bream max 8-10lb, Roach, *Permits:* Available from Darts farm shop. E.A. licence required, *Charges:* Adult: 1 rod - £3.50, 2 or more rods £4.50. O.A.P/Child (under 16): 1 rod - £2.50, 2 or more rods £3.50, *Season:* All year round; Night Fishing by arrangement, *Methods:* Barbless hooks, do not encourage keep nets, disinfectant tanks for dipping tackle

Exeter & District A.A. (Fennick Ponds)
Contact: Terry Reed (Hon. Sec.), PO Box 194, Exeter, EX2 7WG, *Mobile:* 07970 483913, exeteranglingassociation@yahoo.co.uk, *Water:* Two very prolific ponds. Recently re-opened after major enhancement programme, *Species:* Tench, Carp, Crucians, Roach and Rudd, *Permits:* Exeter Angling Centre, Smythen Street (Off Market Street Exeter). Bridge Cafe, Bridge Road, Exeter. Exmouth Tackle & Sport, The Strand, Exmouth. Tackle Trader, Wharf Road, Newton Abbot. Exe Valley Angling, West Exe South, Tiverton, *Charges:* £25 adults, £2 for Juniors (annual). Day and week tickets depending on water, ask at agent, *Season:* Different on each water. Details in association handbook or from agents, *Methods:* Different restrictions on each water. Details in association handbook.

Exeter & District A.A. (Sampford Peverall Ponds)
Contact: Terry Reed (Hon. Sec.), PO Box 194, Exeter, EX2 7WG, *Mobile:* 07970 483913, exeteranglingassociation@yahoo.co.uk, *Water:* Two ponds, *Species:* All coarse fish present with Carp to 20lb, *Permits:* Exeter Angling Centre, Smythen Street (Off Market Street Exeter). Bridge Cafe, Bridge Road, Exeter. Exmouth Tackle & Sport, The Strand, Exmouth. Tackle Trader, Wharf Road, Newton Abbot. Exe Valley Angling, West Exe South, Tiverton, *Charges:* £25 adults, £2 for Juniors (annual). Day and week tickets depending on water, ask at agent, *Season:* Different on each water. Details in association handbook or from agents, *Methods:* Different restrictions on each water. Details in association handbook.

Exeter & District Angling Association (Exeter Canal)
Contact: Terry Reed (Hon. Sec.), PO Box 194, Exeter, EX2 7WG, *Mobile:* 07970 483913, exeteranglingassociation@yahoo.co.uk, *Water:* This very old waterway is approximately 12ft deep throughout its six mile length, *Species:* Carp to 40lb, Tench, Chub, Roach and specimen Pike to 30lb, *Permits:* Exeter Angling Centre, Smythen Street (Off Market Street Exeter). Bridge Cafe, Bridge Road, Exeter. Exmouth Tackle & Sport, The Strand, Exmouth. Tackle Trader, Wharf Road, Newton Abbot. Exe Valley Angling, West Exe South, Tiverton, *Charges:* £25 adults, £2 for Juniors (annual). Day and week tickets depending on water, ask at agent, *Season:* Different on each water. Details in association handbook or from agents, *Methods:* Different restrictions on each water. Details in association handbook.

Exeter Ship Canal
Contact: Exeter City Council, River & Canal Manager, Civic Centre, Exeter, EX1 1RP, 01392 274306, *Water:* 5.25 miles of canal, both banks; upper 2 miles free permits, *Species:* Roach, Bream, Tench, Carp, Pike & Eels, *Permits:* River & Canal Office, Canal Basin, Haven Rd, Exeter, EX2 8DU, *Charges:* Free permits with proof of identity or E.A. licence. Lower level 3.25 miles on Exeter & District A.A. permit, *Season:* Open all year, *Methods:* No live or dead bait coarse fish.

Hogsbrook Lakes
Contact: Desmond & Maureen Pearson, Russett Cottage, Greendale Barton, Woodbury Salterton, Exeter, EX5 1EW, 01395 233340, *Water:* One 1.5 acre, One 2 acre lake, *Species:* Bream, Tench, Roach, Rudd, Golden Rudd, Carp, *Permits:* At lakeside from bailiff, Night fishing by prior arrangement, *Charges:* Day ticket £4 per day (One Rod) £1 extra per rod, Junior £2. Night £6 (One Rod) £1 extra per rod, *Season:* Open all year, *Methods:* Barbless hooks, keepnets by arrangement, No Carp in nets or sacks, All Carp anglers must have unhooking mats.

Home Farm Fishery
Contact: Mr F Williams, Home Farm, Mamhead, Kenton, Exeter, EX6 8HP, 01626 866259, *Water:* 1 lake approx one acre, *Species:* Carp 20lb plus, Roach to 2lb, Tench to 4lb, Rudd to 12oz, *Permits:* From the cabin by the lake, *Charges:* £5 up to two rods, weekly ticket £25 max two rods, concessions for children. Night fishing by arrangement, *Season:* Open all year, *Methods:* No groundbaiting with boilies, no tiger nuts.

Luccombes Coarse Fishery
Contact: Julian Harrod, Towsington Lane, Exminster, EX6 8AY, 01392 832858, *Mobile:* 07748 568316, jenga22@hotmail.com, *Water:* Five medium sized ponds set in 9 acres, *Species:* Carp to 21lb. Tench to 6.5lb, Skimmer Bream, Rudd and Roach, *Permits:* Season tickets available from the above, *Charges:* £5 day tickets on the bank. £3 after 4.30pm. £3 junior (under 16 accompanied). £100 season ticket (12 months), *Season:* Open all year from 6am to half hour before dark, *Methods:* No keepnets (except in matches) Barbless hooks ONLY, No nuts or seeds with the exception of hemp and sweetcorn.

Pengellies Carp Ponds
Contact: Mr Carr, Shillingsford Abbot, Exeter, EX2 9QH, 01392 832286, *Water:* Two small ponds totalling 1/4 acre, *Species:* Carp to 15lb, Roach, *Charges:* Tickets from office, £10 per day up to 3 rods; lake can be prebooked for exclusive fishing, *Season:* Open all year dawn to dusk; night fishing by arrangement only, *Methods:* Barbless hooks only, no boilies

South View Farm
Contact: Mr R.K.Gorton, South View Farm, Shillingford Saint George, Exeter, EX2 9UP, 01392 832278, *Mobile:* 07799 198498, southviewfarmfishery@btinternet.com, *Water:* 3 Lakes totalling 3 acres, *Species:* Mirror, Common up to 28lb & Ghost Carp 15lb, Roach 2.5lb, Rudd 2.5lb, Perch 3.5lb, Bream, Green & Gold Tench to 3.5lb, *Permits:* Tickets on the bank, *Charges:* £5 for two rods, Juniors (under 16, must be accompanied) £4. Evening ticket after 5pm £3 adult, £2 junior, *Season:* Open all year round, *Methods:* Barbless hooks, No boilies, No keepnets

Upham Farm Ponds
Contact: S.J.Willcocks, Upham Farm, Farringdon, Exeter, EX5 2HZ, 01395 232247, cjjj@uphamfarm.freeserve.co.uk, *Water:* 6 Well stocked ponds, *Species:* Carp 26lb, Tench 8lb 8oz, *Permits:* Day tickets on bank, *Charges:* £5/day (concessions for O.A.P's, Junior), *Methods:* Barbless hooks, No keepnets

EXMOUTH

Squabmoor
Contact: South West Lakes Trust, 01837 871565, info@swlakestrust.org.uk, *Water:* Ranger Tel 01647 277587, *Species:* Good head of Carp to 25lb. Roach to 3lb 2oz, Tench, *Permits:* See South West Lakes Trust coarse advert, *Charges:* Full day £4.50, Concession £3.50, 24 Hour £8.50, Season Day £80, Season Concession £60, Season Child (under 16) £35, Season Day & Night £120, Additional Fisheries £20 each, *Season:* Open all year 24 hours a day, *Methods:* No child under 14 years may fish unless accompanied by an adult over 18 years. No child under 16 may fish overnight unless accompanied by an adult over 18 years, and then only with permission of parent or legal guardian (letter to this effect must be produced)

HATHERLEIGH

Legge Farm Coarse Fishery
Contact: Graham Hall, Church Road, Highampton, Beaworthy, EX21 5LF, 01409 231464, legge_farm@yahoo.com, *Water:* 1.25 Acre lake & two other ponds, *Species:* Carp (common to 15lb), Tench, Perch to 4.3lb, Roach, Rudd, Crucians, Grass Carp, Bream, *Permits:* EA licences sold on site, *Charges:* Adults £5, O.A.Ps & evenings after 4pm £3.50, juniors £3, *Season:* All year 7am - Dusk, *Methods:* Barbless hooks, Landing nets, No radios or keepnets.

HOLSWORTHY

Clawford Vineyard
Contact: Clawton, EX22 6PN, 01409 254177, john.ray@clawford.co.uk, *Water:* 10 lakes totalling over 30 acres of water, *Species:* Common, Mirror, Crucian, Ghost & Grass Carp, Tench, Roach, Rudd, Orfe, Barbel, Golden Tench, Blue Tench, Golden/Pink Orfe, Green Rudd, Gold Carp, Goldfish, Catfish, Ide, Chub, *Charges:* On application, *Season:* Open all year, *Methods:* No live or deadbait. No particles or nuts except hemp or sweetcorn. Barbless hooks only. No carp whatsoever in keepnets. Full rules at the fishery

Eastcott Farm & Lodges
Contact: Mrs C. Whitmill, Eastcott Farm, North Tamerton, Nr Holsworthy, EX22 6SB, 01409 271172, eastcott@fsmail.net, *Water:* One Lake approx 0.75 acres, *Species:* Carp & Rudd, *Permits: Charges:* Day ticket £2.50, Under 16 & OAP £1.50, Residents free, *Season:* Open all year, *Methods:* Barbless hooks, No keepnets.

Exemoor Farm
Contact: Mr A R Mills, Week St. Mary, Holsworthy, EX22 6UX, 01566 781366, *Water:* Half acre lake, *Species:* Tench 4/5lb, Golden Orfe, Rudd, Crucian, Common 13lb & Mirror Carp, *Charges:* £3 Per rod per day, cheaper rates after 5pm, *Season:* Open all year, *Methods:* No boilies or hemp

Simpson Valley Fishery
Contact: Simpson Farm, Holsworthy, EX22 6JW, 01409 253593, *Water:* 4 lakes. New two acre specimen lake fishing in 2003, *Species:* Carp to 23lb, Tench 8lb, Roach 2lb, Rudd 1lb, Gudgeon near to British record, Chub 4lb, *Charges:* £5 per day - 2 rods, £3 Juniors and O.A.P's (2002 prices), *Season:* Open all year dawn to dusk, *Methods:* Barbless hooks only. No Carp in keepnets

Wooda Fisheries
Contact: C.J. Pickett, Pancrasweek, Holsworthy, EX22 6DJ, 01409 241934, *Water:* 3 lakes - 1 general, 1 intermediate and 1 specimen, *Species:* Carp, Tench, Perch, Bream & Roach, *Permits:* On site, *Charges:* £5 per day, *Season:* All year, *Methods:* Barbless hooks only, no keepnets.

Woodacott Arms
Contact: Len Sanders, Woodacott Cross, Thornbury, Holsworthy, EX22 7BT, 01409 261358/261237, woodacottarms@aol.com, *Water:* 2 Lakes, 1.25 Acre, 1 Acre, *Species:* Carp 23lb, Tench 7lb, Bream 3lb, Rudd 1.5lb, Roach 1.5lb, Perch 4.5lb, *Charges:* Adults: Day Tickets 2 Rods £5, Juniors: 2 Rods £3, *Methods:* Barbless Hooks, No keepnets, No Boilies or Peanuts.

HONITON

Fishponds House
Contact: Tracy Semmens, Fishponds House, Dunkeswell, Honiton, EX14 0SH, 01404 891358, fishpondshouse@aol.com, *Water:* 2 Lakes each over 1 acre, *Species:* Carp to 20lb, Rudd, Roach and Tench, *Charges:* £6.00 per day, Children under 11yrs £3.00 per day, *Season:* Open all year dawn to dusk, *Methods:* Barbless hooks, No boilies, No keepnets

Hartsmoor Fisheries
Contact: John Griss, Bolham Water, Clayhidon, Cullompton, EX15 3QB, 01823 680460, *Water:* Two day ticket lakes - 2 acres and 1.25 acres, One syndicate lake -3.5 acres, plus one 5 acre lake being developed, *Species:* Roach and Rudd to 2lb, Tench 6lb, Bream 7lb, Barbel 4.5lb, Perch 3lb, Crucians 3.5lb (not hybrids!), Blue Orfe 2.5lb, Chub 5lb, Carp 26.5lb (syndicate 33.5lb) Gudgeon 4oz, *Permits:* Day tickets on the bank, Syndicate - get your name on the waiting list , *Charges:* £5 per day. £5 per night by arrangement, *Season:* Day tickets dawn to dusk all year round, *Methods:* Barbless hooks. No nuts of any kind. No Carp over 2lb in keepnets. Loose feed and groundbait is permitted

Milton Farm Ponds
Contact: Milton Farm, Payhembury, Honiton, EX14 0HE, 01404 850236, *Water:* 5 Lakes approx 2 acres, *Species:* Carp to 22lb, Tench 7lb, Roach, Bream, *Permits:* Collected on bank, *Charges:* £3.50/person/day - no charge for extra rods, £2.50 children 14 or under, *Season:* Open all year round, *Methods:* No groundbaiting with boilies

ILFRACOMBE

Ilfracombe & District Anglers Association (Coarse)
Contact: David Shorney, Victoria Cottage, 8b St Brannocks Road, Ilfracombe, EX34 8EG, 01271 865874, orphaneannie@amserve.net, *Water:* No Club waters. Use Slade reservoir and Mill Park at Berrynarbor, *Species:* Carp, Bream, Perch, Roach, Rudd, Gudgeon and Pike, *Permits:* From Agents: Variety Sports, 23 Broad street, Ilfracombe and The Post Office, Slade, Ilfracombe, Devon, EX34 8LQ, *Charges:* Annual fee combines Sea & Coarse plus licence and permits, *Season:* January to December. Open charity competition in June, *Methods:* Barbless hooks. No Carp in keepnets

Lower Slade
Contact: South West Lakes Trust, 01837 871565, info@swlakestrust.org.uk, *Water:* Ranger Tel 01288 321262, *Species:* Mirror & Common Carp to 20lb plus. Bream to 5lb plus. Perch to 2lb 4oz, Roach, Rudd, Gudgeon and Pike, *Permits:* See South West Lakes Trust coarse advert, *Charges:* Full day £4.50, Concession £3.50, 24 Hour £8.50, Season Day £80, Season Concession £60, Season Child (under 16) £35, Season Day & Night £120, Additional Fisheries £20 each, *Season:* Open all year, 24 hours a day, *Methods:* No child under 14 years may fish unless accompanied by an adult over 18 years. No child under 16 may fish overnight unless accompanied by an adult over 18 years, and then only with permission of parent or legal guardian. (letter to this effect must be produced)

Mill Park Coarse Fishing Lake
Contact: Brian & Mary Malin, Mill Park, Mill Lane, Berrynarbor, Ilfracombe, EX34 9SH, 01271 882647, millpark@globalnet.co.uk, *Water:* 1.5 acre lake between Ilfracombe and Combe Martin, *Species:* Bream, Carp, Perch, Roach, Rudd, Tench, Golden Orfe, Golden Tench, Crucian Carp, *Charges:* Adult £4.50, Junior £2.50, Adult+Junior £6, Reduced rates for residents of touring and camping site; All juniors (-16) must be accompanied by adult, *Season:* Lake open all year; day ticket 8am-9pm or dusk (whichever is earlier), *Methods:* Barbless hooks only, Dip all nets, No night fishing

KINGSBRIDGE

Bickerton Farm Fishery
Contact: Mr Graham Tolchard, Bickerton Farm, Hallsands, Kingsbridge, TQ7 2EU, 01548 511220, *Water:* 1/3 acre & 3/4 acre ponds, *Species:* Carp 15lb, Roach, Rudd, Perch, Tench, Bream, *Charges:* £3 Under 16's, £4 per rod Adults, Two rods £5 & £7, *Methods:* Barbless hooks, No keepnets unless fishing match

Coombe Water Fisheries
Contact: J.W. Robinson, Coombe Farm, Kingsbridge, TQ7 4AB, 01548 852038, *Water:* 3 Lakes, *Species:* Carp to 25lb, Bream to 4lb, Tench to 3lb, Roach to 2.5lb, *Permits:* No E.A. licence required. Lakes are covered by general E.A. licence, *Charges:* £5 day-ticket, £2.50 Under 16. 1/2 day ticket £3, *Season:* All year dawn to dusk. Night fishing by arrangement only, *Methods:* Barbless hooks, No ground bait, no Carp over 1lb in keepnets.

Slapton Ley National Nature Reserve
Contact: Nick Binnie, Slapton Ley Field Centre, Slapton, Kingsbridge, TQ7 2QP, 01548 580685, *Water:* 180 acre Freshwater Lagoon, *Species:* Pike, Perch, Roach, Rudd, *Permits:* Hired rowing boats only, *Charges:* Dependent on number in boat e.g. £18 for 2 anglers, *Season:* No close season, *Methods:* No bank fishing, barbless hooks, no keepnets.

Valley Springs Coarse and Trout Fishery (Coarse)
Contact: J. Bishop, Sherford, Nr Kingsbridge, TQ7 2BG, 01548 531574, valleyspringscottages@btopenworld.com, *Water:* 2 Lakes totalling approx 3 acres, Trout & Coarse, *Species:* Coarse Fish - Carp to 32lb, Tench to 4.5lb, Roach/Rudd to 2lb, *Charges:* £7per day including EA Rod Licence, *Season:* Usually open daily all year. Please ring first if making a long trip, *Methods:* Barbless hooks.

LYME REGIS

Summerleaze Pond
Contact: Summerleaze Farm, Kilmington, Axminster, EX13 7RA, 01297 32390, *Water:* 1 coarse fishing lake, *Species:* Carp, Roach, Perch. Best Carp 17lb, *Charges:* On site, £3 adults, £1.50 children under 16, *Season:* Open all year, dawn to dusk, *Methods:* Please ask at fishery.

NEWTON ABBOT

Exeter & District A.A. (Abrook Pond)
Contact: Terry Reed (Hon. Sec.), PO Box 194, Exeter, EX2 7WG, *Mobile:* 07970 483913, exeteranglingassociation@yahoo.co.uk, *Water:* Good looking pond with rustic bridges and plenty of lily pads, *Species:* Tench, Beam, Roach and Carp to mid twenties, *Permits:* Exeter Angling Centre, Smythen Street (Off Market Street Exeter). Bridge Cafe, Bridge Road, Exeter. Exmouth Tackle & Sport, The Strand, Exmouth. Tackle Trader, Wharf Road, Newton Abbot. Exe Valley Angling, West Exe South, Tiverton, *Charges:* £25 adults, £2 for Juniors (annual). Day and week tickets depending on water, ask at agent, *Season:* Different on each water. Details in association handbook or from agents, *Methods:* Different restrictions on each water. Details in association handbook.

Finlake Holiday Park
Contact: Tony Irving (Bailiff) Ext 230, Nr Chudleigh, TQ13 0EJ, 01626 853833, *Water:* 1 Acre - 30 Peg, *Species:* Crucians 1-4lb, Bream to 4lb, Tench 2-4lb, Skimmers, Roach to 2.75lb, Golden Orfe 12 inches, Rudd 1.5lb, Golden Rudd 8 inches, No Carp, *Permits:* On entry at security, *Charges:* £3 Adult, £2.50 to 14yrs, *Season:* All year round, Winter opening times: 8am - Dusk, Summer opening times: 8am-6pm every day except Tuesdays & Thursdays which are 8am - 3pm, *Methods:* Barbless hooks. No keep nets. No boilies, nuts, floating baits, pellets or paste. Strictly no ground bait, landing nets essential

Newton Abbot Fishing Association (Coarse Ponds)

Contact: Clive Smith (membership secretary), PO Box 1, Bovey Tracey, Newton Abbot, TQ13 9ZE, 01626 836661, newtonfishing@yahoo.com, *Water:* 17 coarse ponds in the Newton Abbot Area. Also member of S.L.A.C. (Somerset Levels Association of Clubs) with stretches of the Parret, Brue and Isle, *Species:* Carp to 36lb, Tench to12lb, Bream to 8lb, Roach to 2lb, Perch to 3lb 9oz, Rudd to 1.5lb, *Permits:* From Tackle Trader, Newton Abbot. Abbot Angling, Newton Abbot. Oakford Filling Station, Kinsteignton. Sporting Lines, Torquay, Handy Baits, Paignton. Brixham Bait & Tackle, *Charges:* Day Tickets: £5 senior, £2 junior. Associate licence £41 senior (1 year fishing majority of waters). Full member £46 adult. £13 junior, £23 OAP/conc. (must live within 20 miles of Newton Abbot), *Season:* Ponds and lakes are open 24 hours a day, 365 days a year. Rivers are controlled by the national close season for coarse fish; Rocombe Ponds and Wapperwell Ponds open from dawn to dusk, *Methods:* Barbless or crushed barbs. 2 rods 1 April to 30 September. 3 rods 1 October to 31 March. No lead shot. No nut baits. No fires. No dogs. No keepnets at Rocombe.

Preston Ponds

Contact: Newton Abbot Fishing Association, newtonfishing@yahoo.com, *Water:* See entry under Newton Abbot Fishing Association. 4 ponds at Kingsteignton. Key Transport: Popular match water (full members only). Eddison Pond: small water. Sawmills: about 3 acres coloured by run off from local clay works but don't be put off! New Cross: Extremely deep former clay pit, *Species:* Key Transport: Skimmers, Bream, big Roach, Rudd, Perch, Tench and Crucians to over a pound. Eddison Pond: Most species with Tench, Crucians and mid-double Carp. Sawmills: Skimmers, Bream, Perch, Tench Carp and Roach to over 1lb with odd Perch to 3lb, Carp to 20lb a rumours of a single large Catfish!. New Cross: Some good Roach, Perch, the odd Tench.

Rackerhayes Complex

Contact: Newton Abbot Fishing Association, newtonfishing@yahoo.com, *Water:* See entry under Newton Abbot Fishing Association. 6 waters just outside Newton Abbot. Island Pond 5 acres (full members only), First Pond 2 acres, Dores Pond 9 acres, Linhay Pond 3 acres, Weedy Pond (just under 1 acre) and Wheel Pond (juniors only)., *Species:* Island Pond: most species, numerous Carp over 30lb.Tench over 10lb. Good sized Roach, Rudd, Pike, Bream and Eels. First Pond: Good head of Carp to 28lb, Tench, Roach, Bream etc. and a large number of jack Pike. Wheel Pond: Carp to 14lb, Roach, Rudd, Perch, Golden Orfe, Tench and occasional small Pike. Linhay Pond: Most coarse species with some excellent Bream. Dores Pond: Very large head of Carp to 30lb, superb Tench averaging 6lb and up to 11lb 15oz. Weedy Pond: most coarse fish including good Tench and some large Carp, *Permits:* See main entry.

Spring Ponds

Contact: Newton Abbot Fishing Association, newtonfishing@yahoo.com, *Water:* See entry under Newton Abbot Fishing Association. Three small farm ponds, *Species:* Middle pond has been heavily re-stocked. Top and bottom ponds well stocked with Carp averaging 2lb. OPdd Carp to low double plus Tench, Roach and Bream. Almost guaranteed action.

West Golds

Contact: Newton Abbot Fishing Association, newtonfishing@yahoo.com, *Water:* A tidal water that is incorporated in the local flood defence system. Extreme care should be taken as flash tidal flooding is common, *Species:* Dace, Roach, Skimmers, Mullet and Carp to over 20lb. Stock changes with flow of higher tides.

NORTH TAWTON

North Tawton Angling Specimen Group

Contact: Mr. J.D. Mansfield, 4 Taw Vale Close, North Tawton, EX20 2EH, 01837 82122, *Water:* Any Lake or River, Sea fishing from shore only, *Species:* Any species listed in the British records, *Charges:* Membership £8/year, *Season:* June 1st - May 31st, *Methods:* Abide by regulations laid out on lake or river the group are fishing

Spires Lakes

Contact: Barry Ware, Riverside, Fore Street, North Tawton, EX20 2ED, 01837 82499, *Water:* Two lakes, 30 peg match lake and 2 acre lake, *Species:* Carp 30lb, Tench 5lb, Roach 1lb 8oz, Rudd 1lb, Bream 3.5lb, Perch 1.5lb, Orfe 4lb, Ghost Carp 1lb, *Permits:* On site kiosk, self service, *Charges:* £5 Day ticket, £3.50 Evening, £3 Junior & O.A.Ps, *Season:* Dawn to dusk, *Methods:* Barbless hooks, No boilies, No tiger or peanuts.

OKEHAMPTON

Alder Lake

Contact: Mr Bob Westlake, Alder, Lewdown, Okehampton, EX20 4PJ, 01566 783397, bobwestlake@aldersportswear.com, *Water:* 4 Acre Lake, *Species:* Perch, Carp to 25lb, Bream to 8.25lb, Specimen Roach and Tench. Plus natural stock of Trout, *Charges:* £4 per rod per day, *Season:* No closed season, *Methods:* No restrictions. Night fishing allowed.

Millaton Farm Coarse Fishery

Contact: Gareth or Jessica Charles-Jones, Millaton Farm, Bridestowe, Okehampton, EX20 4QG, 01837 861100, *Water:* 3 large lakes, 2 small (from 0.75 to 2 acres), *Species:* Carp - Koi 9lb, Ghost 10.5lb, Mirror 15lb, Common 14lb, Crucian 2.5lb, Leather. Tench, Bream 4lb, Perch 1lb, Roach, Rudd, American Sun Bass 2oz., *Permits:* Up to 5 day tickets allowed. You MUST RING day before to book space before setting out, *Charges:* £5 per day per rod, *Season:* Dawn to dusk all year round, *Methods:* Barbless hooks only. No boilies, hemp, peanuts. Groundbait in moderation. No keepnets, dogs, radios.

DEVON - STILLWATER COARSE

Millaton-Wrigley Fishing Syndicate

Contact: Mr Vic Barnett (Syndicate Sec.), 5 Weir Close, Mainstone, Plymouth, PL6 8SD, 01752 708206, victor.barnett@talk21.com, *Water:* 3 small ponds, each cannot be seen from the other. A very private and secluded fishery. Potential to increase the water to five ponds in the near future as they are already there but need to be worked on, *Species:* Carp, Tench, Golden Tench, Bream, Perch, Gudgeon, Roach, Rudd, Large Brown Goldfish (2.5lb), Gold Carp, *Permits:* To join the syndicate costs in the first year are: £10 joining fee, £50 for year. After the first year cost is £50 p.a. 5 day tickets - price on booking (around £4.50 per day). More details from the above contact or phone 01837 861100, allowing for a long ring please, *Charges:* As above, *Season:* No close season, *Methods:* Barbless hooks only. No Carp over 2lb to be retained in keepnets. Knotless nets only. No boilies. All spawning fish to be returned to the water immediately after photographing or weighing. Syndicate members may camp overnight and generally come and go as they wish

Stowford Grange Fisheries

Contact: H. Vigers & Sons, Stowford Grange Farm, Lewdown, Okehampton, EX20 4BZ, 01566 783298, *Mobile:* 07771 798363, *Water:* 2.5 acre, 1 acre and 1.25 acre lakes, *Species:* Roach, Rudd, Carp 20lb, Bream 10lb 2oz, Tench 6lb 4oz, Perch 4lb 14oz, Gudgeon, Golden Tench, *Permits:* At the farm, *Charges:* On application, *Season:* Open all year, *Methods:* Barbless or whisker barbs, no boilies in bottom lake, no nuts, no large carp in nets. Okehampton,

Week Farm

Contact: John & Grenville Hockridge, Bridestowe, Okehampton, EX20 4HZ, 01837 861221, accom@weekfarmonline.com, *Water:* 2x 0.5 acre lakes, 0.25 acre lake, *Species:* Mixed Carp (Common, Mirror, Crucian), Bream; in 0.25 acre Roach, Rudd, Green Tench, *Charges:* £4/day + £1 extra rod, £2/evening, children + OAP half price, *Methods:* Barbless hooks only, all nets to be dipped, night fishing by arrangement, no dogs

PAIGNTON

New Barn Angling Centre

Contact: Andrew & Callie Buchanan, Newbarn Farm, Totnes Road, Paignton, TQ4 7PT, 01803 553602, info@newbarnfarm.com, *Water:* 6 ponds up to 1 acre suitable for juniors (parent supervision), beginners, pleasure and specimen anglers, *Species:* Carp to 27lb, Ghost Carp to 17lb, Tench to 6.5lb, Roach to 2lb 12oz, Bream to 5lb, Perch to 4lb, Rudd to 2lb 4oz, Eels (mirror lake only) 7lb 8oz, *Permits:* No EA rod licence required. Purchase day tickets on arrival, *Charges:* £5 for 1 rod, 2nd rod /£1, juniors (u.14) £3, *Season:* Open all year 7am to dusk (6am June to August). Night fishing only available to holiday guests. 8 fishing shelters around main lake, first come first served, *Methods:* Barbless hooks only; no keepnets; no nuts; all baits eff.: maggots, luncheon meat, sweetcorn, boilies, bread & pellets; sensible ground baiting allowed; float fishing and ledgering; summer time good for floating dog biscuits

Town Parks Coarse Fishing Centre

Contact: Mr Paul Gammin, Town Park Farm, Totnes Road, Paignton, 01803 523133, *Water:* 2 acre lake + 2.5 acre lake 30 pegs + 25 peg lake available to clubs / associations / block bookings, phone for details, *Species:* Common 19lb, Crucian 2.5lb, Mirror Carp 31lb, Bream 6lb 4oz, Tench 8lb 12oz, Roach 2lb 7oz, Perch 4lb 2oz, Rudd 2lb 7oz, Eel 6lb 2oz, *Permits:* No EA Rod licence required, *Charges:* Full day £5, 5 hours £4, Summer evening £3, Night fishing £7, 24 hrs £10, *Season:* All year, Dawn - Dusk. Night fishing by appointment, *Methods:* Barbless hooks, Ground bait, Boilies etc in moderation. No tiger nuts or peanuts

PLYMOUTH

Plymouth & District Angling Club

Contact: Mr Brian Morrell, 20 Pinehurst Way, Ivybridge, PL21 9UL, 01752 895472, *Water:* 3 ponds at Cadover Bridge, two at St. Germans and one at Dellamare (pure Tench) - ranging in size from 0.5 to 2 acres, *Species:* Carp to 29lb 8oz, Tench 6lb, Bream 8lb 8oz, Rudd 11lb 6oz Roach 2lb 8oz and Crucians, *Permits:* Clive's Tackle and Bait, 182 Exeter St, Plymouth. Tel: 01752 228940, *Charges:* Seniors £35. Juniors £10. Disabled and OAP's £15, *Season:* Open all year. St Germans and Cadover 24 hours, *Methods:* Barbless hooks. No Carp in keepnets. Unhooking mats for all Carp.

Plymouth Command Angling Association (Ponds)

Contact: Mr Vic Barnett Hon.Sec, 5 Weir Close, Mainstone, Plymouth, PL6 8SD, 01752 708206, victor.barnett@talk21.com, *Water:* Two lakes of .5 and .9 of an acre for coarse fishing within ten minutes of Plymouth, plus several other accesses to associated waters in the Southwest open to members, *Species:* Carp, Tench, Bream, Perch, Roach, Rudd, Crucians, Goldfish, Eels, Goldcarp and some Koi, *Permits:* Membership is open to all serving members of HM Forces. Associate membership is also open to ex-serving members of HM Forces, no matter when the time was served, *Charges:* Costs for full membership or associate membership are available on application or enquiry at the above contact, *Season:* No close season for coarse fish, *Methods:* Barbless hooks only at the coarse fishery. Knotless keepnets to be used as per EA guidelines on minimum 3 metres length. No trout pellets in any form allowed. Only Carp friendly and proven pellets are to be used. All spawning fish are to be returned to the water immediately. No Carp over 2lb to be kept in keepnets.

Sunridge Fishery

Contact: RM and M Hammett, Sunridge Nurseries, Worston, Yealmpton, Plymouth, PL8 2LN, 01752 880438, *Mobile:* 0777 9445168, sunridgenurseries@yahoo.co.uk, *Water:* Approx half acre private lake that can be reserved for exclusive use. Established 28 years, *Species:* Mirror and Common Carp up to 22lb, *Permits:* From above at the Nurseries, *Charges:* £5 adult day, £3 child/OAP, *Season:* Open all year dawn to dusk, Night fishing by arrangement only, *Methods:* Barbless hooks only, No keepnets (except by prior arrangement)

SEATON

Horriford Fishing

Contact: Mr Pady, Horriford Farm, Colyford, Colyton, EX24 6HW, 01297 552316, horriford@aol.com, *Water:* 3 ponds, *Species:* Bream (5lb), Roach (1lb), Tench (5lb), Carp (8-10lb), Perch (2lb), Rudd (1.5lb), *Permits:* From farmhouse, *Charges:* Day ticket £4. Half day ticket £2.50, *Season:* Open all year dawn to dusk, *Methods:* Barbless hooks only

Wiscombe Park Fishery

Contact: Mike Raynor, Wiscombe Park Fishery, Colyton, EX24 6JE, 01404 871474, *Mobile:* 07860 222342, michael@wiscombe.globalnet.co.uk, *Water:* Half acre lake, *Species:* Carp, Tench, Bream, *Permits:* Self-service (No booking), *Charges:* £3.50/day, Reduced rates for O.A.Ps & Children, Children (u.15) free if accompanied by permit holding adult, *Season:* All year, *Methods:* Single rod

SOUTH BRENT

Hatchlands Coarse Fishery

Contact: Malcolm Davies, Greyshoot Lane, Rattery, South Brent, TQ10 9LL, 01364 73500, *Water:* Two acre lake, *Species:* Carp, Tench, Roach, Bream, Rudd and Gudgeon, *Permits:* No EA licence required. Block EA licence held by fishery, *Charges:* £5 per person per day, *Season:* Open all year, *Methods:* Barbless hooks only; No large Carp in keepnets

Little Allers Coarse Fishery

Contact: M & J Wakeham, Little Allers Farm, Avonwick, South Brent, 01364 72563, *Mobile:* 07855 427510, *Water:* 2 Acre lake, *Species:* Carp, Bream, Tench, Roach, Rudd, *Permits:* On the bank, *Charges:* £5 per day adults, £3 under 16, £2.50 evening ticket after 5pm, *Season:* Open all year dawn to dusk, *Methods:* Barbless hooks only, No carp in keepnets

SOUTH MOLTON

Dunsley Farm

Contact: Mr and Mrs Robins, Dunsley Farm, West Anstey, South Molton, EX36 3PF, 01398 341246, *Water:* Half acre lake, *Species:* Roach, Rudd, Carp and Tench, *Permits:* At the farmhouse, *Charges:* £3 adults. £1.50 children, *Methods:* Children under 16 must be accompanied by an adult.

Oaktree Fishery

Contact: George Andrews, Bottreaux Mill, West Anstey, South Molton, EX36 3PU, 01398 341568, oaktreefishery@btinternet.com, *Water:* Three 2 Acre lakes, *Species:* All Carp, Tench, Bream, Roach, Perch, Koi Carp, Catfish, *Permits:* On site only, *Charges:* Day tickets: Adults from £5, Specimen lake £6, Junior/OAP from £4, Specimen lake £5, Eve tickets: Adult £3.50, Specimen lake £5, Junior/OAP £3.50 Specimen lake £4, *Season:* Open all year 24hrs, *Methods:* Barbless hooks only. No nut type baits. See board at fishery.

TAVISTOCK

Milemead Fisheries (Coarse Lakes)

Contact: Mr Harry Dickens, Mill Hill, Tavistock, PL19 8NP, 01822 610888, *Water:* Two Lakes of 2 acres each. Match Lake available for bookings, please phone for details. Regular Sunday open matches and Thursday evening matches in the summer, *Species:* Carp to 15lb, Tench to 4lb, Bream to 4lb, Roach to 2lb, Rudd to 1.5lb, Crucians to 1lb, *Permits:* Available from lakeside tackle and bait shop, *Charges:* Adult £5, Concession £4, Evening tickets available, *Season:* All year, 7am to Dusk, *Methods:* Barbless Hooks, All nets to be dipped prior to fishing, Please read the rule boards

TIVERTON

Coombe Farm Fishponds

Contact: Mrs Curtis, Coombe Farm, Cadleigh, Tiverton, EX16 8HW, 01884 855337, *Water:* 3 lakes totalling 0.5 acre, *Species:* Carp to 20lb, Roach, Tench to 4lb, Bream to 1.5lb, *Charges:* £3 per day, *Season:* Open all year, *Methods:* No boilies.

Tiverton & District Angling Club

Contact: John Smallwood, Exe Valley Angling, 19 Westexe South, Tiverton, EX16 5DQ, 01884 242275, *Water:* 11.5 Miles on Grand Western Canal, 1.25 acre mixed fishery lake at Exebridge. 0.75 miles river Culm at Stoke Cannon. Various stretches on several rivers in Somerset, *Species:* Canal: Carp, Bream, Tench, Roach, Perch, Pike, Eels. Lakeside: Carp, Bream, Roach, Tench, Eels, Crucian Carp, *Permits:* Please ring Exe Valley for details. Also available from: Exeter Angling Centre, Enterprise Angling Taunton, Topp Tackle Taunton, Country Sports - Cullompton & Minnows Caravan Park - beside Grand Western Canal, *Charges:* Senior: Day £4, Annual £20. Conc: Day £2.50, Annual £8, *Season:* Canal: Closed March 1st - May 31st inc, except 1 5-mile section (Basin to Halburton - ring for details). Lakeside: Open all year, Weekends full members only, Maximum five day permits per day, *Methods:* Canal Methods: Any. Restrictions: Fish from permanent pegs, No night fishing, No cars on bank, No digging of banks or excessive clearance of vegatation. Lakeside Methods: Any. Restrictions: No night fishing, No boilies, Trout pellets or nuts, One rod only, Fishing from permanent pegs, No dogs, Nets to be dipped. Ring Exe Valley Angling for full details

West Pitt Farm Fishery

Contact: Susanne Westgate, Whitnage, Nr. Tiverton, EX16 7DU, 01884 820296, *Mobile:* 078 555 82374, susannewestgate@yahoo.com, *Water:* 3 lakes up to 1.25 acres, *Species:* Common & Mirror Carp, Bream, Tench, Roach, Rudd, Crucians, Golden Tench, Chub, Golden Orfe, *Permits:* Self service day tickets £4.50 per day (correct money please), *Charges:* £4.50/day,. £3.50 evenings, *Season:* All year, no closed season. Open dawn till dusk, *Methods:* No Boilies, Barbless Hooks. Nets to be dipped. Groundbait in moderation

TORRINGTON

Bakers Farm

Contact: Mr & Mrs Ridd, Bakers Farm, Moortown, Torrington, EX38 7ES, 01805 623260, *Water:* 1 acre lake, *Species:* Mirror & Common Carp, Tench, Roach & Rudd, *Charges:* £4/rod/ day, *Methods:* Barbless Hooks, No large carp in keepnets

Darracott

Contact: South West Lakes Trust, 01837 871565, info@swlakestrust.org.uk, *Water:* Ranger Tel 01288 321262, *Species:* Roach up to 1lb. Mixed bags to 20lb plus of Roach, Rudd, Bream and Tench. Perch to 2.25lb. Carp to 15lb, *Permits:* See South West Lakes Trust coarse advert, *Charges:* Full day £4.50, Concession £3.50, 24 Hour £8.50, Season Day £80, Season Concession £60, Season Child (under 16) £35, Season Day & Night £120, Additional Fisheries £20 each, *Season:* Open all year 24 hours a day, *Methods:* No child under 14 years may fish unless accompanied by an adult over 18 years. No child under 16 may fish overnight unless accompanied by an adult over 18 years, and then only with permission of parent or legal guardian (letter to this effect must be produced).

Great Torrington Anglers Association (Coarse)

Contact: Paul Martin, 67 Calf Street, Torrington, EX38 7BH, 01805 623658, paul@olmargames.fsbusiness.co.uk, *Water:* Coarse fishing on local reservoirs, open to anglers from Torrington and surrounding areas, *Permits:* No day tickets sold by club, *Charges:* Annual membership Adult £5, Junior £3.

Stevenstone Lakes

Contact: Alan & Rebecca Parnell, Deer Park, Stevenstone, Torrington, EX38 7HY, 01805 622102, parnellaj@yahoo.co.uk, *Water:* Three lakes, total of six acres in a parkland setting, *Species:* Mirror Carp 23lb, Common 13lb, Tench 6lb, Rudd 1lb, Eels 3lb, *Permits:* Only at Deer Park, *Charges:* Contact Alan & Rebecca Parnell for details of season tickets which are strictly limited. A few day tickets may be available at £10 per day, *Season:* Open 7am to sunset from 1 April to 30 September, *Methods:* Barbless hooks only, no boilies, no nut type baits, no fish over 2lb in keepnets, no dogs, no litter. Unhooking mats essential

UMBERLEIGH

Bridleway Cottages

Contact: Fiona Gordon, Golland Farm, Burrington, Umberleigh, EX37 9JP, 01769 520263, golland@btinternet.co.uk, *Water:* 2 half acre lakes, *Species:* Carp, Tench and Roach, *Permits:* From the farmhouse, *Charges:* On request, *Season:* Open all year, *Methods:* Barbless hooks only.

WINKLEIGH

Okehampton Coarse Fishing Club

Contact: Mrs Paisey, 68 Moyses Meadow, Okehampton, EX20 1JY, 01837 83746, *Water:* Enclosed still water. Brixton Barton Farm, *Species:* Common Carp to 8lb, Roach, Rudd, *Permits:* Fishing only with a member, *Charges:* £3.50, *Season:* 12 months, sunrise to sunset, *Methods:* Barbless hooks. No fish over 2lb in keepnets.

Stafford Moor Fishery

Contact: Andy or Debbie Seery, Dolton, Winkleigh, EX19 8PP, 01805 804360, *Water:* 6 acre specimen lake, 100 pegs match fishery (bookings available); 2 acre pleasure lake. 4 acre Carp balling water (3lb to 10lb fish). 3 acre lake with Tench, Crucians and Bream, *Species:* Carp 30lb, Tench, Bream, Roach, Rudd, Eels, Umberleigh. Specimen lake at Stafford Moor. Specimen lake pre-booking only, *Charges:* £5 pleasure/day, £3.50 conc./ OAP/Junior; £6 specimen/day £6 night, £4 conc./OAP/Junior., *Season:* All year, *Methods:* The method is banned, max. 6 pints of bait (incl. 2 pints of trout pellets), max. 2 kg groundbait, barbless hooks from size 16 upwards (max. size 6), night fishing by arrangement

YELVERTON

Coombe Fisheries

Contact: Mr Stephen Horn, Yelverton, Nr Plymouth, 01822 616624, *Mobile:* 078999 58493, stephenchorn@agriplus.net, *Water:* Two 1 acre lakes, *Species:* Coarse fish: Rudd, roach, Tench, Bream + various Carp (24lb), *Permits:* Local Post Office and (also mobile phone 07788 715470), *Charges:* £4/day, £2.50/ evening, *Season:* No close season, Dawn to dusk, *Methods:* Barbless hooks, No peanuts.

DEVON
Stillwater
Trout

ASHBURTON
Venford
Contact: South West Lakes Trust, 01837 871565, info@swlakestrust.org.uk, *Species:* Brown Trout, *Charges:* Free to holders of a valid Environment Agency Licence, *Season:* 15 March - 12 October, *Methods:* Angling by spinning, bubble float & bait

AXMINSTER
Lower Bruckland Fishery
Contact: David Satterley, Lower Bruckland Farm, Musbury, Axminster, EX13 8ST, 01297 552861, *Mobile:* 0421 429077, info@fishing4trout.co.uk, *Water:* 2x 2 acre lakes, *Species:* Tringle Lake: Rainbows to 30lb & Wild Browns, Serpentine Lake: Rainbows, *Permits:* Available at Angler's Hut by car park, *Charges:* Tringle: £16/day, £12/half day, £8/evening - Serpentine: 4-fish £18, 2-fish £12.50, *Season:* All year, *Methods:* Tringle: Catch & Release, max hook 10, Barbless - Serpentine: Catch & Keep, any method except Spinners

BARNSTAPLE
Blakewell Fisheries
Contact: Mr Richard & John Nickell, Blakewell Fisheries, Muddiford, Barnstaple, EX31 4ET, 01271 344533, info@blakewellfisheries.co.uk, *Water:* 5 Acre Lake, *Species:* Rainbow to 22lb 11oz. Brown to 8lb 8oz and Brook Trout to 4lb 12oz, *Permits:* On Site, *Charges:* 5 Fish £22, 4 Fish £20, 3 Fish £18, 2 Fish £16, *Season:* All Year, *Methods:* Fly Only

BEAWORTHY
South Hay Fishery
Contact: Gill and Reg Stone, South Barn Farm, South Hay, Shebbear, Beaworthy, 01409 281857, R.D.Stone@btinternet.com, *Water:* 2 acre Trout lake, 2 Miles of River Torridge, *Species:* Rainbow Trout (lake), Brown Trout, Sea Trout, Salmon (river), *Charges:* Lake £5 per day plus £1.50 per lb, River £10 per day, *Season:* Lake - all year, River - Mid March to End September, *Methods:* Fly only.

BIDEFORD
Fosfelle Country House Hotel (Game)
Contact: Hartland, Bideford, 01237 441273, *Water:* Pond approx half acre, *Species:* Rainbow & Golden Trout, *Charges:* £7.50 half day - 2 Trout, *Season:* Open all year, *Methods:* Displayed on site.

Torridge Fly Fishing Club
Contact: Mr W.H. Akister (secretary), Ebroch, North Down Rd, Bideford, EX39 3LT, 01237 475906, *Water:* 2 x 4 acre reservoirs situated 2 miles east of Bideford, *Species:* Stocked Rainbow Trout from 1.5 to 8lb. Natural Browns to 5lb, *Permits:* 2 day tickets allowed each day, *Charges:* Day tickets: £10 per day (3 fish limit) to be obtained at Summerlands Fishing Tackle, Westward Ho!, Tel. 01237 471291; Season tickets: £130 (waiting list: membership limited to 25), *Season:* 14th April - 16th December for Rainbow Trout, 14th April - 30th September for Brown Trout, *Methods:* Floating Fly Lines only

CHAGFORD
Fernworthy
Contact: South West Lakes Trust, 01837 871565, info@swlakestrust.org.uk, *Species:* Brown Trout, *Permits:* Self Service Kiosk, *Charges:* Full day £9.25, Season £120, Reduced day £7.25, Season £90, Child/Wheelchair £2, Season £30, *Season:* Opens 1 April 2001 - 12 October, *Methods:* Catch & Release operates. Barbless hooks only.

CHRISTOW
Tottiford
Contact: South West Lakes Trust, 01837 871565, info@swlakestrust.org.uk, *Water:* Ranger Tel 01647 277587, *Species:* Brown Trout Boat Fishery, fish to 6lb, *Permits:* Kennick Self Service, *Charges:* £17 for boat & fishing, *Season:* Opens 15 March 2001 - 12 October, *Methods:* Boat only Fishery. Fly fishing only. Catch & release allowed with barbless hooks.

CHUDLEIGH
Kennick
Contact: South West Lakes Trust, 01837 871565, info@swlakestrust.org.uk, *Water:* Ranger Tel 01647 277587, *Species:* Premier Rainbow Fishery Bank & Boat. 2001 average 3.4 fish per rod day, *Permits:* Self Service Kiosk - Boats may be booked in advance: 01647-277587, *Charges:* Full day £16.25, Season £385. Reduced day £13, Season £290, Child/Wheelchair £3, Season £90. Evening Monday - Friday £13. Season Permits can be used on any Premier Fishery only. Boats £10 per day inc. 2 fish extra to bag limits. 'Wheelie Boat' available for disabled anglers (must be booked at least 48 hrs in advance), *Season:* Opens 23 March 2002 - 31st October, *Methods:* No child under 14 years may fish unless accompanied by an adult over 18 years

Kennick Fly Fishers Association
Contact: Mike Boston, 5 Shirburn Rd, Torquay, TQ1 3JL, 01803 325722, *Water:* 45 acres, *Species:* Rainbow + wild Brown Trout, *Permits:* Club members able to obtain SWLT discounted tickets, *Charges:* Membership fee for club is £8 annual subscription, *Methods:* i.a.w. SWLT byelaws

CULLOMPTON
Goodiford Mill Fishery (Trout Lakes)
Contact: David Wheeler, Goodiford Mill, Kentisbeare, Cullompton, EX15 2AS, 01884 266233, paul@culmvalley.fsnet.co.uk, *Water:* 3 Lakes set in 20 acres, *Species:* Rainbow & Brown Trout, *Charges:* £20 - 4 fish, £17 - 3 fish, Evening £14 - 2 fish. Children under 14 must be accompanied by an adult, *Season:* All year, *Methods:* Max 10 longshank. Full rules on application.

HATHERLEIGH

Half Moon Fishery (Trout Lake)
Contact: Half Moon Inn, Sheepwash, Nr Hatherleigh, EX21 5NE, (01409) 231376, lee@halfmoon.demon.co.uk, *Water:* See also entry under Torridge. 3x 2 acre trout lakes, *Species:* Rainbow Trout up to 3lb, *Permits:* Day tickets available to residents and non-residents, *Charges:* £10/2-fish, £15.50/4-fish.

HOLSWORTHY

Mill Leat Trout Fishery
Contact: Mr Birkett, Thornbury, Holsworthy, EX22 7AY, 01409 261426, cottages@mill-leat.fsnet.co.uk, *Water:* Two lakes totalling 3 acres, *Species:* Rainbow Trout, *Charges:* £5 plus £1.50 per lb. No Limit, *Season:* 1st April - 31st October, *Methods:* Fly only

HONITON

Hollies Trout Farm
Contact: Bobby Roles, Sheldon, Honiton, EX14 4QS, 01404 841428, lacy121@clara.net, *Water:* Spring fed lake, *Species:* Rainbow & Brown Trout, *Charges:* Full day £19/4-fish or £15/3-fish or £5.50 and fish at £1.75/lb. £4.50 - 4 hours (£3 after 5pm) and fish at £1.75/lb, Concessions for OAP's and under 12's, *Season:* Open all year dawn to dusk, *Methods:* Fly only, dry or wet

HONITON

Otter Falls
Contact: Beth Anderson, Old Spurtham Farm, New Road, Upottery, Nr Honiton, EX14 9QD, 01404 861634, hols@otterfalls.fsnet.co.uk, *Water:* Two acre Trout lake, *Species:* Rainbow Trout to 16lb. (lake record 21.5lb), *Permits:* As above, *Charges:* £25 Full day, £15 Half day. Catch and release, *Season:* No closed season - bookings only, *Methods:* Fly only. Barbless hooks. No keepnets, no livebait.
Stillwaters
Contact: Michael Ford, Lower Moorhayne Farm, Yarcombe, Nr Honiton, EX14 9BE, 01404 861284, info@land-own.demon.co.uk, *Water:* 1 acre lake. 1 Sea trout rod on River Axe at the Sea Pool, *Species:* Trout up to 14lb in lake. Sea Trout of average size in river, *Charges:* From £25 per day for River Axe fishing - 1 rod only. £10 per session on stillwaters lake, *Season:* Mar 1st - Nov 1st, *Methods:* Fly only

IVYBRIDGE

Mill Leat Trout Farm
Contact: Chris Trant, Ermington, Nr Ivybridge, PL21 9NT, 01548 830172, chris@millgallery.com, *Water:* 0.75 Acre lake, *Species:* Rainbow Trout average 2 to 4.5lb, *Permits:* EA Licence required, *Charges:* 2 fish £9, 4 fish £16 or £3 charge then £1.50/lbs, *Season:* Open all year - booking advisable, *Methods:* No lures

KINGSBRIDGE

Valley Springs Coarse and Trout Fishery (Trout)
Contact: J. Bishop, Sherford, Nr Kingsbridge, TQ7 2BG, 01548 531574, valleyspringscottages@btopenworld.com, *Water:* 2 Lakes totalling approx 3 acres, Trout & Coarse, *Species:* Rainbow & Brown Trout, *Charges:* £7 to fish plus fish caught at £2 per lb including EA Licence, *Season:* Usually open daily all year. Please ring first if making a long trip, *Methods:* Barbless hooks, Traditional fly fishing methods only.

NEWTON ABBOT

Watercress Fishery
Contact: Mr Paul Cook, Kerswell Springs, Chudleigh, Newton Abbot, TQ13 0DW, 01626 862168, kirsty.cook@btinternet.com, *Water:* 3 spring fed lakes totalling approx 5 acres. Alder lake (specimen lake) Tiger, Brown & Rainbow, *Species:* Rainbow, Brown, Tiger trout, *Permits:* On site. No EA rod licence required, *Charges:* Day £20 - 5 fish. £17 - 4 fish. Half day £14 - 3 fish. £11 - 2 fish. Alder lake (specimen lake) 4-fish £30. 3-fish £24. 2-fish £17, *Season:* Open all year, 8am to 1 hour after sunset, *Methods:* Rules on notice board at fishery.

OKEHAMPTON

Meldon
Contact: South West Lakes Trust, 01837 871565, info@swlakestrust.org.uk, *Species:* Brown Trout, *Charges:* Free to holders of a valid Environment Agency Licence, *Season:* 15 March - 12 October, *Methods:* Angling by spinning, fly or bait

Roadford
Contact: South West Lakes Trust, 01837 871565, info@swlakestrust.org.uk, *Water:* Ranger Tel 01409 211514, *Species:* Brown Trout Fishery - Boat & Bank (boats may be booked in advance: 01409 211514), *Permits:* Angling & Watersports Centre at Lower Goodacre, *Charges:* Full day £13, Season £280, Reduced day £11, Season £225, Child/Wheelchair £3, Season £60, Evening Mon-Fri £11. Boats £10 per day, *Season:* Opens 23 March 2002 - 12th October, *Methods:* Fly fishing only. Catch and release operates - Barbless hooks only. No child under 14 years may fish unless accompanied by an adult over 18 years.
Roadford Fly Fishing Club
Contact: Rod Dibble, 25 Pine View, Gunnislake, PL18 9JF, 01822 834188, rodneydibble@hotmail.com, *Water:* Club fishing at Roadford Lake, *Species:* Brown Trout, *Methods:* Fly only

PLYMOUTH

Drakelands
Contact: Mr Elford, Higher Drakelands, Hemerdon, Plympton, Plymouth, 01752 344691, *Water:* 1.75 acre lake, *Species:* Brown Trout, Rainbow Trout, *Charges:* Ticket to fish £3 plus fish @ £1.85/lb, 1/2 day ticket £11 - 4 hrs (2 fish), £14.50 - 6 hrs (3 fish), £18 - 8 hrs (4 fish), £21 - 8 hrs (5 fish), *Season:* Open all year, Tuesday - Sunday, *Methods:* Barbless hooks only.

SEATON

Wiscombe Park Fishery (Trout Lakes)
Contact: Mike Raynor, Wiscombe Park Fishery, Colyton, EX24 6JE, 01404 871474, *Mobile:* 07860 222342, michael@wiscombe.globalnet.co.uk, *Water:* Two half Acre lakes, *Species:* Rainbow Trout, Brown Trout, *Permits:* Self-service (No booking), *Charges:* £17/day (8 fish limit), £12/4hrs (3 fish), £8.50/2 hrs (2 fish), Children u.15 free (accompanied by permit holding adult), *Season:* All year, *Methods:* Fly fishing (singles)

166

SOUTH BRENT

Avon Dam
Contact: South West Lakes Trust, 01837 871565, info@swlakestrust.org.uk, *Species:* Brown Trout, *Charges:* Free to holders of a valid Environment Agency Licence, *Season:* 15 March - 12 October, *Methods:* Angling by spinning, fly or bait.

Hatchlands Trout Lakes
Contact: Malcolm Davies, Greyshoot Lane, Rattery, South Brent, TQ10 9LL, 01364 73500, *Water:* 6 acres, 2 lakes, *Species:* Rainbow, Brown, Golden, Blue and Brook Trout, *Permits:* No EA Permit required, *Charges:* Prices from £10 for 2 fish. Other prices on application. Sporting ticket from £16, Catch and Release £12, *Season:* Open all year, *Methods:* Barbless hooks on catch and release

Somerswood Lake
Contact: S.A. Goodman, Brent Mill Farm, South Brent, TQ10 9JD, 01364 72154, *Water:* 2 acres in Avon valley, *Species:* Rainbow Trout, *Permits:* At farmhouse, *Charges:* Full day £16 for 4 fish, 1/2 day £10 for 2 fish, *Season:* Open all year, *Methods:* Fly

SOUTH MOLTON

Wistlandpound
Contact: South West Lakes Trust, 01837 871565, info@swlakestrust.org.uk, *Water:* Ranger Tel 01288 321262, *Species:* Intermediate Rainbow Trout Fishery. Trout to 6lb, *Permits:* Post Office in Challacombe (01598) 763229, The Kingfisher, Barnstaple, (01271) 344919. Lyndale News, Combe Martin (01271) 862039, Variety Sports, Ilfracombe (01271) 862039, *Charges:* Full day £11, Season £190, Reduced day £10, Season £170, Child/Wheelchair £2, Season £40, *Season:* Opens 15 March - 12th October, *Methods:* Fly fishing only. Catch and release - barbless hooks

TAVISTOCK

Milemead Fisheries (Trout Lake)
Contact: Mr Harry Dickens, Mill Hill, Tavistock, PL19 8NP, 01822 610888, *Water:* 2 acre spring fed lake, max 10 anglers at any one time, *Species:* Rainbow, Blue and Brown Trout from 1.5lb to 10lb plus, *Permits:* Available from lakeside tackle and bait shop, *Charges:* 2 fish - £12. 3 fish - £16. 4 fish - £19. 5 fish - £22, *Season:* Open all year 8.30 am to dusk, *Methods:* Fly fishing only, no catch and release, please read the rule boards.

Tavistock Trout Farm & Fishery
Contact: Abigail Underhill, Parkwood Road, Tavistock, PL19 9JW, 01822 615441, abigail@tavistocktroutfishery.co.uk, *Water:* 5 Lakes totalling approx 4 acres, *Species:* Rainbow Trout, Brown Trout, *Charges:* Full day 4 fish permit - Osprey Lake £34, Full day 4 fish Kingfisher and Heron Lakes £16.50, *Season:* Open all year 8am - dusk, *Methods:* Max hook size 10.

TIVERTON

Bellbrook Valley Trout Fishery
Contact: Mike Pusey, Bellbrook Farm, Oakford, Tiverton, EX16 9EX, 01398 351292, mike_pusey@notes.interliant.com, *Water:* 7 Lakes totalling 6.75 acres, *Species:* Rainbow Trout (25lb 12oz), Goldies (14lb 2oz), Exmoor Blue (8lb 6oz) and Wild Brown Trout (7lb 8oz), *Charges:* Normal lakes from £6 + pay by weight (evening) to specimen lakes £39/day (4 fish), Super specimen tickets from £50. Many other tickets available, *Season:* Open all year 8.00am / dusk (No later than 9.00pm), *Methods:* Fly only, some catch & release available

Bickleigh Mill
Contact: Bickleigh Mill, Bickleigh, Nr Tiverton, EX16 8RG, 01884 855419, general@bickleighmill.freeserve.co.uk, *Water:* Bickleigh Mill fishing ponds, *Species:* Rainbow Trout, *Permits:* Only at above, *Charges:* On request, *Season:* Easter to end of September, *Methods:* Rod supplied

TORRINGTON

Great Torrington Anglers Association (Trout)
Contact: Paul Martin, 67 Calf Street, Torrington, EX38 7BH, 01805 623658, paul@olmargames.fsbusiness.co.uk, *Water:* Fly fishing on local reservoirs and canal fishing, *Permits:* No day tickets sold by club, *Charges:* Annual membership Adult £5-00, Junior £3-00.

TOTNES

Newhouse Fishery
Contact: Adrian Cook, Newhouse Farm, Moreleigh, Totnes, 01548 821426, *Water:* 4 Acre lake, *Species:* Rainbow Trout, Brown Trout, *Permits:* No EA rod licence required, *Charges:* 5 Fish £20, 4 Fish £17, 3 Fish £14, 2 Fish £11, *Season:* Open all year, *Methods:* Fly only, Barbed hooks

YELVERTON

Burrator
Contact: South West Lakes Trust, 01837 871565, info@swlakestrust.org.uk, *Species:* Low Cost Rainbow & Brown Trout, *Permits:* Esso Garage, Yelverton, *Charges:* Full day £9.25, Season £120, Reduced day £7.25, Season £90, Child/Wheelchair £2, Season £30, *Season:* Opens 15 March 2001 - 12th October, *Methods:* Catch & Release operates. Barbless hooks only.

DORSET River Fishing

THE 'HAMPSHIRE' AVON

For detailed description of the Hampshire Avon and tributaries, see under Hampshire River fishing.

RIVER AVON PEWSEY - CHRISTCHURCH

Fisheries located between Pewsey and Salisbury are predominantly managed for Brown Trout fly fishing. A mixture of Coarse, Salmon and Trout fishing is available on the main river between Salisbury and Christchurch.

Christchurch Angling Club (Game)
Contact: S. Richards, 15 Roeshot Crescent, Highcliffe, BH23 4QH, 01425 279710, steve@christchurchanglingclub.fsnet.co.uk, *Water:* Largest club on the river Avon, mainly mid/lower Avon, Burgate-Christchurch, also Fishing on River Stour between Gains Cross and Christchurch. Stillwater Coarse fishing at Cranebrook. Various other stillwaters. Sea Trout at Christchurch Harbour. Please telephone the secretary for full details, *Species:* Salmon, Sea Trout, Rainbow Trout & Brown Trout, *Permits:* Direct from local Tackle shops, *Charges:* Adult £110, Junior £45, Concession £65, *Season:* Rainbow Trout all year round. Brown Trout: 1st April to 15th October; Salmon 1st Feb. to 31st Aug, Sea Trout 1st July 31st Oct, *Methods:* See rules for individual waters

Royalty Fishery
Contact: Davis Tackle, 75 Bargates, Christchurch, 01202 485169, davis@bonefishadventure.com, *Water:* Approx 1 mile of double bank fishing. Lowest beat on the river. Controlled by Christchurch Angling Club., *Species:* Roach 3lb, Chub 8lb, Dace 1lb, Barbel 14lb, Pike 38lb, Bream 11lb, Perch 4lb, Carp 31lb, Tench 7lb, Salmon 40lb, Sea Trout 15lb, *Permits:* Tickets available from Davis Tackle only, *Charges:* Tel: 01202 485169. Free for Christchurch Angling Club members. Day tickets from £6, *Season:* Coarse:16th July-14th March. Sea Trout 15th April-15th October. Salmon February 1st-31st August, *Methods:* No spinning, No night fishing. No Barbel, Carp or game fish to be kept in keepnets.

Winkton Fishery
Contact: Davis Tackle, 75 Bargates, Christchurch, BH23 1QE, 01202 485169, davis@bonefishadventure.com, *Water:* Approx 1 mile of fishing. Lower river near Christchurch, *Species:* Roach to 3lb 10oz, Chub to 6lb, Dace to 1lb, Barbel 13lb, Pike to 30lb, Perch to 3lb, *Permits:* Davis Tackle only as above, *Charges:* £7 per day (2 roads, coarse only), Block bookings for clubs available. Please call 01202 485169, *Season:* June 16 - March 14, 7am to 2 hours after sunset, *Methods:* No spinning. Coarse only: No Barbel or game fish to be placed in keepnets.

FROME

The Frome rises through chalk on the North Dorset Downs near Evershot, and flows south through Dorchester, and finally Wareham, where it confluences with the River Piddle in Poole harbour. The River Frome is well known for its excellent Salmon, Brown Trout and Grayling fishing. There are also good numbers of coarse fish in certain areas; although access is limited sport can be very rewarding. Salmon and Trout fishing is generally controlled by syndicates and local estates.

Frome, Piddle & West Dorset Fishery Association
Contact: R.J. Slocock, 01929 471274, *Water:* An amalgamation of of riparian owners with an interest in the welfare of river fisheries in their locality. Information can be obtained concerning estate waters from the contact above.

Dorchester Fishing Club
Contact: Mr J.Grindle (Hon. Sec.), 36 Cowleaze, Martinstown, DT2 9TD, 01305 889682, *Mobile:* 07810 555316, john@36cowleaze.freeserve.co.uk, *Water:* Approx 6.5 miles of double bank on the Frome near Dorchester, Brown trout fly fishing, *Species:* Brown trout, Grayling, *Permits:* John Aplin, Dorchester (01305) 266500. Web site, *Charges:* Day tickets and membership available. Please telephone John Aplin for day tickets and John Grindle for membership details, *Season:* April 1st - Oct 14th, *Methods:* Dry fly and Nymph only. Barbless hooks are encouraged.

River Frome (Town Section)
Contact: Purbeck Angling Centre / Deano, 01929 550770, *Water:* One mile stretch of the River Frome, *Species:* Roach, Dace, Grayling, Eels, Pike, Salmon, Trout, Sea Trout, Mullet, Bass, Flounder, Carp and Perch, *Permits:* Enquiries to Purbeck Angling Centre, *Charges:* Free fishing on public section. Enquiries to Purbeck Angling Centre, *Season:* Normal closed seasons apply.

Wessex Fly Fishing & Chalk Streams Ltd. (Frome)
Contact: 01305 848460, sally.slocock@virgin.net, *Water:* See entry under Piddle, *Charges:* from £19 to £65.

PIDDLE AND WEST DORSET STREAMS

'West Dorset' streams include the River Brit, Asker, Bride and Char. These streams are relatively short, 'steep' water courses supporting populations of mainly Brown Trout and Sea Trout. The River Piddle rises at four major springs near Alton St. Pancras, initially flowing south before turning east at Puddletown towards Poole Harbour, where it confluences with the River Frome. This is a relatively small river known primarily for its Salmon, Brown Trout and Sea Trout. Other fish species can be found in the River Piddle including, Roach, Dace, Pike and Perch. Much of the fishing is controlled by local syndicates and estate waters; further information about these groups can be obtained from the aforementioned Frome, Piddle and West Dorset Fishery Association.

Environment Agency - Piddle Fishery
Contact: Conservation Officer, Environment Agency, Rivers House, Sunrise Business Park, Blandford Forum, DT11 8ST, 01258 456080, *Water:* 3km of bank fishing on Lower Piddle, *Species:* Salmon & Sea Trout, *Permits:* 14 permits per annum, *Charges:* £199 plus vat (£34.82), subject to annual review.
Manor of Wareham
Contact: Guy Ryder, The Estate Office, Manor of Wareham, Cow Lane, Wareham, BH20 4RD, 01929 552666, *Water:* Stretch on river Piddle single bank fishing, *Species:* Brown Trout and Sea trout, *Charges:* Season tickets only. Price on application, *Season:* EA byelaws, *Methods:* EA byelaws
Wessex Fly Fishing & Chalk Streams Ltd. (Piddle)
Contact: Richard Slocock, Lawrences Farm, Tolpuddle, Dorchester, DT2 7HF, 01305 848460, sally.slocock@virgin.net, *Water:* 5 Lakes & Pools totalling 4 acres for Rainbow Trout. Plus 16 Beats on Rivers Piddle & Frome for Brown Trout, *Permits:* At above address, *Charges:* Rivers: Minimum £19 day, Max £65, *Season:* Rivers: April 1st to October 15th. Lakes 1st March to 30th November, *Methods:* Fly Fishing only, Most river beats are catch & release using barbless hooks.

STOUR

The River Stour in Dorset is well known by anglers across the country for quality of its fishing. Over the years many British record captures have been made here, for example the current Roach record stands at 4lb 3oz, taken from the Stour near Wimborne.
The Stour rises on the Greensand at St. Peters Pump in Stourhead Gardens and flows through Gillingham near by where it is joined by the Shreen Water and the River Lodden. The Stour stretches out for 96 km, passing through the Blackmoor Vale down to the sea at Christchurch; the total fall over this distance is approximately 230m. Other notable tributaries along its length include the River Tarrant confluencing near Spetisbury, the River Allen at Wimborne and the Moors River coming in near Christchurch. The Stour confluences with the River Avon at the 'Clay Pool' in Christchurch, before flowing into the harbour area and ultimately out into the English Channel.

Blandford & District Angling Club
Contact: Peter Brundish, 10 Windmill Road, Blandford Forum, DT11 7HG, 01258 453545, *Water:* 4 miles of Dorset Stour (Crown Meadows and Nutford), *Species:* Roach to 1.5lb, Bream to 8lb 10oz, Perch to 3lb 2oz, Carp to 17lb, Chub, Pike to 25lb, *Permits:* Conyers Tackle Shop, Market Place, Blandford Tel 01258 452307. Todber Manor Fishing Tackle Shop, Tel: 01258 820384. Or from the secretary, *Charges:* Senior £27.50, O.A.P. £16.50, Junior £8.50, Day tickets £4. Please enquire for family membership, *Season:* Normal coarse season, *Methods:* Boilies can be used in small amounts.

Dorchester & District Angling Society

Contact: W. Lucy, Secretary, 7 Celtic Crescent, Dorchester, DT1 2QJ, 01305 264873, *Water:* 4 miles on Dorset Stour, 1.5 miles Dorset Frome plus lakes at Kingcombe and West Knighton. R. Brue Somerset plus water sharing agreements and Federation waters on Somerset Levels, *Species:* Roach, Dace, Chub, Pike, Gudgeon, Perch, Eels, Carp, Bream, Grayling, *Permits:* Anglers Tackle Store, Weymouth, Aplins Tackle Dorchester, Weymouth Angling Centre, Surplus International, Dorchester, *Charges:* Prices under review for 2002. Members guest tickets, no day tickets, half-year membership from December 1, *Season:* June 16th - March 14th, Stillwater open all year, *Methods:* Various, specific to particular waters.

Durweston Angling Association
Contact: Mr Vernon Bell (secretary), Endcote, Durweston, 01258 451317, *Water:* 2 miles River Stour (including Weir & Mill Pool), *Species:* Bream, Roach, Rudd, Gudgeon, Dace, Eels, Chub, Pike, Perch, *Permits:* The White Horse Public House, Stour Paine. The Mill House, Durweston (after 9 a.m.), *Charges:* Day tickets: £3, River permit £27.50/adult, £16/youth, Charges may change in 2002, *Season:* Close season 14th March - 16th June.
Gillingham & District A A (Stour)
Contact: Simon Hebditch (Hon. Secretary), 5 Ham Court, Shaftsbury Rd, Gillingham, SP8 4LU, 01747 824817, *Mobile:* 07990 690613, ditch@ham5.fsnet.co.uk, *Water:* 7 miles Upper Stour - Gillingham to Marnhull. Also Turners Paddock lake at Stourhead. Mappowder Court 4 lakes at Mappowder, *Species:* Roach 3lb, Chub 4lb 8oz, Barbel 6lb, Pike 21lb, Dace 1lb, Bream 6lb, Gudgeon 3oz, Perch 3lb, Tench 3lb, Carp 10lb, Eels 4lb. Trout, Grayling 2lb 8oz, *Permits:* Mr P Stone (Treasurer) The Timepiece, Newbury, Gillingham, Dorset, SP8 4HZ. Tel: 01747 823339. Mr J Candy, Todber Manor Fisheries Shop, Tel: 01258 820384, *Charges:* £4 day ticket, £22 Season ticket. £11 Juniors and concessions. (probable charges for 2002), *Season:* June 16 to March 14, *Methods:* Best stick float with maggot casters and bread. Large lump of bread for Chub.

Muscliffe & Longham
Contact: Ivor Brittain, Bournemouth, 01202 514345, ivorbri@ntlworld.com, *Water:* 1.5 miles river Stour at Muscliffe and quarter mile at Longham, *Species:* Chub, Barbel, Roach, Dace, Pike, Eels, Minnow, Gudgeon and Perch, *Permits:* Free (owned by Bournemouth Council), *Charges:* Free. E.A. licence required, *Season:* 16th June to 14th March, *Methods:* No restrictions.

Ringwood & District Angling Club (Stour)
Contact: Mr Les Aves, 60 Station Road, Alderholt, Fordingbridge, SP6 3AL, 01425 656245, *Mobile:* 07973 729959, lesaves@barbel4.freeserve.co.uk, *Water:* 11 stretches on Stour including total control of Throop fishery and various stretches upstream to Stourpaine, *Species:* Throop - Barbel to 14lb, Chub 7lb. Middle regions good general Roach, Chub, Bream, Pike, Perch, some Trout, Grayling and Carp, *Permits:* As above and local tackle shops, *Charges:* Adult £90, Junior £40, concessions for OAP's and disabled; Throop day tickets £7.50. Concessions, O.A.P.'s, Disabled and Juniors available from local tackle dealers, *Season:* As per coarse season, *Methods:* All on reverse of ticket.

Stalbridge Angling Association (Stour)
Contact: 01963 362291, *Water:* 2.5 miles Stour, 3 Lakes (Buckland Newton), *Species:* Bream, Tench, Roach, Dace, Pike, Chub, Carp, Rudd, *Permits:* Stalbridge Angling 01963 362291, *Charges:* Senior Annual £20 no joining fee, Junior (under 17 years) & senior citizens £8 no joining fee. Husband and wife ticket £30, Reg Disabled/OAP's £8. Day Tickets £4 senior, £2 junior, *Season:* No closed season on Lakes, *Methods:* No boilies on ponds, no braided lines, no fixed method feeders or fixed leads. Full rules available with permit.

Sturminster & Hinton A.A
Contact: S. Dimmer, 38 Grosvenor Rd, Stalbridge, DT10 2PN, 01258 472788 or 01963 363291, steve@dimmer.freeserve.co.uk, *Water:* 14 miles mid River Stour, 3 small lakes (Stoke Wake Lake & High Bench Lake) members only, *Species:* Roach, Chub, Tench, Bream, Perch, Carp, Pike, *Permits:* Harts Garden Supplies, Kevs Autos or S. Dimmer (Membership Secretary) 01963 363291(evenings), *Charges:* £4/day, £10/week, Juniors £3/season, Adults £17.50 + £5 joining fee, *Season:* March 14th - June 16th, *Methods:* No dogs, Radios, No live baiting, No night fishing, One rod, second rod for Pike only.

Throop Fisheries
Contact: Ringwood Angling Club, *Water:* See entry under Coarse Fisheries - Bournemouth. 10 miles on Dorset Stour.

Wareham & District Angling Society
Contact: Mr. Abrams, 114 Portland Rd, Weymouth, 01305 783145, denning_tackle@yahoo.co.uk, *Water:* River waters on North Dorset Stour and the Frome. 3 lakes Wareham area, *Species:* Coarse, *Permits:* Wessex Angling, Poole, Dorset Tel: 01202 668244; Dennings Tackle, Wyke Regis, *Charges:* Senior £35, Ladies / O.A.P's £16, Junior £15. Membership runs from June 1st to May 31st, *Season:* One lake open during Coarse closed season, *Methods:* Barbless, No litter, No cans, Variations as per membership book

Wimborne & District Angling Club (Stour)
Contact: G.E.Pipet (chairman), 12 Seatown Close, Canford Heath, Poole, BH17 8BJ, 01202 382123, *Water:* 10 miles River Stour, 16 lakes, 1 mile River Avon, *Species:* Trout & Coarse Fisheries, *Permits:* Certain waters are available on Guest Tickets £6 from Wessex Angling Centre, 321 Wimborne Rd, Oakdale, Poole, Dorset, *Charges:* £70 plus £8 joining fees, *Methods:* Barbless hooks on Coarse stillwaters, No floating baits.

Dorset Stillwater Coarse

BOURNEMOUTH
East Moors Lake
Contact: Mr. Nicolas Hoare, East Moors Farm, East Moors Lane, St. Leonards, Ferndale, Nr Bournemouth, 01202 872302, *Water:* 1.5 acre lake, *Species:* Carp: common, mirror, ghost, leather, purple blushing; Tench, Gold Tench, Roach, Perch, Rudd, Chub & Pike, *Charges:* Members only, Country/ Holiday membership available - Please telephone for details, *Methods:* Barbless hooks only, no boilies, no keepnets, no dogs. Children under 14 must be accompanied by an adult

Throop Fisheries (Coarse Lake)
Contact: Ringwood Angling Club, *Water:* Northern edge of Bournemouth. 10 Miles of river bank on Dorset Stour & Stillwater Mill Pool., *Species:* Barbel, Chub, Carp, Roach, Tench, Perch, Dace, Pike, *Permits:* Yeovil Angling Centre - Tel. 01935 476777, Ringwood Tackle - Tel. 01425 475155, Bournemouth Fishing Lodge - Tel. 01202 514345, *Charges:* Prices on application & list, *Season:* 16th June - 14 March (Open every day between these dates), *Methods:* No night fishing.

BRIDPORT
Mangerton Valley Coarse Fishing Lake
Contact: Clive & Jane Greening, New House Farm, Mangerton Lane, Bradpole, Bridport, DT6 3SF, 01308 458482, jane@mangertonlake.freeserve.co.uk, *Water:* 1.6 acre lake, *Species:* Carp to 20lb (Common and Mirror), Roach, Tench, Bream, *Permits:* From Post Office, *Charges:* £5 day, £3 half day, £2 evening, *Season:* Possibly closed March-April-May (please ring first), *Methods:* Barbless hooks. No boilies or beans. No nuts, No dogs. Night fishing by arrangement. All chidren under 12 to be accompanied by an adult

CHRISTCHURCH

Avon Tyrrell Lakes

Contact: Richard Bonney, Avon Tyrrell House, Bransgore, Christchurch, BH23 8EE, 01425 672347, info@avontyrrell.org.uk, *Water:* Two lakes totalling approx 2.5 acres, *Species:* Carp, Tench, Roach, Bream, Perch and Rudd, *Permits:* On site from reception, *Charges:* £5 Day Tickets Adults. £2.50 Juniors(Under 16).Season Tickets also available, please note Night Fishing only available on a season ticket, *Season:* Open mid June to Mid March 8am to 8pm, *Methods:* Barbless Hooks, No keepnets, No nut baits. See rules on site

Christchurch Angling Club (Coarse Ponds)

Contact: S. Richards, 15 Roeshot Crescent, Highcliffe, Christchurch, BH23 4QH, 01425 279710, steve@christchurchanglingclub.fsnet.co.uk, *Water:* Various coarse ponds including Blashford and Ivy Lakes and Cranebrook. Please telephone the secretary for full details. See entry under Hampshire Avon, *Methods:* See rules for individual waters

Hordle Lakes

Contact: M.F. Smith, Hordle Lakes, Golden Hill, Ashley Lane, Hordle, Nr New Milton, 01590 672300, *Mobile:* 07778 954799, *Water:* Seven spring fed lakes set in 11 acres, *Species:* Double figure Carp. Tench, Roach, Rudd, Bream and Perch, *Permits:* At the fishery, *Charges:* Adults £7 per day. OAPs £5. Kiddies pool £3, *Season:* Open all year 8am to dusk, *Methods:* All fish to be returned immediately. No groundbaiting, loose feeding only. Barbless hooks only, no larger than size 6. No Boilies, beans, nuts, trout bait or floating crust/biscuit. Full rules at the fishery.

Mudeford Wood Angling Club

Contact: 27 Hurn Road, Christchurch, BH23 2RJ, 01202 484518, *Water:* Contact Loni's Angling Ctre (Christchurch).Half acre lake, *Species:* Carp, Tench, Roach, Rudd, *Permits:* Loni's Angling Ctre (Christchurch), Barrack Road, Christchurch. Limit of 3 day tickets per day, *Charges:* £5 per rod per day, *Season:* Closed 31st March 2002 - 1st June 2002, fishing from 7am till one hour after sunset, *Methods:* Barbless hooks only, no boilies, no keepnets.

Orchard Lakes

Contact: Mr R Southcombe, New Lane, Bashley, New Milton, BH25 5TD, 01425 612404, *Water:* 3 small lakes, largest 2 acres, *Species:* Carp, Tench, Bream, Roach, Rudd, Perch, *Permits:* Day tickets on the bank, *Charges:* From £5/ day main & Tench lake; £4 on Match Pool, *Season:* Open all year 7am to dusk, *Methods:* Barbless hooks only. No keepnets

Sopley Farm PYO

Contact: Sopley Farm PYO, Sopley, Christchurch, 01425 672451, *Water:* 8 acre lake. 1000 yard perimeter, *Species:* Carp, Bream, Roach, Rudd, *Permits:* At each PYO Farm Shop, *Charges:* £40 Season. £5 Day. £3 Half Day. £3 day OAP and u14, *Season:* June to October when PYO's are open. 9.30am to 6.30pm, *Methods:* Barbless Hooks, No keepnets

Whirlwind Lake

Contact: Mr & Mrs Pillinger, Whirlwind Rise, Dudmore Lane, Christchurch, BH23 6BQ, 01202 475255, *Water:* Secluded lake, *Species:* Common, Crucian and Mirror Carp, Roach, Rudd, Tench, Chub etc, *Permits:* On site and local fishing tackle shops. Davis Tackle, 75 The Bargates, Christchurch 01202 485169. Pro Tackle, 258 Barrack Road, Christchurch 01202 484518. Advanced booking advisable, limited number available, *Charges:* Adults £7.50 day ticket. £5 half day (Limited places). Children (must be accompanied) £5 day, £2.50 half day, *Season:* Open all year, *Methods:* Barbless hooks only. No keepnets, No boilies.

CORFE

Arfleet Lakes

Contact: Rempstone Fisheries, 01929 424721, fishing@rempstone.com, *Water:* 1 acre spring fed lake, *Species:* Carp to 27lb, Roach, Rudd, *Permits:* Local Tackle shops or on Telephone number above, *Charges:* £6.50 day - 2 rods, Concession children under 12, *Season:* Opens April 1st 2002. Night fishing by arrangement only, *Methods:* No Trout pellets, no keepnets, barbless hooks only.

CRANBORNE

Gold Oak Fishery

Contact: Mr J Butler, Gold Oak Farm, Hare Lane, Cranborne, 01725 517275, *Water:* 7 small lakes, *Species:* Carp to 20lb, Green + Golden Tench to 5-6lb, Perch 2.5lb, Roach 2lb, Chub 3lb, Bream 3lb, *Permits: Charges:* Summer day - £7 Adult, £5 Junior. 1/2 day - £5 Adult, £3 Junior. Eve - £3 Adult, £1 Junior. Winter day - £5 Adult, £3 Junior. 1/2 day - £3 Adult, £2 junior, *Season:* All year, *Methods:* No large fish in keepnets, Barbless hooks, Dogs on lead.

Martins Farm Fishery

Contact: Mr Ball, Martins Farm, Woodlands, Nr Verwood, 01202 822335, *Water:* 2.5 acre spring fed lake, *Species:* Carp, Tench, Perch, Roach, Rudd, *Permits:* Tel: 01202 822335, *Charges:* £6 Adult day ticket, £3 Juniors, *Season:* Closed 16th March - 16th June, *Methods:* No keepnets, barbless hooks, No hemp/boilies.

Wimborne & District Angling Club (Coarse Lakes)

Contact: G.E.Pipet (chairman), 12 Seatown Close, Canford Heath, Poole, BH17 8BJ, 01202 382123, *Water:* 11 coarse lakes, 10 miles river Stour, 1 mile river Avon. 5 trout lakes. See also entry under Stour, *Species:* Mixed Coarse, *Permits:* Certain waters are available on guest tickets. £6 from Wessex Angling, 321 Wimborne Rd, Oakdale, Poole, *Charges:* £70 plus £8 joining fees, *Methods:* Barbless hooks on coarse stillwaters. No floating baits.

DORCHESTER

Dorchester & Dist. Angling Society (Coarse Lake)

Contact: W. Lucy, Secretary, 01305 264873, *Water:* See entry under Stour. Coarse lakes at Kingcombe and West Knighton, *Species:* Carp, Tench, Perch and Roach, *Season:* Lakes open all year, *Methods:* Barbless hooks only. No boilies or bivvies on lakes.

Gillingham & District A A (Mappowder Court)
Contact: Simon Hebditch (Hon. Secretary), 01747 824817, *Mobile:* 07990 690613, ditch@ham5.fsnet.co.uk, *Water:* Mappowder Court Fishing Complex (4 lakes), Mappowder Nr Dorchester. (see also entry under river fishing Stour), *Species:* Crucian/Crucian cross 2lb, Carp 22lb, Tench 4lb, Eels 3lb, Roach 2lb, Rudd 1lb, Gudgeon, Perch 2lb, Bream 3lb, Barbel 1lb, Grass Carp 8lb, *Permits:* Mr P Stone (Treasurer) The Timepiece, Newbury, Gillingham, Dorset, SP8 4HZ. Tel: 01747 823339. Mr J Candy, Todber Manor Fisheries Shop, Tel: 01258 820384. Kings Stag Garage, Kings Stag, Nr Hazelbury Bryan, *Charges:* £4 day ticket, £22 Season ticket. £11 Juniors and concessions. (probable charges for 2002), *Season:* Open all year, *Methods:* Barbless hooks. Mainly pole fishing.

Hermitage Lakes (Coarse)
Contact: Nigel Richardson, Common Farm, Hermitage, Cerne Abbas, Dorchester, DT2 7BB, 01963 210556, *Water:* Half acre lake, *Species:* Carp, *Charges:* Day ticket £4, *Season:* Closed 14th March - 16th June, *Methods:* Barbless hooks, No keepnets.

Luckfield Lake Fishery
Contact: John Aplin, 1 Athelstan Road, Dorchester, DT1 1NR, 01305 266500, *Water:* 1.5 acre clay pit in beautiful surroundings, *Species:* Carp - 23lb, Tench - 9lb+, Roach - 3lb+, *Permits:* As above, *Charges:* Day £5, Night £6, 1/2 season £30, Full season £60, *Season:* 16th June - 14th March, *Methods:* No keepnets, Barbless hooks.

Lyons Gate Fishing Lakes
Contact: Lyons Gate, Nr Cerne Abbas, Dorchester, DT2 7AZ, 01300 345260, *Water:* Five lakes totalling approximately 3.5 acres, *Species:* Top lake: Carp to approx 20lb, Roach and Rudd. Carp only lake. Bream and Stugeon lake. Three island lake with Carp, Roach, Rudd and Tench, *Charges:* £4 per day (2 rods), *Season:* Open all year dawn to dusk, *Methods:* No night fishing, Barbless hooks only. No groundbaiting - loose feed only. Full details at the fishery.

Pallington Lakes
Contact: Mr Simon or Mrs Tini Pomeroy, Pallington, Dorchester, DT2 8QU, 01305 848141, pallatrax@aol.com, *Water:* 3 lakes and a stretch of the river Frome, *Species:* Lakes: Carp to 33lb, Tench to 12lb 3oz, Perch to 4lb 13oz, Grayling to 3lb 4oz, Roach, Bream, Chub, Rudd, *Permits:* As above, *Charges:* Lakes: Day £7, Evening £4, 24 hours £13. Juniors half price. Extra charge for third rod. River by arrangement, *Season:* All year round. Ticket office open daily 8 to 10am and 4 to 5pm. Otherwise fishing by appointment only, *Methods:* Barbless hooks, No keepnets. No nut baits. All anglers must be in possesion of a fish antiseptic. All Carp anglers must have min. 36 landing net and unhooking mat

GILLINGHAM

Culvers Farm Fishery
Contact: V.J. Pitman, Culvers Farm, Gillingham, SP8 5DS, 01747 822466, *Water:* One 1.5 acre lake. One 3 acre lake, *Species:* Carp, Bream, Roach and Tench, *Permits:* *Charges:* Day £5. Half Day £3. OAP's and under 16 £3 all day, *Season:* Open all year. No night fishing, *Methods:* Barbless hooks only. No Boilies. No keepnets allowed on Middle Mead. Lower Mead - keepnets permitted

LYME REGIS

Wood Farm Caravan Park
Contact: Jane Pointing, Axminster Road, Charmouth, DT6 6BT, 01297 560697, holidays@woodfarm.co.uk, *Water:* 2 ponds totalling approx 1 acre, *Species:* Carp, Rudd, Roach, Tench & Perch, *Permits:* Rod Licences sold, *Charges:* £3.30 day ticket. £13.50 week. £29 season, *Season:* All year, *Methods:* No boilies, keepnets. Barbless hooks only

STALBRIDGE

Stalbridge Angling Association (Coarse Lake)
Contact: 01963 362291, *Water:* See also entry under Stour. Buckland Newton Lakes - 3 lakes.

STURMINSTER NEWTON

Sturminster & Hinton A.A (Coarse Lakes)
*Contact:*steve@dimmer.freeserve.co.uk, *Water:* See entry under Stour. 3 small lakes (Stoke Wake Lake & High Bench Lake) members only.

Todber Manor Fisheries
Contact: John Candy, Manor Farm, Todber, Sturminster Newton, DT10 1JB, 01258 820384, *Mobile:* 07974 420813, *Water:* Two acre canal style lake; one acre Specimen Lake; 2x 1 acre small Carp lakes & other species i.e. Roach, Tench, Rudd, *Species:* Roach, Skimmers, Tench, Gudgeon, Crucians, Perch and Barbel. Specimen Lake Carp 20lb plus, *Permits:* As above, *Charges:* £4 per day. Specimen Lake £20 for 24 hours, *Season:* Open all year, *Methods:* Barbless hooks only. No keepnets on specimen lake

WAREHAM

Wareham & District Angling Society (Coarse Lakes)
Contact: denning_tackle@yahoo.co.uk, *Water:* See entry under Stour - 3 lakes including Breach Pond.

WEYMOUTH

Osmington Mills Holidays
Contact: Reception, Osmington Mills, Weymouth, DT3 6HB, 01305 832311, holidays@osmingtonmills.fsnet.co.uk, *Water:* 1 Acre Lake, *Species:* Carp, Tench, Bream, Roach, *Permits:* Caravan Park reception, On bank, *Charges:* £6 per day Adults, £3 under 16, £3.50 Evening ticket after 5pm, *Season:* May 23rd - March 15th, *Methods:* Barbless hooks, No keepnets, No particle bait.

Radipole Lake
Contact: Mr D.Tattersall, Council Offices, North Quay, Weymouth, DT4 8TA, 01305 206234, *Mobile:* 07980 730069, davidtattersall@wpbc.weymouth.gov.uk, *Water:* 70 acres plus, *Species:* Carp to 20lb, Eels, Roach to 2lb, Dace, Pike, Mullet, *Permits:* Anglers Tackle Store, 64 Park Street, Weymouth, 01305 782624. Weymouth Angling Centre, 24 Trinity Road, Weymouth 01305 777771, *Charges:* Day - Junior £2, Adult £4, 60+ £3; Monthly - Juniors £5, Adult £16, 60+ £10; Annual - Adult £35, 60+ £25, Junior £11, *Season:* 16th June - 14th March, *Methods:* 2 Rod max, Barbless hooks only, No bivvies

Warmwell Holiday Park
Contact: John Aplin - Fishery Manager, Warmwell, Nr Weymouth, DT2 8JE, 01305 257490 or 0589 680464, *Water:* 3 lakes. 2 acre specimen lake - 20 swims pre-booking only. 2 mixed fishing lakes, *Species:* Carp to 40lb. Perch to 4lb, Rudd, Crucians, Eels, *Permits:* Very limited winter day tickets available from fishery manager on number above, *Charges:* Day tickets £20 for 12 hours, dawn to dusk, *Season:* Winter season dawn to dusk, *Methods:* Barbless hooks. No nuts, beans or pulses. 2 rods max. No keepnets. No remote control boats. Unhooking mats must be used. Minimum 10lb line.

WIMBORNE
Crooked Willows Farm
Contact: Mr & Mrs VJ Percy, Mannington, Wimborne, BH21 7LB, 01202 825628, *Water:* 1.5 acres, *Species:* Carp to 20lb, Tench to 6lb, Chub 4lb, Roach, Rudd + Crucians, *Permits:* Available on bank, *Charges:* £4/day, Juniors £2, *Season:* Dawn to Dusk all year round, *Methods:* Barbless hooks only, no groundbait, NO keepnets

Environment Agency - Little Canford Ponds
Contact: Conservation Officer, Environment Agency, Rivers House, Sunrise Business Park, Blandford Forum, DT11 8ST, 01258 456080, *Water:* Approx. 2 acres, *Species:* Carp, Bream, Roach, Perch Tench, Rudd, Pike, *Charges:* Adult £42, Conc. £21, Junior £21, under 12 years free (subject to annual review).

Whitemoor Lake
Contact: 400 Colehill Lane, Colehill, Wimborne, BH21 7AW, 01202 884478, *Water:* 2 Acre lake and half acre canal, *Species:* Carp 25lb, Tench 7lb, Perch 4-9lbs, Roach 2lb, Rudd 1-8lbs, *Permits:* Minster Sports (Wimborne), Bournemouth Fishing Lodge (Bournemouth), *Charges:* Adults £6-00, Juniors £3-50, O.A.P.'s £4-00, *Season:* No close season, *Methods:* No barbed hooks, No keepnets

Dorset Stillwater Trout

BRIDPORT
Mangerton Mill
Contact: Mr Harris, Mangerton Mill, Mangerton, Bridport, DT6 3SG, 01308 485224, *Water:* 1 Acre lake, *Species:* Rainbow Trout, *Permits:* Post Office, *Season:* 1st April - 31st December, *Methods:* Max hook size 10

CRANBORNE
Wimborne & District Angling Club (Trout Lakes)
Contact: Mr J Burden, 35 Hardy Crescent, Wimborne, BH21 2AR, 01202 889324, *Water:* 5 Trout lakes plus Brown Trout on the river Avon. See also entry under Stour, *Charges:* £70 plus £8 joining fees.

DORCHESTER
Flowers Farm Fly Fishers
Contact: Alan.J.Bastone, Flowers Farm, Hilfield, Dorchester, DT2 7BA, 01300 341351, *Water:* 5 lakes total 3.75 acres, *Species:* Rainbow & Brown trout. Best fish in 2001 - 11lb Rainbow and 5lb Brown, *Permits:* Some 25 and 50 fish tickets available. Prices on request (tel/fax: 01300-341351), *Charges:* £20 per day, £15 half day, £11.50 evening, *Season:* Open all year 5.30am to dusk, *Methods:* Single fly, Max size 10, Bank fishing only.

Hermitage Lakes (Trout)
Contact: Nigel Richardson, Common Farm, Hermitage, Cerne Abbas, Dorchester, DT2 7BB, 01963 210556, *Water:* 3 half acre lakes, *Species:* Rainbow & Brown trout, *Charges:* Day (4 fish) £15, Half day (3 fish) £12, Evening (2 fish) £9, *Season:* Open all season, *Methods:* Max size 10 longshank.

Wessex Fly Fish. Trout Lakes & Chalk Streams Ltd.
Contact: 01305 848460, sally.slocock@virgin.net, *Water:* See entries under Piddle and Frome. 5 clearwater lakes and pools totalling 4 acres, *Charges:* Lakes: Day £26, £22/6hrs, £18/4hrs, £15/evening, conc. £16, *Season:* Lakes: March 1st - November 30th, *Methods:*

LYME REGIS
Amherst Lodge
Contact: Darren Herbert or B. Stansfield, Amherst Lodge, Uplyme, Lyme Regis, DT7 3XH, 01297 442773, *Mobile:* 07765 817206, *Water:* 6 stream fed Trout lakes totalling 4 acres, *Species:* Rainbow to 8lb. Brown Trout to 6lb (catch and release only), *Permits:* Go to rod room on arrival, *Charges:* From £13 for two fish bag. Catch & release £15 day. £11 half day. £8 evening, *Season:* Open all year 9am to dusk. Must book if arriving before 9am, *Methods:* Traditional fly fishing only.

WIMBORNE
Whitesheet Trout Lakes
Contact: Christchurch Angling Club, 01425 279710, steve@christchurchanglingclub.fsnet.co.uk, *Water:* 3 lakes totalling 7 acres. See Christchurch Angling Club main entry under River Avon, Hampshire, *Species:* Rainbow + Brown Trout, *Permits:* On site, *Season:* Open all year dawn to dusk, *Methods:* Fly only.

GLOUCS Stillwater Coarse

CIRENCESTER

Swindon Isis Angling Club Lake No1
Contact: Peter Gilbert, 31 Havelock St, Swindon, SN1 1SD, 01793 535396, *Water:* 6 acre mature gravel pit at Cotswold Water Park (Water Park Lake 19), South Cerney, Cirencester, *Species:* Tench (9lb) lake with Carp to 30lb, Rudd to 2lb12oz, odd big Bream, usual Roach and Perch + good Pike, *Permits:* Tackle shops in Swindon, Cirencester, Chippenham and Calne, *Charges:* Club Permits: Senior £34.50. OAP and disabled £12. Juniors £8. The club permit contains two free day tickets and more day tickets can be obtained for £5 each; year starts 1 April, *Season:* Open all year round. Club cards start 1st April, *Methods:* No bans

FAIRFORD

Milestone Fisheries (Coarse)
Contact: Sue or Bob Fletcher or Andy King, London Road, Fairford, GL7 4DS, 01285 713908, *Water:* 3.5 acre mixed coarse lake. 56 acre Pike lake, *Species:* Well stocked with Carp 26lb, Tench 9.5lb, Bream 11lb, Roach 3.5lb, Rudd, Perch 4.5lb. Separate 56 acre Pike lake 33lb, *Permits:* Day tickets available from fishery office - above address (also fax: 01285-711113), *Charges:* £5.00 per day (2 rods) Junior £3.00 per day, £8 day & night. Pike lake - Day ticket £8, Night ticket £8, day & night ticket £13, *Season:* No closed season, open every day except Dec 25th. Night fishing by arrangement. Pike lake Open from 1st October to end of April, *Methods:* No keepnets, no dogs, barbless hooks only. Pike lake - Barbless & semi - barbless hooks, Minimum of 12lb b.s. line. Traces min 18lbs, 36 soft mesh landing net, unhooking mat, strong wire cutters.

GLOUCESTER

Huntley Carp Pools
Contact: John Tipper - Frank Morris, 14 Thoresby Ave, Tuffley, Gloucester, GL4 0TE, 01452 505313, *Water:* 2 x 4 acre lakes. 1 with Carp to 27lb. 1 with general fish, Carp, Tench, Perch, Bream, Roach, Rudd, Crucian, *Species:* Carp: to 27lb. Coarse: Carp to 20lb, Bream 4lb, Perch 3lb, Tench 5lb, Roach/Rudd 2.75lb, *Permits:* Only from above, *Charges:* To be advised, *Season:* 16th June - 30th April, *Methods:* No keepnets, barbless hooks.

WOTTON-UNDER-EDGE

Lower Killcott Farm Fishing
Contact: Lower Kilcott Farm, Nr Hillesley, Wotton-Under Edge, GL12 7RL, 01454 238276, *Mobile:* 07967 280574, *Water:* 1 acre lake, *Species:* Carp to 20lb, Roach, Rudd, *Charges:* £5 day, £3 half day, *Season:* Open all year, *Methods:* Barbless hooks only, no keepnets or boilies.

GLOUCS Stillwater Trout

DURSLEY

Great Burrows Trout Fishery
Contact: Vernon Baxter (Manager), North Nibley, Nr Dursley, 01453 542343, *Mobile:* 07754 502134, *Water:* Two acre lake, *Species:* Brown Trout, Rainbow Trout (triploid) stocked from 2lb to 5lb, *Permits:* From V. Baxter on site, *Charges:* Day tickets: 2 fish - £14. 3 fish £16. 4 fish £20. 5 fish £24. 6 fish £30, *Season:* Open all year except Christmas day. Fishing from 8am to one hour after sunset, *Methods:* Fly only. No lures. Barbless hooks only. Max hook size 12 longshank. No static fishing. No catch and release except for Brown Trout. Breeding fish to be returned if caught. No wading, fishing from platforms. Knotless landing nets only. EA Licence required.

FAIRFORD

Milestone Fisheries (Trout Lakes)
Contact: Sue or Bob Fletcher or Andy King, Milestone Fisheries, London Road, Fairford, GL7 4DS, 01285 713908, *Water:* 10 acre lake and 2 acre lake, *Species:* 10 acre lake: Brown trout, Rainbow trout 2lb - 20lb. 2 acre lake: Rainbow trout 1lb - 1.25lb (bank fishing only). Also Blue/Golden Trout and doubles only pool 10lb - 23lb, *Permits:* Day tickets & Season tickets plus a limited number catch and release (take first fish - not available when water temperature is high), *Charges:* 10 acre lake: Day & season tickets. Bank (Boats & Float tube for hire) Day ticket 5 fish £30, 1/2 day 3 fish £20. 2 Acre lake: bank fishing only. Catch and take only £12 for 5 fish (top pool), *Season:* No closed season (Return all browns), *Methods:* Catch & take or Catch & release on ten acre lake only. (Barbless hooks on Catch & release), Fly fishing only

LECHLADE

Lechlade & Bushyleaze Trout Fisheries
Contact: Tim Small, Lechlade & Bushyleaze Trout Fisheries, Lechlade, GL7 3QQ, 01367 253266, tim@timtrout.co.uk, *Water:* Lechlade - 8 acres. Bushyleaze - 20 acres, *Species:* Lechlade - Rainbows to 27lb, Browns to 18lb. Bushyleaze - Rainbows to 17lb, Browns to 9lb, *Charges:* Lechlade: £40 full day, 4 fish. £30 half day, 2 fish. £20 evening, 1 fish. Bushyleaze: £30 full day, 6 fish. £25 full day, 4 fish. £20 half day, 3 fish. £15 evening, 2 fish. Season tickets available for both lakes. Discounted day tickets for juniors, *Season:* Open all year, *Methods:* Fly only. Boat hire and float tube hire.

HAMPSHIRE River Fishing

THE 'HAMPSHIRE' AVON

The River Avon is one of England's most famous rivers, and is revered by all anglers for the quality of fish that live in it. This river creates a certain mystique that captivates the attentions of fishers from all walks of life.

The River Avon rises in the Vale of Pewsey and, with its tributaries the Bourne and Wylye, drains the chalk of Salisbury Plain. The River Nadder, which is joined by the Wylye near Salisbury, drains the escarpment of the South Wiltshire Downs and the Kimmeridge clays of the Wardour Vale. The River Ebble and Ashford Water also drain the South Wiltshire Downs and join the Avon downstream of Salisbury and Fordingbridge respectively.

Below Fordingbridge, a number of streams drain the New Forest area. The Avon finally drains into Christchurch harbour, where it is joined by the Rivers Stour and Mude before discharging into the English Channel.

AVON HAMPSHIRE

Bickton Mill

Contact: Simon Cooper, Fishing Breaks, Walton House, 23 Compton Terrace, N1 2UN, 020 7359 8818, info@fishingbreaks.co.uk, *Water:* Extensive fishing on well stocked carriers south of Fordingbridge, *Species:* Brown and Rainbow Trout, *Charges:* £65 per person per day, *Season:* April to October, *Methods:* Dry Fly and Nymph.

Britford (Coarse)

Contact: London Angler's Association, Izaak Walton House, 2A Hervey Park Road, E17 6LJ, 02085 207477, admin@londonanglers.net, *Water:* Several stretches of the Hampshire Avon, *Species:* Roach 3lb, Barbel 10 lb, Chub 7 lb, plus specimen Dace, Grayling, Perch & Pike, *Permits:* Members only, Address as above, *Charges:* Senior: £35 - Junior, OAP, reg. disabled: £18.50 - Husband & wife: £52 - Club affiliated membership available on request, *Season:* Current EA byelaws apply, *Methods:* See members handbook

Britford (Game)

Contact: London Angler's Association, Izaak Walton House, 2A Hervey Park Road, E17 6LJ, 02085 207477, admin@londonanglers.net, *Water:* Several stretches of the Hampshire Avon, *Species:* Trout & Salmon, *Permits:* Members only, Address as above, *Charges:* Senior: £35 - Junior, OAP, reg. disabled: £18.50 - Husband & wife: £52 - Club affiliated membership available on request, *Season:* Current EA byelaws apply, *Methods:* See members handbook

Christchurch Angling Club (Coarse River)

Contact: S. Richards, 15 Roeshot Crescent, Highcliffe, Christchurch, BH23 4QH, 01425 279710, steve@christchurchanglingclub.fsnet.co.uk, *Water:* Largest club on the river Avon, mainly mid/lower Avon, Burgate - Christchurch, including the Royalty Fishery as of 1.4.01, also Fishing on River Stour between Gains Cross and Christchurch plus various coarse ponds including Blashford and Ivy Lakes and Cranebrook. Please telephone the secretary for full details, *Species:* Roach (3lb), Chub (7lb), Dace (1lb), Barbel (14lb), Pike (30lb), Bream (11lb), Perch (4lb), Carp (40lb), Eels (5lb), Cucian Carp (4lb), Grayling (3lb), Tench (9lb), *Permits:* Day tickets available for Rivers & Stillwaters from local Tackle Shops, *Charges:* Adult £110, Junior £45, Concession £65, *Season:* Coarse: 16th June to 14th March. Salmon: 1st Feb to 31st August. Rainbow Trout all year round. Brown Trout: 1st April to 15th October, *Methods:* See rules for individual waters

Ringwood & District Angling Club (Hampshire Avon)

Contact: Mr Les Aves, 60 Station Road, Alderholt, Fordingbridge, SP6 3AL, 01425 656245, *Mobile:* 07973 729959, lesaves@barbel4.freeserve.co.uk, *Water:* Between - Severals fishery at Ringwood upstream to Fordingbridge including Ibsley, *Species:* Barbel to 14lb, Chub to 7lb, Roach 3lb+, Pike 30lb+, Bream 10lb+, Perch, Carp, Dace, Salmon, Sea Trout, Brown Trout, *Permits:* As above and local tackle shops, *Charges:* Adult £90, Junior £40, Concessions, O.A.P.'s, Disabled £62 (Joining fee-£15 adult, £5 junior). Severals day tickets £7.50. Concessions for O.A.P's, Disabled, Juniors. Prices subject to seasonal review, *Season:* Slight variations to coarse season due to Salmon fishing, Current E.A. byelaws apply,

DUN

Holbury Lakes (River Dun)

Contact: Stewart M Guest, Holbury Lakes, Holbury Lane, Lockerley, Romsey, SO51 0JR, 01794 341619, *Water:* 0.6 miles on the river Dun. See also entry under stillwater Trout, Romsey, *Species:* Brown Trout, *Charges:* Half day 2 fish-£19. Day 4 fish-£33. Season (26 full days) £700. 10 fish ticket (catch within 4 months, any number of visits) £120. 25 fish ticket £250. Half day river £28. Half day 2 fish on lakes/river £30.

HAMPSHIRE
Stillwater
Coarse

FORDINGBRIDGE
Cranborne Fruit Farm
Contact: Cranborne Fruit Farm, Alderholt, Fordingbridge, 01425 672451, *Water:* 3 acre lake, *Species:* Carp, Bream, Roach, Rudd, *Permits:* At all local tackle shops, *Charges:* £5 Day. £4 day OAP, *Season:* January to November.

Lake Farm Fishery
Contact: P.S. Birch, Lake Farm, Sandleheath, Fordingbridge, SP6 3EF, 01425 653383, PHIL@birch50.fsnet.co.uk, Water;, 3 acre lake, *Species:* Carp to 25lb, *Charges:* Day tickets £6 at lakeside, *Season:* Open all year 8am to sunset, *Methods:* Barbless hooks only, no keepnets

New Forest Water Park
Contact: Mark Jury, Hucklesbrook Lakes, Ringwood Road, Fordingbridge, SP6 2EY, 01425 656868, *Mobile:* 07939 273388, info@newforestwaterpark.co.uk, *Water:* 19 acre lake, 11 acre lake, *Species:* Pike to 35lb plus, Carp to 40lb plus, Roach, Rudd and Perch in 11 acre lake. Carp to 32lb, Tench to 10lb, Roach to 3lb, Rudd to 2lb in 19 acre lake, *Permits:* From Clubhouse (After 10 a.m.) or on bank. No EA licence required, *Charges:* Day ticket: £6 for 2 rods, £9 for 3 rods. 24hrs ticket £15 for 2 rods, £22.50 for 3 rods bookable in advance, *Season:* All year round, *Methods:* Barbless hooks, No nut baits, No keepnets, No live bait

RINGWOOD
Blashford Lakes
Contact: Christchurch Angling Club, S. Richards, 15 Roeshot Cresent, Christchurch, BH23 4QH, 01425 279710, steve@christchurchanglingclub.fsnet.co.uk, *Water:* Series of former Gravel Pits. Fishing available to members of Christchurch Angling Club. See entry under Hampshire Avon. Includes Spinnaker lake Rockford lake, Roach pit, *Species:* Carp-44lb+. Pike-30lb+. Bream-14lb+. Perch-4lb+. Roach, Tench, Rudd, *Permits:* Available from S. Richards or local tackle shops, *Charges:* Adults-£110. Junior-£45. OAP/Conc-£65 For Season, *Season:* 16th June-14th March. Night fishing available with prepaid permit, *Methods:* See individual fishery rules.

Hurst Pond
Contact: Ringwood Tackle, 01425 475155, *Water:* 1.5 acre pond at Hedlands Business Park, Blashford, Ringwood, Hants, *Species:* Carp 18lb, Tench 6.5lb, Roach 2.5lb, Rudd 2lb, Perch 3lb 12oz, Crucians 2.5lb, Eels 5lb, *Charges:* £5 per day. Limited night fishing, £10 - 24hr ticket, *Season:* Open all year.

Moors Valley Country Park
Contact: Andy Beale (Head Bailiff), Horton Road, Ashley Heath, Nr Ringwood, BH24 2ET, 01425 470721, mvalley@eastdorset.gov.uk, *Water:* The Moors Lake covers an area of 9 acres. Maximum depth 2 meters., *Species:* Tench to 6lb, Carp to 10lb, Roach to 2lb, Perch to 2lb, Rudd 2lb, Pike to 20lb. Most river species ie Dace/Gudgeon etc, *Permits:* Fishing is from the bays marked by wooden posts on the west bank and has disabled access. Permits from visitor centre, *Charges:* £3.00 Adults (17-65yrs), £2.50 65yrs plus, £2.00 Junior (Up to 16yrs). Car park charges vary throughout the year, pay and display, *Season:* Moors lake from 16th June to 14th March, *Methods:* Rod licence for 12yrs plus, one ticket per rod, fishing from 8-30am to dusk, no keepnets, no boilies, barbless hooks, wooden bays only, float/ledger/feeder/dead bait for pike.

Ringwood & District A.A. (Coarse Lakes)
Contact: Mr Les Aves, 60 Station Road, Alderholt, Fordingbridge, SP6 3AL, 01425 656245, *Mobile:* 07973 729959, lesaves@barbel4.freeserve.co.uk, *Water:* 4 lakes at Hightown plus Northfield on outskirts of Ringwood, *Species:* Hightown - Mixed fishery with Carp to 38lb 14oz, Tench, Bream, Roach, Rudd, Pike, Eels. Northfield - Big Carp to 30lb, Tench to 12lb, Bream, Roach, Rudd, Pike, *Permits:* From above and local tackle shop, *Charges:* Adult £90, Junior £40, concessions for OAP's and disabled; day tickets £7.50 plus night options available at Ringwood Tackle, West St, Ringwood, 01425-475155. Prices may change for 2002, please enquire, *Season:* All year fishing available, *Methods:* All on reverse of ticket

HAMPSHIRE
Stillwater
Trout

FORDINGBRIDGE
Damerham Fisheries
Contact: Mike Davies, The Lake House, Damerham, Fordingbridge, SP6 3HW, 01725 518446, *Water:* 6 lakes. 1.5 mile Allan River, *Species:* Rainbow Trout (Sandy, Lavender, White + Electric Blue Rainbow Trout), *Permits:* Season Rods, *Charges:* Full Rod £1,500 (30 days), 1/2 Rod £780 (15 days), 1/4 Rod £530 (10 days). Guest Rod £60. Please phone to confirm prices, *Season:* March - October, *Methods:* Fly only.

Rockbourne Trout Fishery
Contact: Rockbourne Trout Fishery, Rockbourne Road, Sandleheath, Fordingbridge, SP6 1QG, 01725 518603, *Mobile:* 07802 678830, rockbourne@talk21.com, *Water:* 6 Spring fed lakes & 3 chalkstream beats on the Sweatford water, *Species:* Rainbow / Brown Trout, Triploids, *Permits:* From the fishery, *Charges:* 5 fish £40. 4 fish £35. 3 fish £30. 2 fish £20. Junior/novice 1 fish catch and

release lake £10, age limit 16yrs, *Season:* All year, *Methods:* Fly only, max hook size 10lb, no droppers, tandem/ double/treble hooks, no dogs

ROMSEY

Holbury Lakes

Contact: Stewart M Guest, Holbury Lakes, Holbury Lane, Lockerley, Romsey, SO51 0JR, 01794 341619, *Water:* 4 lakes totalling 6.5 acres plus 0.6 miles on the river Dun, *Species:* (in lakes) Rainbow Trout to 13lb 9oz, Blue Trout to 11lb 2oz and Brown Trout to 7lb 4oz, *Charges:* Half day 2 fish-£19. Day 4 fish-£33. Season (26 full days) £700. 10 fish ticket (catch within 4 months, any number of visits) £120. 25 fish ticket £250. Half day river £28. Half day 2 fish on lakes/river £30.

STOCKBRIDGE

John O ' Gaunts

Contact: Mrs E Purse, 51 Mead Road, Chandlers Ford, SO53 2FB, 01794 388130 or 02380 252268, *Water:* 2 Lakes approx 7 acres in Test Valley, *Species:* Rainbow Trout (various sizes), *Permits:* Available from Fishery Tel: 02380 252268 or 01794 388130, *Charges:* £32/day-4-fish, £18/half day-2-fish, *Season:* February 1st - November 30th inclusive, *Methods:* Fly and Nymph only

WINCHESTER

Dever Springs

Contact: Mr N. Staig and Miss P. Ball, Barton Stacey, Winchester, SO21 3NP, 01264 720592, pippa@deversprings.freeserve.co.uk, *Water:* Two lakes totalling 6 acres plus a half mile stretch of the river Dever, *Species:* Rainbow Trout - British record holder at 36lb 14oz. Brown Trout - British record holder at 28lb 2oz, *Permits:* EA rod licence required, *Charges:* 4 fish £55. 3 fish £42. 2 fish £32, *Season:* Open all year, *Methods:* Fly only. Max hook size 12, single wet or dry fly.

SOMERSET River Fishing

AXE

The River Axe emerges from the Mendip Hills at Wookey Hole and from here to below Wookey the river is Trout water. The river deepens as it crosses low lying land at the foot of the Mendips to the sluices at Bleadon and Brean Cross, the tidal limit. Fish species in the lower reaches include Bream, Roach, Tench, Dace and Pike.

Taunton Fly Fishing Club

Contact: Mr G. Woollen, Graylings, Frog Lane, Chard, TA20 3NX, 01460 65977, *Water:* Large sections Rivers Tone and Axe plus Otterhead Lakes, *Species:* Sea Trout, Brown Trout, Grayling, *Permits:* For Otterhead Lakes: Topp Tackle, Station Rd. Taunton; Enterprise Angling, East Reach, Taunton, *Charges:* Full Club Membership: £110 - Otterhead Day tickets: £5, *Season:* 1st April - 15th October, *Methods:* Fly only.

Weston-super-Mare A.A

Contact: Weston Angling Centre, 25a Locking Road, Weston-super-Mare, BS23 3BY, 01934 631140, *Water:* River Axe, River Brue, South Drain, North Drain. Summer Lane Pond, Locking Pond, *Species:* Bream, Tench, Roach, Carp, Gudgeon, Perch, Rudd, some Dace, Chub, *Permits:* Weston Angling Centre, *Charges:* Season £20, Week £10, Day £4, *Season:* Old River Axe, Summer Lane and Locking Ponds - year round, *Methods:* No boilies, No nuts.

BARLE

Dulverton Angling Association

Contact: P. Veale, Lance Nicholson Fishing,Tackle & Guns, 9 High Street, Dulverton, TA22 9HB, 01398 323409, lancenich@lancenich.f9.co.uk, *Water:* New Association. Contact for further details, *Species:* Brown Trout, *Charges:* Adults £10. Junior £1.

Fly Fishing in Somerset (Barle)

Contact: R.M. Gurden, 3 Edbrooke Cottages, Winsford, Nr Minehead, TA24 7AE, 01643 851504, *Mobile:* 07814 243991, complete.angling@virgin.net, *Water:* 5 miles on the Barle, *Species:* Wild Brown Trout, Salmon, *Season:* March 15 to September 30, *Methods:* All waters fly only.

BRIDGWATER AND TAUNTON CANAL

Cut in 1827 the canal provided a good commercial waterway between the two towns. The canal has been recently restored for navigation but there is only infrequent boat traffic. The canal offers excellent coarse fishing from the towpath for Roach, Bream, Tench, Rudd, Perch & Pike.

HUNTSPILL RIVER / SOUTH DRAIN / CRIPPS RIVER / NORTH DRAIN

The Huntspill River is a man made drainage channel, excavated in the 1940s and connected to the River Brue and South Drain via the Cripps River. The North Drain was dug c1770 to drain low lying moors to the north of the River Brue. The Huntspill is a notable coarse fishery and is often the venue for national and local match fishing competitions. Catches consist primarily of Bream and Roach. The North and South Drain and Cripps River contain similar species and also offer good sport for the coarse angler.

Bridgwater Angling Association

Contact: Mr M Pople, 14 Edward Street, Bridgwater, TA6 5EU, 01278 422397, *Water:* 6 miles on the Bridgwater & Taunton Canal, Fishing on the rivers Cripps, North & South Drain, King's Sedgemoor Drain, Langacre Rhine & The Huntspill. Stillwater fishing at Combwich, Walrow, Dunwear & Screech Owl and Bridgwater Docks, *Species:* All types of Coarse Fish, *Permits:* Available from Tackle outlets throughout Somerset area including Somerset Angling, 74 Bath Rd, Bridgwater, Tel: 01278 431777 & Thyers Tackle, 1a Church Street, Highbridge, Tel: 01278 786934. Further information on Bridgwater A.A. available from Watts News, Edward Street, Bridgwater. Open: Mon-Sat 5am-7pm, Sunday . 5am-4pm. Tel: 01278 422137, *Charges:* Adult season £26, Junior (12-17yrs) £6, Senior Citizens £9, Disabled £9, Junior (7-11yrs) £3.Day tickets £3.50, enquire at outlets, *Season:* E.A. byelaws apply. Bridgwater and Taunton Canal open all year, *Methods:* Full rules and map with permits.

Taunton Angling Association (Bridgwater & Taunton Canal)
Contact: Mr. J.Helyer, 40 Albemarle Road, Taunton, TA1 1BA, 01823 257559, kgregson@compuserve.com, *Water:* 7 miles on Bridgwater & Taunton Canal, *Species:* Roach 2lb, Bream 7lb, Eels 2lb, Rudd 2lb, Perch 2lb, Pike 27lb, Tench 7lb, *Permits:* Topp Tackle, 63 Station Road, Taunton, (01823) 282518. Enterprise Angling (01823) 282623. Somerset Angling, Bath Road, Bridgwater (01278) 431777. Street Angling, High Street, Street (01458) 447830. Wellington Country Sports, 5 Lancer Court, High Street, Wellington (01823) 662120, *Charges:* Season £23. Day tickets £4 Senior, £2 Junior, *Season:* Closed 14th March - 16th June, Ponds and canal open all year, *Methods:* Barbless hooks on stillwaters. All fish (including Pike and Eels) to be returned alive.

BRISTOL AVON
The River Avon flows from its sources near Sherston and Tetbury to its confluence with the Severn at Avonmouth some 117 kilometres and is fed by many tributaries on its way. The headwaters of the River Avon, the Tetbury and Sherston branches join at Malmesbury. Both are important Trout streams where fishing is strictly preserved and there is little opportunity for the visiting angler to fish these waters.

Bristol, Bath & Wiltshire Amalgamated Anglers
Contact: Jeff Parker, 16 Lansdown View, Kingswood, Bristol, BS15 4AW, 0117 9672977, *Water:* Approx 80 miles Coarse Fishing on Bristol Avon & Somerset Rivers & Streams. Stillwaters at Lyneham, Calne, Malmesbury, Bath and Pawlett near Bridgwater. Trout only water on Cam Brook. Too much to list here, please contact the secretary for full details, *Species:* All coarse species, *Permits:* Full Membership available from the Secretary. Veterans over 70 years contact the secretary for details of discounted membership. Full members only may fish at Tockenham Reservoir, Burton Hill lake at Malmesbury & Shackells Lake. Day Tickets for all waters except Burton Hill & Tockenham are available at Tackle Shops. Limited night fishing, *Charges:* Adults £30 (discount for early purchase). Adult and child £35. Concessions £10. Night fishing full members £50 per season, *Methods:* No metal cans/glass bottles in possesion; no fresh water fish as live bait, max. 2 rods per angler, full rules on application

Bathampton Angling Association (Bristol Avon Claverton)
Contact: Dave Crookes, 25 Otago Terrace, Larkhall, Bath, BA1 6SX, 01225 427164, dave@bathampton.org, *Water:* 2.5 miles Bristol Avon up and downstream from Claverton, *Species:* Bream to 6lbs, Chub to 5lbs, Roach to 2.5lbs, Pike to 25lbs, Barbel to 12lbs, *Permits:* Local fishing tackle shops, *Charges:* Adults £20, Combined lady and gent £28. Juniors £5.50. O.A.P £4.50. Registered disabled £5.50. Under 12's free. To year end 31/12/2002. Members only, *Season:* Standard river close season, night fishing on application.

(Box Brook)
Water: 3 miles of Box brook (tributary of Avon). Split into 2 beats at Briddle Hill and Shockerwick, *Species:* Brown Trout (occasional Rainbows) Grayling, *Permits:* Local fishing tackle shops, *Charges:* Adults £20, Combined lady and gent £28. Juniors £5.50. O.A.P £4.50. Registered disabled £5.50. Under 12's free. To year end 31/12/2002.Members only. Special day permit must be purchased before fishing., *Season:* Fishing from 1st April to 15 October inclusive, *Methods:* Traditional Fly/Nymph only

(Bristol Avon Kelston)
Water: 2 miles of Bristol Avon at Kelston., *Species:* Bream to 8lbs, Roach to 2lbs, Pike to 20lbs, Chub to 3lbs, Barbel to 8lbs., *Permits:* Local fishing tackle shops, *Charges:* Adults £20, Combined lady and gent £28. Juniors £5.50. O.A.P £4.50. Registered disabled £5.50. Under 12's free. To year end 31/12/2002. £3 day tickets available to Non-Members. Tickets must be purchased before fishing., *Season:* Standard river close season, *Methods:* Club byelaws apply.

(Bristol Avon Newbridge)
Water: 1.5 miles of Bristol Avon at Newbridge, downstream of Bath, *Species:* Bream to 10lbs, Chub to 4lbs, Roach to 2.5lbs, Pike to 16lbs, *Permits:* Local fishing tackle shops, *Charges:* Adults £20, Combined lady and gent £28. Juniors £5.50. O.A.P £4.50. Registered disabled £5.50. Under 12's free. To year end 31/12/2002. £3 day tickets available to Non-Members.Tickets must be purchased before fishing., *Season:* Standard river close season, *Methods:* Club byelaws apply.

(Bristol Avon Saltford))
Water: 1.5 miles of Bristol Avon at Saltford, *Species:* Bream to 8lbs, Roach to 2lbs, Chub to 3lbs, *Permits:* Local fishing tackle shops, *Charges:* Adults £20, Combined lady and gent £28. Juniors £5.50. O.A.P £4.50. Registered disabled £5.50. Under 12's free. To year end 31/12/2002. £3 day tickets available to Non-Members. must be purchased before fishing., *Season:* Standard river close season, *Methods:* Club byelaws apply.

Malmesbury to Chippenham
Coarse fisheries predominate in this section, although Trout are stocked by fishing associations in some areas. Arguably one of the best fisheries in the country, this section contains a wide range of specimen fish. Local records include: Roach 3lb 2oz, Perch 3lb 3oz, Tench 8lb 5 1/2oz, Bream 8lb 8oz, Dace 1lb 2oz, Chub 7lb 10oz, Carp 20lb 8 1/4oz and Pike 33lb 3oz. Also many Barbel to 12lb have been reported.

Chippenham to Bath

Upstream from Staverton to Chippenham the Avon continues to be an important coarse fishery, both for the pleasure angler and match fisherman. The river flows through a broad flood plain and provides a pastoral setting. In the faster flowing sections chub, Roach, Dace and Barbel can be caught in good numbers.

Bath to Hanham

Between Hanham and Bath much of this length retains a rural character and is an important coarse fishery used by pleasure and match anglers. The National Angling Championships have been held here. Roach, Bream and Chub are the main catches and, in some favoured swims, Dace. Very good catches of Bream are to be had with specimen fish. 'Free' fishing is available through Bath from the towpath side between Newbridge and Pulteney Weir. Carp of 20lb have been reported caught downstream of Pulteney and Keynsham Weirs.

Bristol Avon

Contact: Abbey Angling, 54b High Street, Hanham, Bristol, 0117 9081130, Water: Free stretch from Crewsall Road - Chequers - Hanham Mills, 2.5 miles approx, Species: All coarse fish, Permits: Ea licence required, Charges: Free fishing (Further details contact Abbey Angling), Season: Closed season applies.

Hanham to Avonmouth

Between Netham Dam and Hanham Weir the river is affected by spring tides. The water has a very low saline content and this length of river provides reasonable coarse fishing. Below Netham Dam the river contains mostly estuarine species but some Sea Trout and Salmon have been seen.

Avon Valley Country Park (River Avon)

Contact: Bath Rd, Keynsham, Bristol, BS31 1TP, 0117 9864929, info@avonvalleycountrypark.co.uk, Water: 1.5 miles on River Avon, Species: Tench & Coarse fish, Permits: From above, Charges: £4 Adult entrance to park (includes ticket to fish), £3 Child, £3.50 Senior Citizen, Season: Park open: Easter - 1st November 10am - 6pm. Current E.A. Byelaws apply on the river

Bristol City Docks Angling Club

Contact: Bob Taylor, 27 Flaxpits Lane, Winterbourne, Bristol, BS36 1LA, 01454 773990, rtbr20912@cableinet.co.uk, Water: 3 miles on Bristol Avon from Chequers Weir to Netham. Feeder canal (Netham - docks), Bristol Docks system, Species: Skimmers, Bream, Roach, Dace, Chub, Pike, Eels, Carp, Tench and Perch, Permits: All Bristol tackle shops and Harbour Masters office, or from secretary above on 01454 773990 or 07909 806451, Charges: Season: Senior + 2 Juniors under 12 £14, Seniors £12, Concessions, Disabled, Juniors, O.A.P's £6, Day tickets in advance: Seniors £2.50 + Concessions £1, Day tickets on the bank issued by Bailiff: Seniors £5, Juniors/Conc £2.50, Season: 1st April - March 31st inclusive, River - normal close season applies; Docks and Feeder Canal open all year, Methods: Docks: Pole and Feeder. Pole & Waggler on Feeder Canal. All normal river tactics on the Avon. Daily update information from Tony on 0117 9517250.

PSV Angling Club

Contact: Mike Shillaber, 184 Kingsweston Lane, Bristol, BS11 0LX, 0117 9078492, webmaster@psvfishing.com, Water: PSV Angling Club do not have any specific waters, they control the use of fishing permits for Bristol Docks. Regular matches throughout the south west for members only. New members welcome, Charges: £10 per year. £15 including fishing at Bristol City Docks.

BRISTOL FROME

The Bristol Frome rises at Dodington and offers a fair standard of coarse fishing on the lower sections. The upper section contains limited stocks of Brown Trout, Roach and Perch. This tributary of the River Avon is culverted beneath Bristol and discharges into the Floating Harbour.

Frome Angling Association (River)

Contact: Roger Lee, 51 Welshmill Lane, Frome, BA11 3AP, 01373 461433, Water: 12 miles River Frome - 10 acre lake, Species: River: Roach, Chub, Bream. Lake: Tench, Carp, Roach, Pike, Permits: Haines Angling, Christchurch Street West, Frome, Charges: £10 Senior, £5 Junior U/16, O.A.P's £5, Day tickets £2, Season: 16 June to March 14, unless changes in legislation occur, Methods: No restrictions.

Frome Vale Angling Club

Contact: S. Coles (secretary), 2. Burrough Way, Winterbourne, Bristol, BS36 1LE, 01454 778095, Water: 1 mile river Frome; half acre lake (Winterbourne); 1 acre lake at Brimsham Park, Yate Bristol, Species: Carp, Roach, Bream, Tench, Pike, Perch, Chub - Brimsham Park lake: Carp, Roach, Rudd, Bream, Perch, Permits: As above or from Mr.I.Moss, 69 Long Rd, Mangutsfield, Bristol, Charges: Per season: Seniors £15 - Juniors £7 - OAP's/Disabled £5. Day tickets not available, Season: From June 16th - March 14th. Closed season March 15th - June 15th, Methods: Barbless hooks on all waters. Lakes: barbless hooks, no floating baits, no keepnets, hooks no larger than size 10, no cereal ground baits

RIVER BOYD

The River Boyd rises just south of Dodington and joins the Bristol Avon at Bitton. In the middle and lower reaches coarse fish predominate. The upper reaches above Doynton contain Brown Trout.

BY BROOK

The Broadmead and Burton brooks together form the By Brook which flows through Castle Combe and is joined by several smaller streams before entering the River Avon at Bathford. Brown Trout predominate above the village of Box, mostly small in size but plentiful in number. At Box and below the fishery is mixed and Dace to 14oz and Roach of 2lb are not uncommon.

RIVER MARDEN

The River Marden is fed by springs rising from the downs above Cherhill and joins the river Avon upstream of Chippenham. Brown Trout occur naturally in the upper reaches. Downstream of Calne coarse fish predominate and weights of more than 30lb are regularly caught in matches. The Marden Barbel record stands at over 10lb.

SOMERSET FROME

The Somerset Frome is the main tributary of the Bristol Avon. It drains a large catchment area which is fed from the chalk around Warminster and limestone from the eastern end of the Mendips. There are numerous weirs and mills mostly disused. The tributaries above Frome provide ideal conditions for Brown Trout with fishing on the River Mells. The middle and lower reaches provide excellent coarse fishing.

Airsprung Angling Association (Frome)
Contact: Alan Lampard, 6, Hewitt Close, Trowbridge, BA14 7SG, 01225 764388, *Water:* See also entry under Wiltshire, river fishing, Kennet & Avon Canal. River Frome at Stowford Farm (near Farleigh Hungerford), *Species:* Carp, Bream, Chub, Roach, Rudd, Dace, Tench, Perch, etc, *Permits:* Association Licence only (no day tickets on river), *Charges:* On application, *Season:* Subject to normal close season, *Methods:* Details from Association.

Avon & Tributaries Angling Association
Contact: Mr Miller (Secretary), 5 William St, Bath, BA2 4DE, *Water:* Somerset Frome, Cam, Wellow, Midford Brooks, *Species:* All coarse species and Trout, *Permits:* No day tickets, guest ticket from individual members, *Season:* In rules, *Methods:* In rules.

MIDFORD BROOK

The Midford Brook runs through well wooded valleys with mostly mixed fishing on the lower reaches and Trout fishing in upper reaches. The largest Brown Trout recorded weighed 5lb 6oz.

KENNET AND AVON CANAL

There are some 58 kilometres of canal within the Bristol Avon catchment area which averages one metre in depth and thirteen metres in width. The Kennet & Avon Canal joins the River Avon at Bath with the River Kennet between Reading and Newbury. The canal was opened in 1810 to link the Severn Estuary with the Thames. The canal, now much restored, provides excellent fishing with Carp to 25lb, Tench to 5lb also Roach, Bream, Perch, Rudd, Pike and Gudgeon.

Bathampton Angling Association (Kennet & Avon Canal)
Contact: Dave Crookes, 25 Otago Terrace, Larkhall, Bath, BA1 6SX, 01225 427164, dave@bathampton.org, *Water:* 6.5 miles of Kennet and Avon canal. From Bath to Limpley Stoke hill, *Species:* Bream to 4lbs, Chub to 3.5lbs, Roach to 2lbs, Pike to 10lbs, Carp to 15lbs, Tench to 3lbs. Perch to 2.5lbs, *Permits:* Local fishing tackle shops, *Charges:* Adults £20, Combined lady and gent £28. Juniors £5.50. O.A.P £4.50. Registered disabled £5.50. under 12's free. To year end 31/12/2002. £3 day tickets available to non-members must be purchased before fishing, *Season:* Open all year, *Methods:* Club bye-laws apply.

BRUE

The River Brue is a Trout fishery from its source above Bruton to Lovington. From here to Glastonbury a number of weirs provide areas of deep water and coarse fish predominate, notably Chub and Roach, together with Bream, Dace and Pike. Similar species may be found between Glastonbury and Highbridge where the river is channelled across the Somerset Levels and connected with a number of drainage channels such as the Huntspill River and North Drain.

Glaston Manor Association
Contact: J. Ogden, 10 Dovecote Close, Farm Lane, Street, *Water:* Brue - approx 15 miles both banks; 2/3 miles on Sheppey plus S. Drain from Catcott Bridge back to source, *Species:* Roach, Chub, Bream, Dace, Perch, Gudgeon & Pike, *Permits:* Thatchers Tackle, Wells. Street Angling, High St, Street, Somerset Tel: 01458 447830, *Charges:* Day ticket £4, Junior membership £5, Senior membership £16, OAP and disabled £8 *Season:* Current EA byelaws apply, *Methods:* No live bait permitted, Full rules on day ticket

Merry Farm Fishing
Contact: Mr.Peter Dearing, Merry Farm, Merry Lane, Basonbridge, TA9 3PS, 01278 783655, *Water:* 600 yards on the River Brue, *Species:* Pike 30lb plus, Bream 10lb, Tench 5lb, Chub 6lb, Carp 30lb plus, Roach 1.5lb, Gudgeon, Ruffe, Perch 4lb, *Permits:* Day tickets, *Charges:* £1 per day, *Season:* 16th Jun to 14th March, *Methods:* No restrictions.

CAM AND WELLOW BROOKS

The Cam and Wellow Brooks, rising on the north side of the Mendip Hills, flow through what was a mining area and now provide good quality Trout fishing controlled by local fishing associations.

Cameley Lakes (River Cam)
Contact: J. Harris, Hillcrest farm, Cameley, Temple Cloud, Nr Bristol, BS39 5AQ, 01761 452423, *Water:* Fishing on River Cam. See also entry under stillwater trout, Bristol, *Species:* Rainbow and Brown trout, 1.5 - 5lb, *Permits:* Fishery car park, Cameley, Temple Cloud near Bristol, *Charges:* £20 - 4 fish limit (Day permit.) £15 - 2 fish limit (Half day permit), *Season:* 8am to sundown, *Methods:* Dry fly and Nymph fishing, no larger than 1 inch.

CHEW

The River Chew rises near Chewton Mendip and flows through the Bristol Waterworks Reservoirs at Litton and Chew Valley Lake. The river continues through Chew Magna, Stanton Drew, Publow, Woolard and Compton Dando to its confluence with the River Avon at Keynsham. A mixed fishery for most its length and is particularly good for Roach, Dace and Grayling below Pensford.

Bathampton Angling Association (River Chew)
Contact: Dave Crookes, 25 Otago Terrace, Larkhall, Bath, BA1 6SX, 01225 427164, dave@bathampton.org, *Water:* 1 mile of river Chew at Compton Dando, near Keynsham, *Species:* Roach, Chub, Grayling, Brown Trout, Rainbow Trout, Dace, Perch, *Permits:* Local fishing tackle shops, *Charges:* Adults £20. Combined lady and gent £28. Juniors £5.50. O.A.P £4.50. Registered disabled £5.50. Under 12's free. To year end 31/12/2002. Members only, *Season:* Open all year. Fly only for trout from 15 March to 15 June inclusive, *Methods:* Club bye-laws apply

Keynsham Angling Association
Contact: Mr K. N. Jerrom, 21 St Georges Road, Keynsham, Bristol, BS31 2HU, 01179 865193, *Water:* Stretches on the rivers Avon and Chew, *Species:* Mixed, *Charges:* Members only fishing. Membership details from secretary or Keynsham Pet & Garden Centre, tel: 01179 862366. Adult membership £12. Juniors, OAPs, disabled £4, *Season:* Current EA byelaws apply, *Methods:* Details in members handbook. On rivers Chew and Avon there are no restrictions other than current E.A. byelaws.

Knowle Angling Association
Contact: Keith Caddick, 41 Eastwood Crescent, Brislington, Bristol, BS4 4SR, 01179 857974, derek.ezekial@adsweu.com, *Water:* 5 miles of upper and lower river Chew. Also 3 trout lakes, *Species:* Rainbow and Brown Trout up to 8lb. Planned stocking of 4,600 for 2002 season, *Charges:* £65 annual membership, *Season:* 2 lakes all year round. 1 reservoir April to end December, *Methods:* Fly only on lakes and upper Chew.

EXE & TRIBUTARIES

See detailed description under Devon, River Fishing

Broford Fishing
Contact: P. Veale, Lance Nicholson Fishing, Tackle & Guns, 9 High Street, Dulverton, TA22 9HB, 01398 323409, lancenich@lancenich.f9.co.uk, *Water:* Approx 5 miles bank fishing on Little Exe, *Species:* Wild Brown Trout with occasional Salmon, *Permits:* As above, *Charges:* £10 per day, *Season:* 15th March - 30th September, *Methods:* Fly Only

Fly Fishing in Somerset (Little Exe)
Contact: Mr Robin Gurden, 3 Edbrooke Cottages, Winsford, Nr Minehead, TA24 7AE, 01643 851504, *Mobile:* 07814 243991, complete.angling@virgin.net, *Water:* Upper Exe 3/4 mile double bank, Catherines Brook 3/4 mile double bank. Barle 5 miles, *Species:* Wild Brown Trout, Salmon early and late season, *Season:* March 15 to September 30, *Methods:* All waters fly only.

Nick Hart Fly Fishing (Exe)
Contact: Nick Hart, Exford View, 1 Chapel Street, Exford, Minehead, TA24 7PY, 01643 831101, *Mobile:* 0797 1198559, nick@hartflyfishing.demon.co.uk, *Water:* 1.5 miles of Upper Exe, 3 miles of Middle Exe (see also entries under Devon, Taw and Torridge), *Species:* Up.Exe: Trout to 1lb, Mid.Exe: Salmon to double figures, *Permits:* From Nick Hart Fly Fishing, *Charges:* Trout: £15/day, Salmon: £35/day, *Season:* 15 March - 31 September, *Methods:* Up.Exe: Fly only, Barbless hooks, Catch & Release - Mid.Exe: Spin or Fly Fish year round

ISLE

The River Isle rises near Wadeford and soon after its source is joined by a tributary from Chard Lake. Trout are found as far as Ilminster but below the town coarse fish predominate. The profile of the river is fairly natural though a number of shallow weirs provide increased depth in places. Species caught in the lower stretches include Chub, Dace and Roach.

Chard & District Angling Club
Contact: Mr Braunton, Planet Video & Angling, 19a High Street, Chard, TA20 1QF, 01460 64000, *Water:* Approx 3 miles on the river Isle. Also Chard Reservoir and Perry Street Pond, see entry under coarse fishery, *Species:* Dace, Roach, Chub, Perch, Bream, Gudgeon, *Permits:* Planet Video & Angling, 19a High Street, Chard, Somerset TA20 1QF. Tel: 01460 64000, *Charges:* Membership £15 per year, concessions juniors, OAP's; includes coarse stillwater Perry Street Pond. No day tickets Perry Street or on river., *Season:* Closed season 14th March to 16th June on river.

Ilminster & District A.A.
Contact: P. Lonton, Marshalsea, Cottage Corner, Ilton, Ilminster, 01460 52519, *Water:* Approx 6 miles on the river Isle, *Species:* Roach, Chub, Perch, Bream, Dace, *Permits:* Day tickets from Ilminster Warehouse. Membership details from the secretary. Annual membership tickets from Ilminster Warehouse, Yeovil Angling Centre, The Tackle Shack, Chard Angling, Enterprise Angling, Taunton, *Charges:* £12 annual membership. Day tickets £3. Junior £2, *Season:* Current EA byelaws apply, *Methods:* Club rules apply.

Newton Abbot Fishing Association (River Isle)
Contact: Clive Smith (membership secretary), PO Box 1, Bovey Tracey, Newton Abbot, TQ13 9ZE, 01626 836661, newtonfishing@yahoo.com, *Water:* 1 mile stretch of the river Isle at Hambridge. Popular winter venue. See entry under Devon, Stillwater Coarse, Newton Abbot, *Species:* Pike, Roach, Rudd, Bream, Tench and Dace. Pike fishing can be frantic, *Permits: Charges:* *Season:* Rivers are controlled by the national close season for coarse fish.

KENN AND BLIND YEO

The New Blind Yeo is an artificial drainage channel which also carries some of the diverted water of the River Kenn. Both waters contain good Roach with Bream, Rudd, Carp, Perch, Tench and Pike.

Clevedon & District F.A.C.
Contact: Mr Newton, 64 Clevedon Rd, Tickenham, Clevedon, BS21 6RD, 01275 856107, *Water:* 6 miles - Blind Yeo / River Kenn, *Species:* Roach, Bream, Rudd, Eels, Perch, Pike, Tench, *Permits:* NSAA Permit at all local tackle shops, *Charges:* Season - Seniors: £20, Juniors/OAP: £8; Weekly - £10; Daily - £3, *Season:* June 16th - March 14th inc, *Methods:* Waggler/Stick, Pole, Ledger; No live baits, no coarse fish to be used as dead bait

THE KINGS SEDGEMOOR DRAIN

The Kings Sedgemoor Drain is an artificial drainage channel dug c1790. As well as draining a large area of moor it also carries the diverted water of the River Cary and excess flood flows from the River Parrett. The KSD is a very well known coarse fishery and is used for both local and national match fishing competitions. Fish species present include Roach, Bream, Tench, Perch and Pike.

PARRETT

The River Parrett rises in West Dorset and there is some Trout fishing as far as Creedy Bridge upstream of the A303. Below this point a number of weirs and hatches result in deeper water and slower flows. The resulting coarse fishery contains a wide variety of species including Roach, Bream, Rudd, Chub, Dace, Carp, Crucian Carp and Pike. Similar species are found in the lowest freshwater section at Langport where the Rivers Isle and Yeo join the Parrett to form a wide deep river which becomes tidal below Oath Sluice.

Langport & District Angling Association

Contact: Den Barlow, Florissant, Northfield, Somerton, TA11 6SJ, 01458 272119, den@barlow65.fsnet.co.uk, Water: 5 miles on the river Parrett. Coombe Lake - 2.75 acres, no closed season, Species: All common coarse species except Barbel, Permits: Fosters Newsagency, Bow Street, Langport, Charges: Annual £11, junior £5, disabled/OAP £5.50. Weekly £5. Senior day £3, junior day £1.50, Season: Closed season on river only. Membership from 16th June to 15th June inc. Night fishing permitted on river only from Langport A.A. controlled banks, Methods: Lake: Barbless hooks, No boilies, No Carp in keepnets.

Somerset Levels Association of Clubs

Contact: Newton Abbot Fishing Association, newtonfishing@yahoo.com, Water: See entry under Newton Abbot Fishing Association Devon, Stillwater Coarse. Rights to numerous parts of the Parret, Brue, Isle and other stretches of drain in the Langport area, Species: All coarse species.

Stoke Sub Hamdon & District A.A.

Contact: Mr Derek Goad (Secretary), 2 Windsor Lane, Stoke-sub-Hamdon, (H.Q. Stoke Working Mens Club), 01935 824337, Water: Upper Stretches River Parrett approx 10km. Also Bearley Lake, Long Load Drain (Shared Water), Species: Carp, Tench, Roach, Rudd, Bream, Perch, Dace, Chub, Pike, Eel, Gudgeon, Ruffe. Trout Fishing also available, Permits: Day and season permits from Stax Tackle, Montacute and Yeovil Angling Centre, Yeovil. Season tickets also available from secretary, Charges: Day ticket £4 (Bearley Lake). Season charges £10 includes cost of Bearley Lake Fishing. Juniors/OAPs £5 includes lake fishing. Juniors under 11 must be accompanied by an adult, Season: Trout 1st April - 31st October. Lake all year. Coarse 16th June - 14th March, Methods: Trout: No maggot. Lake: No boilies or nut baits, no night fishing, lake rules apply. River Coarse: No restrictions

Tiverton & District Angling Club (River Parret)

Contact: John Smallwood, Exe Valley Angling, 19 Westexe South, Tiverton, EX16 5DQ, 01884 242275, Water: Various stretches on several rivers in Somerset including Isle, Brue and North Drain. See also entry under stillwater coarse, Devon, Tiverton, Permits: Please ring Exe Valley for details. Also available from: Exeter Angling Centre, Enterprise Angling Taunton, Topp Tackle Taunton, Country Sports - Cullompton & Minnows Caravan Park - beside Grand Western Canal, Charges: Senior: Day £4, Annual £20. Conc: Day £2.50, Annual £8, Season: Coarse: closed 15 March to 16 June. Trout: open from 15 March to 30 September. Salmon: open 14 February to 30 September.

TONE

The River Tone rises on the edge of Exmoor National Park and not far from its source it feeds into and out of Clatworthy reservoir. From here to Taunton there are some twenty miles of fast flowing Trout river, though Grayling, Dace and Roach appear near Taunton where weirs provide increased depth. Through the town and just below, Chub, Dace and Roach predominate but at Bathpool the river becomes wider, deeper and slower. Roach, Bream, Carp, Tench and Pike are the typical species in this stretch which continues to the tidal limit at New Bridge.

Taunton Angling Association (Tone)

Contact: Mr. J.Helyer, 40 Albemarle Road, Taunton, TA1 1BA, 01823 257559, kgregson@compuserve.com, Water: 6 miles on River Tone (See also entry under Taunton and Bridgwater Canal), Species: Roach 2lb, Pike 36lb, Dace 1lb, Bream 10lb, Tench 5lb, Perch 3lb, Carp 30lb, Permits: Topp Tackle, 63 Station Road, Taunton, (01823) 282518. Enterprise Angling (01823) 282623. Somerset Angling, Bath Road, Bridgwater (01278) 431777. Street Angling, High street, Street (01458) 447830. Wellington Country Sports, 5 Lancer Court, High Street, Wellington.(01823) 662120, Charges: Season £23. Day tickets £4 senior, £2 junior, Season: Closed from 14th March to 16th June, Methods: All fish (including Pike and Eels) to be returned alive.

Wellington Angling Association

Contact: M Cave, 60 Sylvan Road, Wellington, TA1 8EH, 01823 661671, Water: Approx 2 miles on River Tone.Both banks from Nynhead weir to Wellington, Species: Brown Trout, Permits: Membership only, Charges: Joining fee £10, annual membership £12, Season: As E.A. season, Methods: No spinning.

WEST SEDGEMOOR DRAIN

This artificial channel was excavated in the 1940s on the lines of existing watercourses. Coarse fish species present include Bream, Roach, Tench and Carp.

Taunton Angling Association (W. Sedgemoor Drain)
Contact: Mr. J.Helyer, 40 Albemarle Road, Taunton, TA1 1BA, 01823 257559, kgregson@compuserve.com, *Water:* 2 miles of West Sedgemoor Drain, easy access for disabled anglers, *Species:* Bream 5lb, Roach 2.5lb, Eels 2lb, Tench 7lb, Pike 29lb, Perch 2lb, Rudd 2lb, Carp 26lb, *Permits:* Topp Tackle, 63 Station Road, Taunton, (01823) 282518. Enterprise Angling (01823) 282623. Somerset Angling, Bath Road, Bridgwater (01278) 431777. Street Angling, High street, Street (01458) 447830. Wellington Country Sports, 5 Lancer Court, High Street, Wellington.(01823) 662120, *Charges:* Season £23. Day tickets £4 senior, £2 junior, *Season:* Closed from 14th March to 16th June, *Methods:* All fish (including Pike and Eels) to be returned alive.

YEO

The River Yeo rises near Sherborne and between here and Yeovil the river is a coarse fishery, though tributaries such as the River Wriggle have Brown Trout. Below Yeovil a number of weirs produce areas of deep water and the resulting fishery contains good Dace together with Roach, Chub, Bream and Pike.

Ilchester & District A.A.
Contact: Mr M Barnes, 44 Marsh Lane, Yeovil, *Water:* River Yeo above and below Ilchester, *Species:* Chub, Roach, Dace, Bream, Gudgeon, Tench and Carp, *Permits:* Tackle shops in Yeovil. Yeovil Angling Centre. Stax Tackle, Montacute. Ilchester Post Office.Newsagents, Ilchester. Club Secretary, *Charges:* Season ticket £10. OAP/junior £5. Weekly ticket £3, *Season:* Open 16th June to 15th March, *Methods:* Current EA byelaws apply. Club rules on ticket and fishery map

N. Somerset Association of Anglers
Contact: Mr Newton, 64 Clevedon Rd, Tickenham, Clevedon, BS21 6RD, 01275 856107, *Water:* Blind Yeo, Kenn, Congresbury Yeo, Brue, Apex Lake, Newtown Ponds & Walrow Ponds, Tickenham Boundry Rhyne, North Drain, *Species:* Roach, Bream, Eels, Perch, Rudd, Carp, Pike, Tench, *Permits:* NSAA Permits available at all local Tackle Shops, *Charges:* Season: Seniors £20. Juniors/OAP/ Disabled £8. Weekly: £10. Day £3, *Season:* June 16th - March 14th inclusive. Apex Lake & Newtown Ponds: June 1st - 28th February incl, *Methods:* Apex Lake and Newtown Ponds: Barbless hooks, No live or dead baits, no floating baits, min. breaking strain line 2.5lb.

Yeovil & Sherborne Angling Association (Yeo)
Contact: Alex Murray, 2 Wisteria Close, Yeovil, BA21 2EE, *Mobile:* 07818 098057, *Water:* 4 miles rivers, Sherborne Castle Lake & discounted tickets Viaduct Fishery, *Species:* Roach, Bream, Carp, *Permits:* Membership details from above and local tackle shops, *Charges:* No day tickets. Club card £10, includes half price fishing at Viaduct.

SOMERSET Stillwater Coarse

BATH

Bathampton Angling Association (Weston Village)
Contact: Dave Crookes, 25 Otago Terrace, Larkhall, Bath, BA1 6SX, 01225 427164, dave@bathampton.org, *Water:* Small pond at Weston village in Bath, *Species:* Carp to 10lbs, Roach to 1.5lbs, Bream to 2lbs, Hybrids to 1lb, Tench to 4lbs., *Permits:* Bacons Tackle Box, 83 Lower Bristol Road, Bath, *Charges:* Adults £20, Combined lady and gent £28. Juniors £5.50. O.A.P £4.50. Registered disabled £5.50. Under 12's free. To year end 31/12/ 2002. Members only special day permits must be purchased in advance at £2 day, *Season:* Open all year, *Methods:* Special rules apply. Available from secretary, on website, from shop.

(Newton Park Pond)
Water: 2.5 acre lake at Newton park, near Bath, *Species:* Bream to 2.5lbs, Chub to 6lbs, Roach to 2lbs, Pike to 24lbs, Carp to 27lbs, *Permits:* Local fishing tackle shops (members only), *Charges:* Adults £20, Combined lady and gent £28. Juniors £5.50. O.A.P £4.50. Registered disabled £5.50. under 12's free. To year end 31/12/2002. Additional special day permit at £3 must be obtained before fishing, *Season:* Open all year fishing times vary according to time of year. No night fishing., *Methods:* Copies of rules available from secretary and tackle shops. Also displayed on notice boards at lakeside, and on website.

(Huntstrete Ponds)
Water: 3 lake complex at Hunstrete, near Pensford. Total 11 acres 120 pegs, *Species:* Bream to 8.5lbs, Chub to 2.5lbs, Roach to 2.5lbs, Pike to 22lbs, Carp to 28lbs, Tench to 9lbs, Perch to 2.5lbs, Crucians to 2lbs, Eels to 7lbs, *Permits:* Local fishing tackle shops (members only), *Charges:* Adults £20, Combined lady and gent £28. Juniors £5.50. O.A.P £4.50. Registered disabled £5.50. Under 12's free. To year end 31/12/2002. Additional special day permit at £2.50 must be obtained before fishing, *Season:* Open all year fishing times vary according to time of year. No night fishing., *Methods:* Copies of rules available from secretary and tackle shops. Also displayed on notice boards at lakeside, and on website.

BRIDGWATER
Avalon Fisheries
Contact: Allan Tedder (Ted), 7 Coronation Road, Bridgwater, TA6 7DS, 01278 456429, *Mobile:* 07855 825059, *Water:* 6 acre match Coarse and 3 acre specimen lakes, *Species:* Carp to mid 20's, Tench 7.5lb, Bream 9lb 2oz, Perch 3lb, Roach, Rudd, *Permits:* Site office and on the bank. Mobile Phone 0966 363413, *Charges:* £5 Adult, £3 Junior / O.A.P / Disabled, *Season:* No closed season - Open dawn to dusk, *Methods:* Barbless on specimen lake, No floating or boilie baits on coarse lake, all nuts banned on both lakes, boilies/night fishing allowed on carp lake only.
Bridgwater Angling Association (Coarse Lakes)
See entry under Taunton and Bridgwater Canal. Various stillwaters. Stillwater fishing at Combwich, Walrow, Dunwear & Screech Owl.
Bridgwater Sports & Social Club
Contact: Duncan & Sandra Smith, Bath Road, Bridgwater, TA6 4PA, 01278 446215, *Water:* 3 large ponds, *Species:* Carp to 26lb, Crucian to 3lb, Bream & Roach to 1.5lb, Perch to 4lb, Tench to 5lb, *Charges:* £25/person - private members fishing, *Season:* Normal open season, *Methods:* No night fishing

Browns Pond
Contact: Phil Dodds, Off Taunton Rd (A38), Bridgwater, 01278 444145, doddphilelen@aol.com, *Water:* 2.5 acres, *Species:* Carp to 22lb, Tench to 5lb, bream to 6lb, Perch to 2lb & Roach, *Charges:* On site. £2 per day, *Season:* Closed May, open June 1st - April 30th; dawn to dusk, *Methods:* No night fishing, barbless hooks only, no live bait, no carp sacks
Burton Springs Fishery (Coarse Lake)
Contact: Tony Evans, Lawson Farm, Burton, Nr Stogursey - Bridgwater, TA5 1QB, 01278 732135, burtonsprings@aol.co.uk, *Water:* Aprox 2 acre lake, *Species:* Mirror, Common, Leather Carp, Ghost Carp to 20lb, Tench to 5 lb, *Permits:* Self Service at fishing lodge, *Charges:* £5 per day, 2 rods, *Season:* Open all year 8am-9pm or dusk, *Methods:* Barbless hooks only, no nuts, only 'carp mesh' keepnets allowed for smaller carp, large carp to be released immediately
Durleigh Reservoir
Contact: Wessex Water, 0845 600 4 600, *Water:* 80 acre reservoir, *Species:* Carp, Roach, Bream, Perch, Tench and Pike, *Permits:* Contact Ranger Paul Martin on 01278 424786, *Charges:* Day Ticket £5, Day Concession £3.50, Evening Ticket £3.50, Book of Tickets £40 for 10, *Season:* Open all year except Christmas day, Boxing day & New Years day.
Plum Lane Fishery
Contact: Julie, Plum Lane, Dunwear, Bridgwater, 01278 421625, *Water:* 1 acre pond, *Species:* Predominately Carp to 10lb plus Tench. Roach and Skimmers, *Permits:* On site, *Charges:* £5 per adult (2 rods). One child can fish with an adult free of charge, *Season:* Open all year, *Methods:* Barbless hooks only. No keepnets. Advice available on site.
Summerhayes Fishery
Contact: Mike or Brian, Somerset Bridge, Bridgwater, TA6 6LW, 01278 781565, *Mobile:* 07703 115502, *Water:* Several lakes - totalling 6 acres, *Species:* Carp, Bream, Tench, Roach, Rudd, Perch, Ghost Carp, *Charges:* On bank £5 day, £3 concessions; disabled access, *Season:* Open all year dawn to dusk, *Methods:* Barbless hooks, no nuts.

Taunton Road Ponds
Contact: Phil Dodds, Off Taunton Rd (A38), Bridgwater, 01278 444145, doddphilelen@aol.com, *Water:* 3.5 acres, *Species:* Carp to 28lb, Tench to 6lb, bream to13lb 6oz, Perch to 3lb, Rudd to 2lb, skimmer Bream to 12oz & Roach to 8oz, *Charges:* On site, £2 per day, *Season:* Closed May, open June 1st - April 30th; dawn to dusk, *Methods:* No night fishing, barbless hooks only, no live bait, no large carp in keepnets, no carp sacks
The Sedges
Contact: Pat & John, River Lane, Dunwear, Bridgwater, TA7 0AA, 01278 445221, *Water:* 2 lakes totalling 7 acres, *Species:* Tench, Rudd, Roach, Bream, Chub, Carp to 32lb, *Charges:* On bank: £5 adult day, children accompanied by adult £4, *Season:* Open all year dawn to dusk, *Methods:* No keepnets in summer months, no carp sacks, barbless hooks, unhooking mats.
Trinity Waters
Contact: John Herring, Hopfield Fish Farms, Straight Drove, Chilton Trinity, Bridgwater, *Mobile:* 0772 0542141, *Water:* Currently 3 lakes: 6.5 acres, 2 acres and 1 acre. (6.5 and 1 acre lakes opening in 2002), *Species:* Rudd - 2lb. Roach - 2lb. Perch - 3lb. Tench - 6lb. Golden Tench - 5lb. Bream - 11lb. Mirror, Common and Grass Carp to 12lb, *Permits:* On site only, *Charges:* £5 per day, £7.50 for two rods. £3 juniors and concessions. Match rates on request, *Season:* Open all year dawn to dusk, *Methods:* Barbless hooks. No keepnets. No fixed rigs.

BRISTOL
Alcove Angling Club
Contact: Mr K.Davis (Membership Secretary), 6 Ashdene Ave, Upper Eastville, Bristol, BS5 6QH, 01179 025737, alcoveacbristol@yahoo.co.uk, *Water:* 4 lakes in Bristol & South Glos, *Species:* Carp, Bream, Roach, Tench, Rudd, Pike, Perch, *Permits:* As above, *Charges:* Adult £35, OAP/Disabled £20, *Season:* No close season, *Methods:* As specified in membership card, Night fishing at Alcove Lido only

Bagwood Lake

Contact: Trench Lane, Woodlands, Patchway, Bristol, BS32 4JZ, 01454 619319, *Water:* One coarse lake, *Species:* Carp, *Permits:* On site, pay in shop, *Charges:* £7 - 12 hour ticket. £13 - 24 hour ticket, *Season:* Open all year - night fishing by arrangement.

Bitterwell Lake

Contact: Mrs M Reid, The Chalet, Bitterwell Lake, Ram Hill, Coalpit Heath, Bristol, BS36 2UF, 01454 778960, *Water:* 2.5 Acres, *Species:* Common, Mirror, Crucian Carp, Roach, Bream, Rudd, Perch, *Charges:* £4 -1 rod. £2 second rod, O.A.P.'s etc, Reg. disabled and arrivals after 4 pm, *Season:* Closed for spawning 4 - 6 weeks May - June, *Methods:* Barbless hooks size 8 max, No bolt rigs, No boilies, No nuts, hemp or groundbait

Bristol, Bath & Wilts Amalgamated Anglers (Lakes)

Contact: Jeff Parker, 16 Lansdown View, Kingswood, Bristol, BS15 4AW, 0117 9672977, *Water:* See entry under Bristol Avon - Various stillwaters, too much to list here, please contact the secretary for full details; Stillwaters at Lyneham, Calne, Malmesbury, Bath and Pawlett near Bridgwater, *Species:* All coarse species, *Methods:* Max. 2 rods; no metal cans or glass allowed on banks; no freshwater fish to be used as livebait / Full rules and maps available

Frome Vale Angling Club (Coarse Pond)

Water: 1 acre lake at Brimsham Park, Yate Bristol. See entry under Bristol Frome.

Ham Green Fisheries

Contact: Mr Hunt, Ham Green, Chapel Lane, Pill, 01275 849885, *Mobile:* 07818 640227, *Water:* Two lakes. 1 acre 25 peg. 2 acre open bank, *Species:* 1 acre lake stocked with Carp, Roach, Rudd, Perch, Pike, Bream, Skimmers, Golden Tench and Golden Orfe. 2 acre lake all the above with Carp to 35lb, *Permits:* Mr Hunt, 21 Station Rd, Portishead, Bristol; also on lake side from baliff. Veals Tackle Shop, 61 Old Market St, Bristol, *Charges:* £5 in advance fron Veals Tackle or £7 on the bank, *Season:* No closed season. 7am to 8pm from 16 June to 13 October. 8am to 5pm from 1 November to 30 April. Night fishing strictly by arrangement, booking essential by telephone to Mr Hunt, *Methods:* No live bait, barbless hooks preferred, no keepnets for fish over 1lb, carp sacks allowed

Kingswood Disabled Angling Club

Contact: Ian Mearns, 0117 9641224, kingswooddisabledac@goldserve.net, *Water:* Bristol based Coarse fishing club meeting monthly. New members welcome. Must be registered disabled at local Social Services Office. Regular fishing trips and matches organised. Please phone for further information, *Charges:* £7.50 adults annual membership.

Paulton Lakes

Contact: Trevor Francis, Paulton, Bristol, BS39 7SY, 01761 413081, *Water:* 2 lakes totalling 2.5 acres, *Species:* Carp, Tench, Roach, Grass Carp, Rudd, Chub, *Permits:* Only from Paulton Builders Merchants, Paulton and A.M. Hobbs, Midsomer Norton. Tel (01761) 413961, *Charges:* £5 per day ticket, *Season:* Open all year, Dawn to dusk, *Methods:* Barbless hooks, No ground baiting, Unhooking mats must be used.

Tan House Farm Lake

Contact: Mr & Mrs James, Tan House Farm, Yate, Bristol, BS37 7QL, 01454 228280, *Water:* Quarter mile lake, *Species:* Roach, Perch, Carp, Bream, Tench, Rudd, *Permits:* Day tickets from Farm House, *Charges:* Adult £3 per rod or £5 for 2 rods, Children & O.A.Ps £2, *Season:* closed April 17th - May 28th, *Methods:* No Ground bait, Dog & cat food, Boilies, Barbless hooks only

CHARD

Chard & District Angling Club (Coarse Lakes)

Contact: Mr Braunton, Planet Video & Angling, 19a High Street, Chard, TA20 1QF, 01460 64000, *Water:* Perry Street Pond - 1.5 acres. Chard Reservoir - 48 acres. Also 3 miles on Isle see entry under associations, *Species:* Roach, Bream, Carp, Tench, Perch, Eels, Rudd, *Permits:* Planet Video & Angling, 19a High Street, Chard, Somerset TA20 1QF. Tel: 01460 64000. Perry Street Ponds - members only, details from secretary, *Charges:* Chard reservoir £5 per day (£3 club members). Perry Street ponds members only, membership £15, *Season:* Open all year, *Methods:* Full list of rules from fishery notice board and membership book

Marshwood Farm

Contact: Martin Wright, Marshwood Farm, Perry Street, Chard Junction, Chard, 01297 680218, t.glaspers@farmersweekly.net, *Water:* 1.5 acre lake, *Species:* Common and Mirror Carp to 25lb, *Permits:* Season £100. 7 day weekly ticket £23. No day tickets. Available in advance from the above, *Season:* Closed from 14th Match to 16th June. Open dawn to dusk - no night fishing, *Methods:* Barbless hooks. Minimum line 6lb. No boilies or tiger nuts. No keepnets or carp sacks. All litter to be removed. No radios, bivvies, barbecues. One rod only to be used.

CHEDDAR

Cheddar Angling Club

Contact: Cheddar Angling Club, P.O. Box 1183, Cheddar, BS27 3LT, 01934 743959, *Water:* 200 acre Cheddar reservoir, *Species:* Pike, Perch, Tench, Roach, Eels, Carp, *Permits:* Permits are NOT available at the reservoir. Only from: Broadway House Caravan Park, Axbridge Road, Cheddar, Somerset. Bristol Angling Centre, 12-16 Doncaster Road, Southmead, Bristol. Thatchers Pet and Tackle, 18 Queen St, Wells. Veals Fishing Tackle, 61 Old Market St, Bristol. Thyers Fishing Tackle, Church St, Highbridge, *Charges:* Seniors season permit £30, Juniors season permit £15, Seniors day permit £5, Juniors day permit £3, *Season:* Pike - 1st October to 31st March. All other species no closed season, *Methods:* No live baiting, Moderate ground baiting, No dead baiting until 1st October. No night fishing, dawn to dusk only. Unhooking mats recommended. Rod limits: seniors maximum 3 rods, juniors one rod only

Stone Yard Fisheries

Contact: Thatchers Angling, 18 Queen St, Wells, BA5 2DP, 01749 673513, *Water:* Small Ponds (15 Anglers) at Litton near Chewton Mendip, *Species:* Carp to approx 18lb, small Tench, *Permits:* Thatchers Angling 01749 673513. 5 tickets per day available from A.M. Hobbs Angling 01761 413961, *Charges:* Day £5 Senior, £2.50 Junior, *Season:* March 1st - October 31st, *Methods:* Barbless hooks only. No Boilies

CLEVEDON

N. Somerset Association of Anglers (Coarse Lakes)

Water: See also entry under River Fishing, Yeo. Apex lake: 6 acre lake, Newtown: 3 acre lake, Walrow ponds: 2 acre lake, 3 acre lake and 6 acre lake, *Species:* Apex: Carp to 18lbs, Bream to 7lb, Pike to 15lb, Roach, Rudd. Newtown: Carp to 24lb, Pike to 27lb, Bream 7lb, Roach, Rudd, Perch. Walrow: Carp to 26lb, Bream 11lb, Tench 10lb, Pike 24lb, Roach, Rudd, Perch, *Permits:* Local tackle shops, purchased in advance of fishing, *Charges:* £3 day, £10 week, £20 season, junior/OAP/disabled £8, *Season:* Apex & Newtown Lakes 1 June - 28 Feb. (incl.), Walrow Pond 16 June - 14 March (incl.), *Methods:* Apex & Newtown Lakes: Barbless hooks, min. 2.5lb BS line, no live or dead bait, no floating bait.

CONGRESBURY

Silver Springs Coarse Fishery

Contact: Liz Patch, Silver Street Lane, Congresbury, BS49 5EY, 01934 877073, *Water:* 4.5 acres, *Species:* Carp to low twenties, Rudd, Roach, Tench, Chub and Bream, *Permits:* On Site, *Charges:* £5 / £3.50 conc, *Season:* All year dawn till half hour before dusk, *Methods:* Barbless hooks

CORFE

Taunton Angling Association (Wych Lodge Lake)

Contact: Mr. J.Helyer, 40 Albemarle Road, Taunton, TA1 1BA, 01823 257559, kgregson@compuserve.com, *Water:* Wych lodge Lake, 5 acre large carp lake, *Species:* Large Carp up to 25lb, Roach, Rudd and Perch all to 2lb, *Permits:* Only from Topp Tackle, Taunton (restricted to 10 pegs). Please bring season ticket as proof of membership when purchasing day permit, *Charges:* £3 per day, *Season:* Open all year, *Methods:* Barbless hooks, no Carp in keepnets, no lighting of fires, no litter.

CREWKERNE

Highlands Dairy Lake

Contact: J.Wyatt, Highlands Dairy Farm, Hewish, Nr Crewkerne, 01460 74180, *Water:* 1 acre lake, *Species:* Carp, Tench, Rudd, Roach, Perch, *Permits:* At house, *Charges:* £4 per day including night fishing. £3 day ticket, *Season:* Open all year, *Methods:* No keepnets for Carp. Barbless hooks only.

Water Meadow Fishery

Contact: Mr. Pike, Pitt Farm, North Perrott, Crewkerne, TA18 7SX, 01460 72856, *Water:* 2 coarse lakes totalling approx 1.75 acres, *Species:* 16 different varieties of coarse fish, *Charges:* On site - £5 day. £3 morning/afternoon. £2 half day/evening, *Season:* Open all year - dawn to dusk, *Methods:* No boilies or keepnets, barbless hooks only, ground baiting in moderation.

FROME

Edneys Fisheries

Contact: Richard Candy, Edneys Farm, Mells, Frome, BA11 3RE, 01373 812294, *Mobile:* 07941 280075, *Water:* 2 lakes, *Species:* Carp, Tench, Roach, Rudd, Perch, Common, Mirror, Linear, Leather and Ghost Carp, *Charges:* Adults £5, Under 14 yrs £3. Evening tickets only available weekdays after 5pm at £3.

Frome Angling Association (Coarse Lake)

Water: 10 acre lake. See entry under River Fishing - Bristol Frome.

Mells Pit Pond

Contact: Mr M.Coles, Lyndhurst, Station Road, Mells, Nr Frome, BA11 3RJ, 01373 812094, *Water:* 1 acre lake, *Species:* Various Carp, Rudd, Roach, Tench, Perch, *Permits:* Tickets issued at bankside, *Charges:* £4/day, Season tickets £50, *Season:* Open all year, *Methods:* Barbless hooks. No keepnets

Parrots Paddock Farm (Coarse)

Contact: Mr. Baker, Wanstrow Rd, Nunnery Catch, 01373 836505, *Water:* 90yd x 75 yd pond, *Species:* Rainbow Trout & Coarse fish, *Permits:* Please phone first, *Season:* Open all year, dawn to dusk, *Methods:* No night fishing, keepnets only for small fish, barbless hooks only, ground bait in moderation.

Shepards Lake
Contact: John Nicholls, Barrow Farm, Witham Friary, Frome, BA11 5HD, 01749 850313, Water: Half acre lake, Species: Carp, Perch and Tench, Charges: £4 adult. £3.50 children and OAPs, Season: February to September. Phone for details, Methods: No restrictions.

Witham Friary Lakes
Contact: Mr. Miles, Witham Hall Farm, Witham Friary, Nr Frome, BA11 5HB, 01373 836239, Water: Two lakes totalling approx. 2 acres, Species: Carp, Roach, Tench, Perch, Gudgeon, Permits: On site, Charges: £4 a day - £6 night ticket (dusk - 8 am), Season: All year, Methods: Barbless hooks only.

HIGHBRIDGE

Emerald Pool Fishery
Contact: Mr Alan Wilkinson, Emerald Pool Fishery, Puriton Road, West Huntspill, Highbridge, TA9 3NL, 01278 794707, Water: 1.5 acre lake Plus 'Sapphire Lake' - new 20 peg disabled angler friendly pool for adults and juniors, Species: Bream, Golden Orfe, Roach, Rudd, Tench, Perch, Carp to low-mid 20's, Sturgeon to 4 feet long, Barbel 5lb, Permits: Enviroment Agency rod licence required on this water, Season: All year, Methods: Barbless hooks only, No Carp sacks, No peanuts or ground bait, All Sturgeon to be released immediately, No fish over 3lb to be retained at all

KEYNSHAM

Avon Valley Country Park (Coarse Pond)
Contact: Bath Rd, Keynsham, Bristol, BS31 1TP, 0117 9864929, info@avonvalleycountrypark.co.uk, Water: Small Coarse pond, Species: Carp to 12lb, Permits: From above, Charges: £4 Adult entrance to park (includes ticket to fish), £3 Child, £3.50 Senior Citizen, Season: Park open: Easter - 1st November 10am-6pm, Methods: Barbless hooks only, no keepnets

Keynsham Angling Association (Coarse Lake)
Contact: Mr K. N. Jerrom, 21 St Georges Road, Keynsham, Bristol, BS31 2HU, 01179 865193, Water: Century Ponds 0.25 acres. See also entry under river Chew, Species: Mixed Fishery, Charges: Day ticket for club members £2.50, Season: Open all year dawn to dusk. Closed alternate Sunday mornings until 1pm, Methods: Barbless hooks and no Boilies

KINGSTON SEYMOUR

Acorn Carp Fishery
Contact: Adrian and Bev Bartlett, Lampley Rd, Kingston Seymour, 01934 833760 or 834050 (lake), Water: 3.5 acres of water full disabled access to every swim, Species: Specimen Carp from 10 to 30lbs, Charges: Day tickets 7am - 7pm £10. Night 7pm-7am £10. 24 hours £15. weekly rates available.

Bullock Farm Fishing Lakes
Contact: Philip Simmons, Bullock Farm, Kingston Seymour, BS21 6XA, 01934 835020, bullockfarm@kingstonseymour1.freeserve.co.uk Water: 4 Lakes totalling 4.75 acres, including specialist Carp lake, Species: Carp - Common, Mirror, Ghost, Crucian, Grass, Purple and Koi. Tench, Roach, Rudd, Chub, Bream, Skimmer Bream, Golden Orfe, Golden Tench, Permits: Only at lakeside, Charges: £5.00 day ticket, £3.00 O.A.P's / Under 14s / Disabled. Season tickets & Match rates available, Season: Open all year round Dawn - Dusk, Methods: No boilies, Barbless hooks, Fish friendly keepnets only, No dogs, u14s to be accompanied by an adult, no loose-fed pellets, Common sense!

Plantations Lake
Contact: Mr or Mrs W.Travis, Middle Lane Farm, Middle Lane, Kingston Seymour, Clevedon, BS21 6XW, 01934 832325, Water: 0.75 acre Carp lake, 2.5 acre Coarse lake. New 1.75 acre match lake open, Species: 12 Species of coarse fish incl. Barbel, Crucian Carp. 3 Species of Carp in Carp lake, Charges: £5 Adult (£1 extra rod), £4.00 Juniors/ O.A.P's/Disabled. Half days (from 2pm) available: adult £4, juniors/OAPs £2.50. Please enquire for membership details, Season: All year, Methods: No boilies, Barbless hooks

LANGPORT

Langport & Dist. Angling Association (Coarse Lake)
Contact: den@barlow65.fsnet.co.uk, Water: Coombe Lake - 2.75 acres. See entry under Parrett, Species: Carp to 30lb, Tench 6.5lb, Roach 1.5lb, Perch 2lb plus, Bream 7lb, Chub 4lb, Permits: See entry under Parrett, Charges: See entry under Parrett, Season: No closed season. No night fishing, Methods: Barbless hooks, no boilies, no Carp in keepnets.

Thorney Lakes
Contact: Richard or Ann England, Thorney Farm, Muchelney, Langport, TA10 0DW, 01458 250811, thorneylakes@langport.totalserve.co.uk, Water: Two 2 Acre lakes, Species: A selection of coarse fish including large Carp, Permits: On the bank, Charges: £5/day, £3/half day after 4 p.m, £3 for O.A.Ps + Children under 16, Season: 16th March - 31st January, Methods: Barbless hooks, No boilies, nuts or pulses, All nets to be dipped on site, No night fishing

MARTOCK

Ash Ponds
Contact: Pat Rodford, Ash Ponds, Burrough Street, Ash, Martock, 01935 823459, Water: Four 1 acre ponds, Species: Carp, Tench and Bream, Permits: On the bank, Charges: £3 for 12 hours, Season: No closed season, Methods:

North Petherton
Follyfoot Farm
Contact: Rupert Preston, Follyfoot Farm, North Pertherton, TA6 6NW, 01278 662979, Mobile: 07748 400904, rpreston@eurobell.co.uk, Water: Three acre Carp lake, Species: Mirror, Koi and Common to 30lb, Permits: On the bank - self service, Charges: £5 per day, Season: Open all year dawn to dusk. Night fishing by prior arrangement only, Methods: No keepnets, barbless hooks only, no dogs or radios. Full rules at the fishery.

SHEPTON MALLET
Bridge Farm Fishery
Contact: John Thorners, Bridge Farm Shop, Pylle, Shepton Mallet, BA4 6TA, 01749 830138, *Water:* 0.25 mile long x 30m wide lake, approx 3 acres, *Species:* Common Carp to 15lb, Roach, Rudd and other coarse fish, *Permits:* From farm shop on arrival, *Charges:* Adults £5, Juniors u.16 £2.50, *Season:* Open all year, dawn to dusk, *Methods:* Barbless hooks only, no keepnets, for carp, no night fishing

SOMERTON
Miners Ponds
Contact: Lower Vobster, Coleford, Somerton, *Water:* 2 ponds totalling 1.5 acres approx, *Species:* Carp 28.25lb, Roach, Tench, Perch and Bream, *Permits:* AM Hobbs Angling, Midsomer Norton, Bath, Tel: 01761 413961; Haines Angling, 47 Vallis Way Frome, Tel: 01373 466406, *Charges:* Day tickets on bank, £5 per day, *Season:* Open June 16th - beginning March, dawn to dusk, *Methods:* No keepnets, no boilies, barbless hooks
Viaduct Fishery
Contact: Mr Steve Long, Viaduct Fishery, Cary Valley, Somerton, TA11 6LJ, 01458 274022, *Water:* Six Coarse Lakes including one specimen lake, *Species:* Mirror Carp 27lb, Crucian Carp, Common Carp 23lb, Perch 5lb, Roach 1.5lb, Bream 6lb, Tench 8lb and Golden Tench, Rudd, Ruffe, *Permits:* Fishery Shop or Pre-Payment Office; EA Rod licences available, *Charges:* Day ticket £5, Under 16 £4, Summer Evening ticket £3, Winter Half day ticket £3. £1 charge for second rod; Match bookings taken, *Season:* All year, *Methods:* All nets to be dipped, no nuts or boilies, barbless hooks size 10 max, no fixed rigs, no braid, fishing from pegs only.

STREET
Godney Moor Ponds
Contact: Nick Hughes, Street Angling Centre, 160 High Street, Street, BA16 0NH, 01458 447830, *Water:* Approx 4 acres, *Species:* Coarse fish including Carp, *Permits:* Only from Street Angling Centre, *Charges:* £4 per day (All genders), *Season:* April to February inclusive. Sunrise to sunset only, *Methods:* No nuts, 2 rods max. Carp fishing in large pond only.

Taunton Angling Association (Walton Ponds))
Contact: Mr. J.Helyer, 40 Albemarle Road, Taunton, TA1 1BA, 01823 257559, kgregson@compuserve.com, *Water:* Walton Ponds, Two ponds, *Species:* Carp 24lb, Tench 3lb, Roach 1lb, Rudd 1lb, Pike 22.5lb, *Permits:* Topp Tackle, 63 Station Road, Taunton, (01823) 282518. Enterprise Angling (01823) 282623. Somerset Angling, Bath Road, Bridgwater (01278) 431777. Street Angling, High street, Street (01458) 447830. Wellington Country Sports, 5 Lancer Court, High Street, Wellington.(01823) 662120, *Charges:* Season £23. Day tickets £4 senior, £2 junior, *Season:* Open all year, *Methods:* Barbless hooks, no Carp in keepnets.

TAUNTON
Frog Lane Carp Fishery
Contact: Frog Lane, Durston, Taunton, 07771 993135, *Water:* 4.5 acre lake, *Species:* Carp to 31lb, Tench, Bream and Rudd, *Permits:* On site, *Charges:* Day: £3.50, 24hrs: £5, *Season:* Open all year, night fishing allowed, *Methods:* Barbless hooks only, no tiger nuts, no keepnets
Ilminster & District A.A. (Coarse Lake)
Contact: P. Lonton, Marshalsea, Cottage Corner, Ilton, Ilminster, 01460 52519, *Water:* Thurlebeare - 1.5 acres, *Species:* Carp 18lb, Bream 6lb, Roach 1.5lb, Perch 2.5lb, Tench 6lb - mixed fishery, *Permits:* Enterprise Angling, Taunton and Ilminster Warehouse. Membership details from the secretary. Annual membership tickets from Ilminster Warehouse, Yeovil Angling Centre, The Tackle Shack, Chard Angling, Enterprise Angling, Taunton, *Charges:* £12 annual membership. Day tickets £3. Junior £2, *Season:* Open all year, *Methods:*

Taunton Angling Association (King Stanley Pond)
Contact: Mr. J.Helyer, 40 Albemarle Road, Taunton, TA1 1BA, 01823 257559, kgregson@compuserve.com, *Water:* King Stanley Pond, *Species:* Carp 20lb, Roach 1lb, Tench 3lb, Rudd 1lb, Perch 1lb, *Permits:* Topp Tackle, 63 Station Road, Taunton, (01823) 282518. Enterprise Angling (01823) 282623. Somerset Angling, Bath Road, Bridgwater (01278) 431777. Street Angling, High street, Street (01458) 447830. Wellington Country Sports, 5 Lancer Court, High Street, Wellington. (01823) 662120, *Charges:* Season £23. Day tickets £4 senior, £2 junior, *Season:* Open all year, *Methods:* Barbless hooks only. No Carp in keepnets.
(Maunsell Ponds)
Water: Three Ponds together comprising Maunsell Ponds, *Species:* Carp 20lb, Tench 5lb, Roach 1lb, Bream 3lb, Crucians 1lb, *Permits:* Topp Tackle, 63 Station Road, Taunton, (01823) 282518. Enterprise Angling (01823) 282623. Somerset Angling, Bath Road, Bridgwater (01278) 431777. Street Angling, High street, Street (01458) 447830. Wellington Country Sports, 5 Lancer Court, High Street, Wellington.(01823) 662120, *Charges:* Season £23. Day tickets £4 senior, £2 junior, *Season:* Open all year, *Methods:* Barbless hooks, no Carp in keepnets.
(Wellington Basins)
Water: Wellington Basins, two small ponds, *Species:* Bream 5lb, Roach 1lb, Perch 1lb, Carp 15lb, Pike 10lb, *Permits:* Topp Tackle, 63 Station Road, Taunton, (01823) 282518. Enterprise Angling (01823) 282623. Somerset Angling, Bath Road, Bridgwater (01278) 431777. Street Angling, High street, Street (01458) 447830. Wellington Country Sports, 5 Lancer Court, High Street, Wellington.(01823) 662120, *Charges:* Season £23. Day tickets £4 senior, £2 junior, *Season:* Open all year, *Methods:* Barbless hooks, no Carp in keepnets.

WEDMORE

Lands End Farm Fishery
Contact: Martin Duckett, Heath House, Wedmore, BS28 4UQ, 07977 545882, *Water:* Match Lake and specimen Lake, total 3 acres, *Species:* Carp to 22lb (Common, Mirror, Ghost, Crucian) Grass Carp to 17lb, Bream to 8lb, Tench and Roach 2lb, Rudd, Chub, Ide, Perch, Barbel, Golden Orfe to 4lb, *Permits:* From offfice on site, *Charges:* £5/day, £3 after 4pm, £4 juniors, £4 conc, *Season:* Open all year. 7am to dusk in the summer, *Methods:* Barbless hooks only, No keepnets, No dog biscuits, boilies or nuts

WELLINGTON

Langford Lakes (Coarse Lakes)
Contact: Mr. Hendy, Middle Hill Farm, Langford Budville, Wellington, 01823 400476, *Water:* 4 lakes totalling 3.5 acres, *Species:* Carp, Roach, Perch, Tench, Bream, *Charges:* Prices on application, *Season:* Open all year dawn to dusk, *Methods:* Natural baits only, barbless hooks, full list at fishery.

WELLS

Emborough Ponds
Contact: Thatchers Tackle, 18 Queen Street, Wells, BA5 2DP, 01749 673513, *Water:* 3.5 acre lake, *Species:* Carp to 25lb, Tench 8lb, small Roach, *Charges:* Limited membership, please enquire at Thatchers Tackle, *Season:* 1 March - 31 December, *Methods:*

WINTERBOURNE

Frome Vale Angling Club (Coarse Lake)
Water: Half acre lake at Winterbourne. See entry under Bristol Frome.

WIVELISCOMBE

Oxenleaze Farm Caravans & Coarse Fishery
Contact: Richard & Marion Rottenbury, Chipstable, Wiveliscombe, TA4 2QH, 01984 623427, enquiries@oxenleazefarm.co.uk, *Water:* 3 Lakes 2 acres, *Species:* Carp 30lb, Tench 9lb, Roach 2lb 6oz, Rudd 2lb 3oz, Bream 8lb, *Permits:* At above address, *Charges:* £5/person/day (2 Rods max), Spectators 50p/person/day, *Season:* 1st April - 31st October, *Methods:* Barbless Hooks, No ground bait

YEOVIL

Ashmead Lakes
Contact: Steve Maynard, Stone Farm, Ash, Martock, TA12 6PB, 01935 823319, *Water:* 11 acres, *Species:* Mirror and Common Carp to over 30lb, *Charges:* Syndicate water. Please phone for details, *Season:* Closed January to mid February, *Methods:* No restrictions.

Stoke Sub Hamdon & District AA
Contact: 01935 824337, *Water:* Bearley Lake (no night fishing) - See entry under River Parrett.

The Old Mill Fishery
Contact: Mike Maxwell, Tucking Mill Farm, Stoford, Yeovil, BA22 9TX, 01935 414771, roz_maxwell@hotmail.com, *Water:* Three 1.5 acre lakes plus fishing on a tributary of the river Yeo and a canal, *Species:* 21 different species of coarse Fish. River contains Roach, Dace, Chub and Barbel, *Permits:* On the bank, *Charges:* Permit for lakes and river £5/day (£2.50 accompanied juniors u.16yrs). £2 evening ticket 5pm onwards in summer. Club bookings taken, *Season:* Open all year 7am to dusk, *Methods:* Barbless hooks only. Keepnets permitted in winter only. No keepnets between April and October. Keepnets always permitted during organised matches.

Yeovil & Sherborne Angling Association (Coarse Lakes)
Contact: Alex Murray, 2 Wisteria Close, Yeovil, BA21 2EE, *Mobile:* 07818 098057, *Water:* Sherborne Castle Lake & discounted tickets Viaduct Fishery. Also see River Yeo entry, *Species:* Roach, Bream, Carp, *Permits:* Membership details from above + local tackle shops, *Charges:* No day tickets. Club card £10, includes half price fishing at Viaduct.

SOMERSET Stillwater Trout

BRIDGWATER

Burton Springs Fishery (Trout Lake)
Contact: Tony Evans, Lawson Farm, Burton, Nr Stogursey, Bridgewater, TA5 1QB, 01278 732135, burtonsprings@aol.co.uk, *Water:* Aprox 1.5 acre lake, *Species:* Brown, Rainbow, Tiger & Blue Trout, *Permits:* Self service at fishing lodge, *Charges:* 4-fish ticket £22, 3-fish £18, 2-fish/ 5hr £15, sporting ticket £10 (catch & release permitted after limit), *Season:* Open all year 8am-9pm or dusk, *Methods:* Barbless hooks only, only Rainbow Trout may be taken

Hawkridge Reservoir
Contact: Wessex Water, 0845 600 4 600, *Water:* 32 acre reservoir, *Species:* Brown and Rainbow Trout, *Permits:* Ranger Gary Howe Tel 01278 671840, *Charges:* Day Ticket £13, Season Ticket £390, Day Concession £11, Season Concession £290, Evening Ticket £8 (no concessions). Book of Tickets - £70 for 6 available only from the ranger. Concession book of tickets £60, *Season:* 20 March -13 November 2002.

Quantock Fishery
Contact: Sue & Neil Bruce-Miller, Quantock Fishery, Stream Farm, Broomfield, Bridgwater, TA5 2EN, 01823 451367, quantock@quantockforce9.co.uk, *Water:* 1 x 2 acre spring fed lake + 1 x 0.5 acre spring fed lake, *Species:* Brown + Tiger Trout, Rainbow Trout to 20lb, *Charges:* Prices on application and booking advisable, *Season:* Open every day all year dawn to dusk, *Methods:* Barbless hooks only, Two fish limit - then catch + release, all fish over 6lb to be returned

BRISTOL

Blagdon Lake
Contact: Bob Handford, Blagdon Lake, Park Lane, Blagdon, BS40 7UD, 01275 332339, bob.handford@bristolwater.co.uk, *Water:* 440 Acre Lake, *Species:* Rainbow Trout best 16lb 4oz, Brown Trout best 10lb 4oz, *Permits:* Woodford Lodge, Chew Valley Lake, Blagdon Lodge and Blagdon Lake, *Charges:* Day bank £15, O.A.P. £13, Junior £7.50, Evening Bank £12 - Day boat £22.50, O.A.P. £20.50, Junior £16, Afternoon £18.50, Evening £15 - Season £540, O.A.P. £340 (Valid at Chew and Barrows also), *Season:* 25 March - 30 November 2002, *Methods:* Fly fishing only.

Bristol Reservoir Flyfishers Association
Contact: Roger Stenner, 18 Stafford Place, Weston-Super-Mare, BS23 2QZ, 01934 417606, *Water:* Fishing on Bristol Waterworks reservoirs. Blagdon, Chew Valley and Barrows. Competitions organised from bank or boat. Tuition offered. Full winter programme of activities including: tackle auctions, fly tying sessions, beginners and improvers casting sessions, *Species:* Rainbow and Brown Trout, *Permits:* Day tickets direct from Bristol Water. Club does not sell day tickets, *Charges:* £3 joining fee. Annual membership £7.50 full members, £5 pensioners and registered disabled, joining fee £1 juniors - annual membership fee juniors free.

Cameley Lakes
Contact: J. Harris, Hillcrest Farm, Cameley, Temple Cloud, BS18 5AQ, 01761 452423, *Water:* One 2.5 acre lake and three 1acre lake plus fishing on the river River Cam, *Species:* Rainbow Trout, Brown Trout 1 - 5lb, *Permits:* Car park, *Charges:* £20 incl VAT Day ticket 4 fish, £15 incl VAT Half Day ticket 2 fish, *Season:* Open all year - 8.00 till sundown, *Methods:* Fly fishing only. Hooks no larger than 1 inch

Chew
Contact: Bob Handford, Woodford Lodge, Chew Stoke, Nr.Bristol, BS40 8XH, 01275 332339, bob.handford@bristolwater.co.uk, *Water:* 1,200 Acre lake, *Species:* Rainbow Trout to 14lb 6oz, Brown Trout to 13lb 3oz, *Permits:* Woodford Lodge, Chew Lake, *Charges:* Day bank £13, O.A.P. £11, Junior £6.50, Evening bank £10 - Day boat £28.50, O.A.P. £26, Junior £21, Afternoon £23, Evening £17.50 - Season £440, O.A.P. £290 (Valid at Barrows also), *Season:* 25 March - 30 November 2002, *Methods:* Fly fishing only.

Litton Lakes
Contact: Bob Handford, 01275 332339, bob.handford@bristolwater.co.uk, *Water:* 7 acre lake and 11 acre lake at Coley, Nr Chewton Mendip, *Species:* Brown & Rainbow Trout, *Permits:* Woodford Lodge, Chew Valley Lake, *Charges:* £90 permit for two rods, fishing both lakes exclusively, *Season:* Open all year, *Methods:* Fly fishing only.

The Barrows
Contact: Bob Handford, 01275 332339, bob.handford@bristolwater.co.uk, *Water:* Three lakes of 25 acres (No. 1) 40 acres (No. 2) 60 acres (No.3) at Barrow Gurney, Nr. Bristol, *Species:* Rainbow Trout (10lb 10oz) Brown Trout (9lb 1oz), *Permits:* Woodford Lodge, Chew Valley Lake, *Charges:* Day bank £10.50, O.A.P. £9, Junior £6, Evening bank £8.50, Season £330, O.A.P. £217, *Season:* 25 March - 30 November 2002, *Methods:* Fly fishing only.

CONGRESBURY

Silver Springs Trout Fishery
Contact: Liz Patch, Silver Street Lane, Congresbury, BS49 5EY, 01934 877073, *Water:* 2.5 acres, *Species:* Rainbows, *Permits:* On Site, *Charges:* 4 Fish £20 - 3 @ £17 - 2 @ £14 - O.A.P./ u16 £18, £15 & £12 respectively, *Season:* All year, *Methods:* Fly only

DULVERTON

Exe Valley Fishery
Contact: Andrew Maund, Exebridge, Dulverton, 01398 323328, enquiries@exevalleyfishery.co.uk, *Water:* 3 Lakes fly only (2 + 1 + 3/4 acre lakes), 1 Small lake any method half acre, *Species:* Rainbow Trout, *Permits:* Day Tickets, *Charges:* Day ticket £5.50 5 fish limit, plus £3.50 per kilo, Half day ticket 3 fish limit, £3.30 plus £3.50 per kilo, *Season:* All year, *Methods:* See above

Wimbleball
Contact: South West Lakes Trust, 01837 871565, info@swlakestrust.org.uk, *Water:* Information Office Hours 01398 371372, *Species:* Premier Rainbow Fishery - Boat & Bank (boats may be booked in advance: 01398-371372). Rod average for 2001: 3.78 fish/rod/day. Biggest fish: Rainbow 11lb 9oz, *Permits:* Self service at Hill Barn Farm, *Charges:* Full day £16.25, Season £385. Reduced day £13, Season £290, Child/Wheelchair £3, Season £90. Evening Monday - Friday £13. Season Permits can be used on any Premier Fishery only. Boats £10 per day inc. 2 fish extra to bag limits. 'Wheelie Boat' available for disabled anglers (must be booked at least 48 hrs in advance). This venue may be booked for competitions, *Season:* Opens 23 March 2002 - 31st October, *Methods:* Fly fishing only. No child under 14 years may fish unless accompanied by an adult over 18 years

FROME

Parrots Paddock Farm (Trout)
Contact: Mr. Baker, Wanstrow Rd, Nunnery Catch, 01373 836505, *Water:* Rainbow Trout. See entry under Stillwater Coarse.

TAUNTON

Hawkridge Fly Fishing Club
Contact: Mrs Sally Pizii, Tumbleweed Cottage, Curry Mallet, Nr. Taunton, TA3 6SR, 01823 480710, *Water:* Primarily fishing on Hawkridge Reservoir. Club meetings 8pm second Tuesday of the month at The Blake Arms, Bridgwater. Visiting speakers & monthly competitions in season. Club trips, fly tying and social evenings.

Otterhead Lakes
Contact: M.G. Woollen, *Water:* See main entry for Taunton Fly Fishing Club under River Axe, Somerset.

WIVELISCOMBE
Clatworthy Fly Fishing Club
Contact: Mr F Yeandle, 51 Mountway Rd, Bishops Hull, Taunton, TA1 3LT, 01823 283959, *Water:* 130 acre Clatworthy reservoir on Exmoor, *Species:* Rainbow and Brown Trout, *Permits:* On site from Lodge, *Charges:* Day Ticket £13/5-fish limit, Concessions £11 OAP's. Evening Ticket £8. 6 Days £70, Concessions £60. Season £390/4-fish limit (only 4 visits/week allowed), Concession £290. Boats £10/day, £6 evening, *Season:* Open 20th March -13th October, *Methods:* Fly Fishing Only
Clatworthy Reservoir
Contact: Wessex Water, 0845 600 4 600, *Water:* 130 acre reservoir, *Species:* Rainbow and Brown Trout, *Permits:* Contact ranger Dave Pursey on 01984 624658, *Charges:* Day Ticket £13, Season Ticket £390, Day Concession £11, Season Concession £290, Evening Ticket £8 (no concessions). Book of Tickets - £70 for 6 available only from the ranger. Concession book of tickets £60, *Season:* 20 Mar - 13 Oct 2002.

YEOVIL
Sutton Bingham Fly Fishers Association
Contact: Dave Stacey or Colin Greenham, 01935 423223 or 01935 824714, *Water:* Hold regular competitions throughout the season. For members only. Tuition available. Fly tying classes held during the close season, *Charges:* New members always welcome. Adult and junior £3 per year.
Sutton Bingham Reservoir
Contact: Wessex Water, 0845 600 4 600, *Water:* 142 acre reservoir, *Species:* Rainbow and Brown Trout, *Permits:* Contact ranger Ivan Tinsley on 01935 872389. Advisable to book boats in advance, *Charges:* Day Ticket £13, Season Ticket £390, Day Concession £11, Season Concession £290, Evening Ticket £8 (no concessions). Book of Tickets - £70 for 6, available only from the ranger. Concession book of tickets £60. Wheelie boat available for wheelchair users., *Season:* 20 March - 13 October 2002.

WILTSHIRE River Fishing

AVON HAMPSHIRE
For detailed description of the Avon, see under Hampshire river fishing.

Chalk Stream Angler Fishery
Contact: Simon Cain, Meadow Barn, Lower Woodford, Salisbury, SP3 4EH, 01722 782602, info@chalkstreamangler.co.uk, *Water:* Approx. 2 mile upper Avon consisting of main river and carrier streams. Disabled access, *Species:* Wild Brown Trout and Grayling, *Charges:* Trout Season £60-£94/rod/day; Grayling period £35/rod/day, *Season:* Trout 15 April - 15 October, Grayling 16 October - 15 December, *Methods:* Upstream dry fly and nymph, Barbless hooks, catch & release, Long trotting for Grayling in the 'Grayling period'
Salisbury & District Angling Club
Contact: Rick Polden - Secretary, 29a Castle Street, Salisbury, SP1 1TT, 01722 321164, chairman@salisburydistrictac.co.uk, *Water:* Several Stretches on River Avon at Little Durnford, Amesbury, Ratfyn Farm & Countess Water. Also fishing on Dorset Stour, River Wylye, Nadder, Bourne & Ratfyn Lake at Amesbury, *Species:* All species Coarse and Game, *Charges:* Full or Associate Membership available. Details from the secretary. Coarse £55 plus £15 initial joining fee. Concessions for Senior Citizens & Juniors; Game £113, *Season:* Lakes: 1st June - 31st March. Rivers: 16th June - 14th March.

Services Dry Fly Fishing Association
Contact: Major (Retd) CD Taylor - Hon Secretary, c/o G2 Sy,HQ 43 (Wessex) Brigade, Picton Barracks, Bulford Camp, Salisbury, SP4 9NY, 01980 672161, *Water:* 7 miles on River Avon from Bulford upstream to Fifield, *Species:* Brown Trout & Grayling, *Permits:* Fishing Restricted to Serving & Retired members of the Armed Forces. for membership details apply to Secretary, *Charges:* On Application, *Season:* 1st May - 15th October. Grayling until 31st December, *Methods:* Only upstream fishing permitted, dry fly exclusively during May & dry fly/nymph thereafter
Wroughton Angling Club
Contact: Mr T.L.Moulton, 70 Perry's Lane, Wroughton, Swindon, SN4 9AP, 01793 813155, *Water:* 1.25 miles Rivers Avon and Marden at Chippenham, Reservoir at Wroughton, *Species:* Roach, Perch, Bream, Pike, Barbel, Chub, Carp, Tench, *Permits:* Mr M. Shayler, 20 Saville Crescent, Wroughton, Swindon, WILTS, Tel.: 01793 637313, *Charges:* £12.50 per season (day tickets £5 seniors), *Methods:* Restrictions - No Boilies, Peanuts, Particle baits, Dog biscuits or Nuts of any description
Upavon Farm
Contact: Peter C Prince, No 3 The Old Tractor Yard, Rushall, Near Pewsey, SN9 6EN, 01980 630008, *Mobile:* 0770 922544, princeproperties@msn.com, *Water:* 0.75 miles on Hampshire Avon in Wiltshire, *Species:* Brown Trout, both stocked and wild, up to 3lb average 1.5lb. Wild Grayling to 2lb average 1lb, *Permits:* Day, Season Permits, *Charges:* Day - £35 weekdays, £45 weekends and public holidays, *Season:* Brown Trout commences 15 April, ends 30 September. Grayling fishing thereafter, *Methods:* Catch and release, barbless hooks excepting annual season ticket holders.

AVON - WILTSHIRE

Avon Springs Fishing Lake
(Wiltshire Avon)

Contact: BJ Bawden, Recreation Road, Durrington, Salisbury, SP4 8HH, 01980 653557, *Mobile:* 07774 801401, barrie@fishingfly.co.uk, *Water:* 1 mile Wiltshire Avon at Durrington, *Species:* Brown Trout and Grayling, *Permits:* Also contact: mobile 07774 801401. Email barrie@fishingfly.co.uk, *Charges:* £45 day ticket, *Methods:* Fly only

BRISTOL AVON

Malmesbury to Chippenham

Coarse fisheries predominate in this section, although Trout are stocked by fishing associations in some areas. Arguably one of the best fisheries in the country, this section contains a wide range of specimen fish. Local records include: Roach 3lb 2oz, Perch 3lb 3oz, Tench 8lb 5 1/2oz, Bream 8lb 8oz, Dace 1lb 2oz, Chub 7lb 10oz, Carp 20lb 8 1/4oz and Pike 33lb 3oz. Also many Barbel to 12lb have been reported.

Airsprung Angling Association
(Bristol Avon)

Contact: Alan Lampard, 6 Hewitt Close, Trowbridge, BA14 7SG, 01225 764388, *Water:* See also entry under Kennet & Avon Canal. Bristol Avon at Bradford on Avon, Pondfields, Staverton Meadows, and between Holt and Melksham, *Species:* Carp, Bream, Chub, Roach, Rudd, Dace, Tench, Perch, etc, *Permits:* Association Licence only (no day tickets on river), *Charges:* On application, *Season:* Subject to normal close season, *Methods:* Details from Association.

Avon Angling Club (Bristol Avon)

Contact: R.P. Edwards, 56 Addison Road, Melksham, SN12 8DR, 01225 705036, *Water:* 4 miles of Bristol Avon. see also entry under Kennet and Avon Canal, *Species:* Roach, Bream, Tench, Chub, Barbel, Perch, Pike, Eels, *Permits:* Haines Tackle, Frome; Robbs Tackle, Chippenham; Wiltshire Angling, Trowbridge; Melksham Angling Centre call 01225 705036, *Charges:* Day ticket £2. Full Licence £12. Junior Licence £4, *Season:* Current EA Byelaws apply, *Methods:* No restrictions.

Bradford-on-Avon & District A.A.

Contact: 4 Fitzmaurice Close, Bradford-on-Avon, 01225 763835, *Water:* 7 miles River Avon at Staverton and Bradford-on-Avon. 2 miles river Frome at Langham Farm nr Tellisford. 5 miles Kennet & Avon Canal, *Species:* Barton Farm: Mainly quality Bream, big Chub, Roach, Tench & Dace. Nets of Bream in excess of 100lb. Canal: Mainly Tench, Bream with good Perch & Roach. Frome: large Bream, Chub, Tench. Quality Roach, Dace and Perch. Avon: Large Bream shoals, big Chub, Carp, Roach and Perch, *Permits:* Club licence and day/weekly permits from Wiltshire Angling (5 Timbrell St. Trowbridge, 01225-763835), St. Margarets News Bradford-on-Avon, Haines Angling, Frome. Season/ week/ day permits available from most tackle outlets in the area, *Charges:* Senior: season: £20 / week: £10 / day: £3 - Junior, OAP, disabled: season: £9 / week: £5 / day: £1.5, *Season:* June 16th - March 14th inc. Canal open all year, *Methods:* Not more than 2 rods at any one time, no more than 4 mtrs apart. Keepnets allowed; Bloodworm allowed from October 31st. No livebaiting.

Calne Angling Association

Contact: Miss JM Knowler, 123a London Road, Calne, 01249 812003, *Water:* River Avon, River Marden and a lake, *Species:* Barbel to 8lb, Pike to 8lb, Carp to 10lb, Bream to 6lb, Rudd to 8oz, Roach to 2.5lb; Wild Carp in lake, *Permits:* T.K.Tackle, *Charges:* Please enquire at T.K.Tackle, *Season:* River: June - March, Lake: open all year, *Methods:* No restrictions

Chippenham Angling Club

Contact: Mr Duffield, 95 Malmesbury Road, Chippenham, SN15 1PY, 01249 655575, sw1/964952@aol.com, *Water:* 8 miles on River Avon. Carp lake at Corsham, *Species:* Barbel, Chub, Roach, Bream, Perch, Pike, Tench, *Permits:* Robs Tackle, Chippenham - Tel: 01249 659210, *Charges:* Please telephone for prices. *Season:* June 16th - March 14th, *Methods:* No boilies or keepnets on Carp lake.

Swindon Isis Angling Club
(Bristol Avon)

Water: Two miles of the Bristol Avon at Sutton Benger near Chippenham. See also entry under Thames, *Species:* Bream 9lb 9oz, Perch 4lb, Tench 8lb, Barbel 11lb, Pike 28lb, Roach 2lb 7oz and usual species, *Permits:* Tackle shops in Swindon, Chippenham, Cirencester and Calne, *Charges:* As per Thames entry, *Season:* From 16th June to 14th March, *Methods:* No Bans

KENNET AND AVON CANAL

There are some 58 kilometres of canal within the Bristol Avon catchment area which averages one metre in depth and thirteen metres in width. The Kennet & Avon Canal joins the River Avon at Bath with the River Kennet between Reading and Newbury. The canal was opened in 1810 to link the Severn Estuary with the Thames. The canal, now much restored, provides excellent fishing with Carp to 25lb, Tench to 5lb also Roach, Bream, Perch, Rudd, Pike and Gudgeon.

Airsprung Angling Association
(Kennet & Avon)

Contact: Alan Lampard, 6, Hewitt Close, Trowbridge, BA14 7SG, 01225 764388, *Water:* Two kilometres on Kennet and Avon Canal from Beehive Pub to Avoncliffe aquaduct at Bradford-on-Avon, *Species:* Carp, Bream, Chub, Roach, Rudd, Dace, Tench, Perch, etc, *Permits:* St Margarets News, 45 St Margarets Street, Bradford-on-Avon, Wilts.; Wiltshire Angling, 01225-763835; West Tackle, Trowbridge, 01225 755472, *Charges:* Day ticket £2. Full licence price on application, *Season:* Open all year, *Methods:* No night fishing. No fishing on match days in pegged areas. No radios etc. No fishing within 25 metres of locks etc. No bloodworm or joker; be aware of overhead cables !

Avon Angling Club (Kennet and Avon)

Contact: R.P. Edwards, 56 Addison Road, Melksham, SN12 8DR, 01225 705036, *Water:* 1 mile of Kennet and Avon Canal. See also entry under Bristol Avon, *Species:* Bream, Tench, Roach, Carp, *Permits:* Haines Tackle, Frome; Wiltshire Angling, Trowbridge; Robbs Tackle, Chippenham, Melksham Angling Centre or call 01225 705036, *Season:* All year.

Devizes A.A. (Kennet & Avon Canal)
Contact: T.W. Fell, 21 Cornwall Crescent, Devizes, SN10 5HG, 01380 725189, *Water:* 15 miles from Semington to Pewsey, also 6.5 acre lake, *Species:* Carp 15 - 23lb, Roach, Tench, Pike to 26lb, Bream, *Permits:* Angling Centre, Snuff St, Devizes, Wiltshire. Tel: 01380 722350. Local tackle shops in Devizes, Melksham, Trowbridge, Chippenham, Calne, Swindon. Wiltshire Angling: 01225-763835, *Charges:* Adult £20 per season. Junior £7.50. Day tickets £3.50 (not sold on the bank). 14 day ticket £8, *Season:* E.A. byelaws apply, *Methods:* Please use barbless hooks

Marlborough & District A.A
Contact: Mr.M.Ellis, Failte, Elcot Close, Marlborough, SN8 2BB, 01672 512922, *Water:* Kennet & Avon Canal (12 miles approx), *Species:* Roach, Perch, Pike, Tench, Bream, Carp, *Permits: Charges:* Full membership £25 plus £5 joining fee, Junior up to 16 £5, Ladies £5, O.A.P's £5, *Season:* Open all year. Membership from 1st Jan - 31st Dec, *Methods:* No live baiting, No bloodworm or joker

Pewsey & District Angling Association
Contact: Don Underwood, 51 Swan Meadow, Pewsey, SN9 5HP, 01672 562541, *Water:* 4 Miles Kennet & Avon canal, *Species:* Roach, Tench, Carp, Bream, Perch, Pike, *Permits:* The Wharf, Pewsey, *Charges:* Day tickets Senior £3 / Junior/OAP £2. Prices may change for 2002, *Season:* No closed season, *Methods:* Rod and line.

NADDER

The River Nadder rises near Tisbury draining the escarpment of the South Wiltshire Downs and Kimmeridge Clay of the Wardour Vale. The River Wylye joins the Nadder near Wilton before entering the main River Avon at Salisbury.
The Nadder is well known as a mixed fishery of exceptional quality; there is a diverse array of resident species including Chub, Roach, Dace, Bream, Pike, Perch, Brown Trout and Salmon. Much of the fishing is controlled by estates and syndicates although two angling clubs offer some access to the river.

Compton Chamberlayne Estate
Contact: Simon Cooper, Fishing Breaks, Walton House, 23 Compton Terrace, N1 2UN, 020 7359 8818, info@fishingbreaks.co.uk, *Water:* Four miles of double bank fishing, divided into 7 beats, *Species:* Brown and Rainbow Trout, *Charges:* £80 per person per day plus VAT, *Season:* May to September, *Methods:* Dry fly and Nymph only.

Tisbury Angling Club
Contact: Mr E.J.Stevens, Knapp Cottage, Fovant, Salisbury, SP3 5JW, 01722 714245, *Water:* 3 miles on River Nadder. 3.5 acre lake and 2.5 acre lake, *Species:* Roach, Chub, Dace, Pike, Bream, Perch, Carp, Brown trout, *Permits:* Phone for details, *Charges:* Adult £4 joining fee and £24 per season. Juniors £7.50 per season. OAPs £12.50 per season. Seniors £5 per day (dawn to dusk) Juniors £3 per day (dawn to dusk). New members welcome, *Season:* 16th June to 14th March, *Methods:* General

SEMINGTON BROOK

The Semington Brook is spring fed from Salisbury Plain and flows through a flat area to its confluence with the River Avon downstream of Melksham. In the upper reaches and in some of its tributaries Brown Trout predominate. Downstream of Bulkington coarse fish prevail with sizeable Bream, Chub, Roach, Dace and Perch.

Lavington Angling Club
Contact: Mr Gilbert, Gable Cottage, 24 High Street, Erlestokes, Nr Devizes, SN10 5TZ, 01380 830425, *Water:* Baldam Mill section of Semington Brook, *Species:* Coarse and Game, *Permits:* Membership details from Mr Gilbert, *Season:* Current EA byelaws apply.

STOUR

See description under Dorset, river fishing.

Stourhead (Western) Estate
Contact: Sonia Booth, Estate Office Gasper Mill, Stourton, Warminster, BA12 6PU, (01747) 840643, sonia@stourhead.com, *Water:* 10 ponds and lakes, largest 10 acres, on the headwaters of the Stour, *Species:* Wild Brown Trout, Perch, Tench, Bream, Roach, Carp, *Charges:* Season permit for fly fishing £100.

THAMES

Swindon Isis Angling Club (Thames)
Contact: Peter Gilbert, 31 Havelock St, Swindon, SN1 1SD, 01793 535396, *Water:* 2 mile of river Thames at Water Eaton near Cricklade, Swindon, *Species:* Barbel 9lb, Chub 4.5lb, Roach 2lb, Bream 7lb, Perch 2lb, *Permits:* Tackle shops in Swindon, Chippenham, Cirencester and Calne, *Charges:* Club Permits: Senior £34.50. OAP and disabled £12. Juniors £8. The club permit contains two free day tickets and more day tickets can be obtained for £5 each; 1/2 year starts 1 November, £12 & £6 all others, *Season:* From 16th June to 14th March, *Methods:* No bans

WYLYE

The River Wylye rises near Kingston Deverill and flows off chalk, draining the western reaches of Salisbury Plain. The river confluences with the River Nadder at Wilton near Salisbury, then joins the main River Avon which flows south to Christchurch.
This river is best described as a 'classic' chalk stream supporting predominantly Brown Trout; hence most fisheries here are managed for fly fishermen. The fishing is predominantly controlled by local syndicates and estates.

Boreham Mill
Contact: Simon Cooper, Fishing Breaks, Walton House, 23 Compton Terrace, N1 2UN, 020 7359 8818, info@fishingbreaks.co.uk, *Water:* Half mile of double bank fishing and Hatch pool south of Warminster, *Species:* Brown Trout, *Charges:* £65 plus VAT per day one person. £115 plus VAT per day 2 people, *Season:* May to September, *Methods:* Dry fly & Nymph only.

Langford Lakes (River Wylye)
Contact: Emma Day, Duck Street, Steeple Langford, Salisbury, 01380 725670, eday@wiltshirewildlife.org, *Water:* Wylye - half mile, *Species:* Brown trout, Grayling, *Charges:* On application, *Season:* April 15th - Oct 14th Trout season. Oct 15th - March 14th Grayling season, *Methods:* Fly Only

Sutton Veny Estate
Contact: Mr & Mrs A.Walker, Eastleigh Farm, Bishopstrow, Warminster, BA12 7BE, 01985 212325, *Methods:* 07836 294633, enquiries@chalkstream.co.uk, *Water:* 4.5 miles on River Wylye. 2 miles of only wild trout, *Species:* Brown Trout and Grayling, *Charges:* £50/day (no beats), Season tickets upon request, Sutton Veny Fishing Syndicate – details on request, *Season:* 15th April - 15th October, *Methods:* Dry fly and upstream nymph only. Catch and release on two miles.

Wilton Fly Fishing Club
Contact: Mr A Simmons, Keepers Cottage, Manor Farm Lane, Great Wishford, SP2 0PG, 01722 790231, *Mobile:* 07866 343593, *Water:* Over 6 miles of chalkstream on the river Wylye (including carriers), *Species:* Wild Trout. Past record 7lb 2oz. Grayling to over 2lb, *Permits:* Season membership only via Secretary: Dr. J. McGill, Garden Croft, Beech Lawn, Epsom Road, Guildford, Surrey GU1 3PE. Tel 01483 504201, *Charges:* Prices on application to secretary, *Season:* Trout 16 April to 15 October. Grayling 16 June to 14 March, *Methods:* Trout - dry fly and upstream nymph only. Grayling dry fly and upstream nymph only in Trout season. Trotting also allowed from 15 October to 14 March.

WILTSHIRE
Stillwater
Coarse

CALNE
Blackland Lakes
Contact: J.or B. Walden, Blackland Lakes Holiday & Leisure Centre, Stockley Lane, Calne, SN11 0NQ, 01249 813672, fishing@blacklandlakes.co.uk, *Water:* One 1 acre, One 0.75 acre, *Species:* Carp to 33lb, Tench to 5lb, Roach to 4lb, Bream to 4lb, Perch to 4lb, *Charges:* 1 rod £7, extra rods £1, concessions OAP's and children, *Season:* Open all year, *Methods:* Barbless hooks, No ground bait, No large fish or Bream in keepnets

CHIPPENHAM
Chippenham Angling Club (Coarse Lake)
*Contact:*sw1/964952@aol.com, *Water:* See entry under Avon. Carp Lake, *Permits:* Members only, no day tickets.

Ivy House Lakes & Fisheries
Contact: Jo, Ivyhouse Lakes, Grittenham, Chippenham, SN15 4JU, 01666 510368, *Water:* 1 Acre + 6 Acre lakes, *Species:* Carp, Bream, Roach, Tench, Chub, Perch, *Permits:* On the bank day tickets, No night fishing, *Charges:* Day tickets £5 per day (1 rod). £3 Ladies O.A.Ps etc. Match booking £4, *Season:* All year, *Methods:* Boilies & Tiger nuts banned, Ground bait in moderation.

Sevington Lakes Fishery
Contact: R.J. Pope, Wellfield House, Parkhouse Lane, Keynsham, Bristol, BS31 2SG, 0117 9861841, *Water:* 2.5 acres in 2 lakes, *Species:* Mirror & Common Carp to 26lb, Crucians, Roach, Perch, Tench & Rudd, *Charges:* Day Ticket: Adult £5, Junior £2.50, *Season:* Open all year - Dawn to dusk, *Methods:* Barbless hooks please.

Silverlands Lake
Contact: Mr & Mrs King, Wick Farm, Lacock, Chippenham, SN15 2LU, 01249 730244, *Mobile:* 07720 509377, kingsilverlands2@btinternet.com, *Water:* One spring fed 2.5 acre lake, *Species:* Carp, Tench, Bream, Pike, *Permits:* Only from the fishery, *Charges:* Day/Night tickets £5, Season tickets 12 months - £100 Adult, £65 1/2 year. £8 - 24 hour ticket, *Season:* Open all year, *Methods:* No nuts, Dogs to be kept on a lead at all times

Wyatts Lake
Contact: L. Beale, Wyatts Lake Farm, Westbrook, Bromham, Nr Chippenham, SN15 2EB, 01380 859651, *Water:* 2 acre lake approx, *Species:* Mirror and Common Carp to 15lb, *Permits:* On site, *Charges:* £4 per person (unlimited rods), *Season:* Open all year 24 hours a day. Night fishing available, *Methods:* Good fishing practices required and expected.

DEVIZES
Devizes A.A. (Coarse Lake)
Contact: T.W. Fell, 21 Cornwall Crescent, Devizes, SN10 5HG, 01380 725189, *Water:* New 6.5 acre lake. Crookwood Lake well stocked, *Permits:* Angling Centre, Snuff St, Devizes, Wiltshire. Tel: 01380 722350. Local tackle shops in Devizes, Melksham, Trowbridge, Chippenham, Calne, Swindon. Wiltshire Angling: 01225-763835, *Charges:* Please phone for details.

Lavington Angling Club (Coarse Lake)
Contact: Mr Gilbert, Gable Cottage, 24 High Street, Erlestokes, Nr Devizes, SN10 5TZ, 01380 830425, *Water:* Two acre Merritts lake, *Species:* Carp, Tench, Roach, Rudd, Bream and Perch, *Permits:* Members only, details from club secretary, *Season:* Closed season from March 14th to June 15th, *Methods:* Keepnet limits. Full details of rules in Club handbook

MALMESBURY

The Lower Moor Fishery (Coarse)

Contact: Geoff & Anne Raines, Lower Moor Farm, Oaksey, Malmesbury, SN16 9TW, 01666 860232, *Mobile:* 07989 303768, *Water:* 7 acre coarse fishing lake, *Species:* Carp, Pike, Perch, Tench, Mirror, *Permits:* From office adjacent to car park, *Charges:* £5/day, *Season:* We observe close season for coarse fishing, *Methods:* Barbless hooks

MELKSHAM

Burbrooks Reservoir

Contact: A.J. Mortimer, 3 Talbot Close, Melksham, SN12 7JU, 01225 705062, *Mobile:* 07946 400707, *Water:* 0.75 acre Lake between Melksham & Calne, and Devizes and Chippenham in the village of Bromham (New Road), *Species:* Mirror, Common & Crucian Carp, Bream, Tench, Roach, Perch, Gudgeon, Chub, *Permits:* Please contact Melksham Angling Centre, Melksham House, Melksham: 01225-793546, or the Spar Shop in Bromham Village: 01380-850337, *Charges:* £4 Adults. £2 ladies, juniors and OAPs, *Season:* Open all year dawn to dusk, *Methods:* No night fishing, Only one rod per person, No hooks above size 8

MERE

Gillingham & District A A (Turners Paddock)

Contact: Simon Hebditch (Hon. Secretary), 01747 824817, *Mobile:* 07990 690613, ditch@ham5.fsnet.co.uk, *Water:* Turners Paddock at Stourhead Nr Mere (see also entry under river fishing Stour), *Species:* Tench 6lb, Bream 7lb, Carp 15lb, Roach 2lb, Rudd 2lb, Hybrids, Perch, Eels 6lb, *Permits:* Mr P Stone (Treasurer) The Timepiece, Newbury, Gillingham, Dorset, SP8 4HZ. Tel: 01747 823339. Mr J Candy, Todber Manor Fisheries Shop, Tel: 01258 820384. Mere Post Office, High Street, Mere, Wiltshire, *Charges:* £5 day ticket, £22 Season ticket. £11 Juniors and concessions. (probable charges for 2002), *Season:* June 16 to March 14, *Methods:* No fish in keepnets for more than 6 hours. Leave no litter. Feeder best for Bream & Tench.

SALISBURY

Longhouse Fishery

Contact: Jonathan Burch, Tinca, The Longhouse, Teffont, Nr. Salisbury, SP3 5RS, 07790 694757, *Water:* 3x 0.25 acre pond; 0.75 acre lake; 15 pegs in total, all deep, *Species:* Common + Mirror + Ghost + Koi + Crucian Carp (23.6lb), Roach + Rudd (2.6lb), Perch (3.9lb), Tench (3lb), *Permits:* Lakeside only, *Charges:* £5/day, £6/night, £7/24hrs, *Season:* All year 24hrs/day, only 10 days closed for pheasant shoot (Oct.-Jan.), *Methods:* Only bans are no particles (pulses) other than hemp or corn

Salisbury & District Angling Club (Coarse Lakes)

Contact: Rick Polden - Secretary, 29a Castle Street, Salisbury, SP1 1TT, 01722 321164, chairman@salisburydistrictac.co.uk, *Water:* Peters Finger Lakes, Steeple Langford and Wellow Lakes. See entry under Avon Hampshire, *Species:* Carp, Tench, Bream, *Charges:* £55 per season. Concessions for Senior Citizens & Juniors, *Season:* 1st June - 31st March.

Tisbury Angling Club (Coarse Lakes)

Contact: Mr E.J.Stevens, 01722 714245, *Water:* See also entry under Nadder. Old Wardour Lake (3.5 acre), 2 miles south of Tisbury and Dinton Lake (2.5 acre), 2 miles north of Tisbury.

Waldens Farm Fishery

Contact: David & Jackie Wateridge, Waldens Farm, Walden Estate, West Grimstead, Salisbury, SP5 3RJ, 01722 710480, *Water:* 5 Lakes for approx 7.5 acres, *Species:* All coarse fish. Specimen Pike Lake. Specimen Carp Lake. 27 peg match Lake for club or private hire, *Permits:* From the bank, *Charges:* Day (dawn to dusk) Adult £6, Junior - O.A.P. £4, Evenings 5 p.m.on £3.50, Match peg fees £4. Night fishing by appointment only, *Season:* Open full 12 months, *Methods:* Barbless hooks, Net dips to be used, Limited Groundbait, No boilies, nuts or cereals. Keepnets allowed.

Witherington Farm Fishing

Contact: Tony or Caroline Beeny, New Cottage, Witherington Farm, Downton, Salisbury, SP5 3QX, 01722 710021, *Water:* 3 Well stocked lakes, *Species:* Carp, Tench, Roach, Bream, Rudd, Chub, Perch, *Permits:* On bank, *Charges:* Full day £5, Half day £3, Full day Junior U16 / Disabled / O.A.P. £3, *Season:* All year Dawn - Dusk, *Methods:* No Boilies, Barbless hooks, All nets to be dipped, No night fishing, No keepnets only in matches.

TROWBRIDGE

Rood Ashton Lake

Contact: Marlene Pike, Home Farm, Rood Ashton, Trowbridge, BA14 6BG, 01380 870272, *Water:* 7 acre lake available for matches - please enquire for details, *Species:* Carp, Tench, Roach, *Permits:* Home Farm and Lake View, *Charges:* 6a.m. - 6p.m. £4.50, O.A.P's / Juniors £3.50. 6 p.m. - 11 a.m. £3.50, O.A.P's / Juniors £2.50. Please enquire for match bookings, *Season:* Open all year, *Methods:* No keepnets (only competitions). No tin cans or boilies, Barbless hooks only. No nuts. No night fishing

Tucking Mill

Contact: Wessex Water, 0845 600 4 600, *Water:* Free coarse fishing for disabled anglers from 16 June 2002 - 14 March 2003, *Species:* Roach, Chub, Tench and Large Carp, *Permits:* The site is regularly used by disabled angling clubs including Kingswood Disabled Angling Club. For more information please contact the club secretary Mr C Goodland, 58 Horthom Close, Patchway, Bristol BS34 5SE or Telephone 0117 975 4789, *Season:* 8am to sunset except in close season.

WARMINSTER

Longleat Lakes & Shearwater

Contact: Nick Robbins, Longleat Estate Office, Longleat, Warminster, 01985 844496, *Water:* Longleat 3 Lakes, Top lake Carp up to 32lb, Shearwater 37 acres, Carp up to 25lb. Longleat, 20 Carp over 20lb, *Species:* Carp, Roach, Bream, Tench, Perch, Rudd, *Permits:* From bailiff on the bank, *Charges:* Upon request, *Season:* Upon request, *Methods:* No keepnets or carp sacks, no boilies except Longleat. No nuts, peas, beans on all lakes, no bolt rigs. Barbless hooks only

Warminster & District Angling Club
Contact: c/o Steves Tackle, 3 Station Road, Warminster, 01985 214934, *Water:* Berkley Lake- 6 acres and Southleigh Lake at Crockerton - 2 acres, *Species:* Well stocked with all coarse fish, *Permits:* Club membership only. Details from Steves Tackle.

WESTBURY
Brokerswood Country Park
Contact: Mrs S.H.Capon, Brokerswood, Westbury, BA13 4EH, 01373 822238, woodland.park@virgin.net, *Water:* 5 Acre lake within 80 acre country park, *Species:* Carp, Roach, Tench, Perch, Dace, *Charges:* Adults £4.50, Children £3, *Season:* Closed Season 8th April - 16th June, *Methods:* Barbless hooks, No boilies, No keepnets
Clivey Ponds
Contact: Mr Mike Mortimer, Lakeside Clivey, Dilton Marsh, Westbury, BA13 4BA, mporsche@aol.com, *Water:* 1 acre lake, *Species:* Roach, Rudd, Bream to 2lb, Perch, Carp to 12lb, Crucians, Tench to 3lb and Gudgeon, *Permits:* On the bank or from Haines Angling Centre, 47 Vallis Way, Frome, *Charges:* £3/Day Ticket. Juniors OAPs etc. £2/day, *Season:* All year, *Methods:* Barbless Hooks only. No Groundbait
Eden Vale A.A.
Contact: A.E.D. Lewis, Secretary, Station Road, Westbury, 01373 465491, *Water:* 5.25 acre lake, *Species:* Carp (Common-15lb, Mirror-10lb), Bream-3lb, Roach-1.5lb, Perch-1lb, Rudd-0.75lb, Pike-15lb, *Permits:* Railway Inn opposite lake (max 8/day), Haines Angling, Badcox, Frome available from July 1st, Mon.-Fri. only, *Charges:* Day: £4 adult - £3 junior. Members (restricted to 15 mile radius of Westbury) at present £15 may increase in 2002. New Members £2.50 joining fee. Applications to Sec. with S.A.E. must be sponsored by two existing members, *Season:* members only May 1st - March 15th, day tickets July 1st - March 15th, *Methods:* No fixed rigs, no keepnets before June 16th, no Carp or Tench in keepnets.

WILTSHIRE Stillwater Trout

CALNE
Pheasant Fly Fishers
Contact: Ian Breaker, 11 Walter Sutton Close, Curson Park, Calne, SN11 0RG, 01249 819068, *Water:* None - A fly fishing club where members fish local waters and go on organised trips further afield, *Permits:* Please contact us on the number above or phone Ricky Baptista on 01225 719175 for more details. Anglers are welcome to attend our regular meetings at the Pheasant Inn, Bath Rd, Chippenham at 8pm on the first Tuesday of each month.

DEVIZES
Mill Farm Trout Lakes
Contact: Bill Coleman, Mill Farm Trout Lakes, Worton, Devizes, SN10 5UW, 01380 813138, *Mobile:* 07761 181369, *Water:* 2 Waters of 3.5 acres, *Species:* Rainbow Trout. All triploids from 2lb to double figures, *Permits:* Great Cheverell Post Office. One mile from fishery and open on Sunday mornings, *Charges:* 5 Fish £26, 4 Fish £23, 3 Fish £18, 2 Fish £14, 1 Fish (2hrs before dusk only) £7, *Season:* All year, 7.30am to dusk. Dec and Jan 8am to dusk. Closed Mondays except Bank Holidays, *Methods:* Fly fishing only.

MALMESBURY
The Lower Moor Fishery (Trout)
Contact: Geoff & Anne Raines, Lower Moor Farm, Oaksey, Malmesbury, SN16 9TW, 01666 860232, *Mobile:* 07989 303768, *Water:* 2 Lakes, 34 acre Mallard lake, 8 acre Cottage lake, *Species:* Rainbow 13lb 4oz & Brown Trout 9lb 3oz, *Permits:* From office adjacent to car park, *Charges:* 4 Fish ticket £22, 2 Fish ticket £14, Junior 2 Fish ticket £12, *Season:* March 16th - Jan 1st 2003, 8 a.m. to dusk, *Methods:* Mallard lake - any type of fly fishing, Cottage lake - nymph or dry fly on floating line.

PEWSEY
Manningford Trout Fishery
Contact: Dr Stewart Owen, Manningford Bohune, By Pewsey, SN9 6JR, 01980 630033, trout4u@barset.co.uk, *Water:* 4 acre lake fed by the Hampshire Avon, *Species:* Rainbow Trout to 18lb. Brown Trout to 10lb, *Permits:* From the Woodbridge Inn, 200yds from the lake, located on A345 between Pewsey and Upavon, *Charges:* Details from the fishery. 4 fish, 2 fish and junior tickets available, *Season:* Open all year from 8am to dusk, *Methods:* Fly fishing only.

SALISBURY
Avon Springs Fishing Lake (Stillwater)
Contact: BJ Bawden, Recreation Road, Durrington, Salisbury, SP4 8HH, 01980 653557, *Mobile:* 07774 801401, barrie@fishingfly.co.uk, *Water:* One 4 acre lake, One 3 acre lake. One mile of upper Avon chalk stream left hand bank, *Species:* Brown Trout 17lb 9oz, Rainbow Trout 15lb 4oz (2001), *Permits:* EA fishing licences available on site. Also contact: mobile 07774 801401, fax 01980-655267. Email barrie@avonsprings.freeserve.co.uk or barrie@fishingfly.co.uk, *Charges:* £35 per day, £25 junior. 1/2 day £28, junior £18, eve £18, *Season:* Open all year 8.30am to 8pm, *Methods:* Fly only no lures

Every care has been taken in compiling this directory and all information is believed correct at the time of printing. The publishers cannot however accept liability for any errors or ommisions. Fishery rules may change throughout the year, if in any doubt always contact the owner.

*Frank Bennet of
Manadon Angling
with a personal best
Mirror of 47lb 12oz*

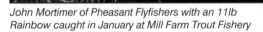

*John Mortimer of Pheasant Flyfishers with an 11lb
Rainbow caught in January at Mill Farm Trout Fishery*

*Young angler with a 6lb
Mirror from Milemead*

GAME

COARSE

SERVICES

HOTELS

SELF CATERING

CAMPING

CARAVANS

BED & BREAKFAST

TUITION

Road Directions
GAME

1. Amherst Lodge
From the A35 Bridport to Honiton road, take the Hunter's Lodge turning onto the B3165 towards Lyme Regis. After 1.4 miles turn right down Cathole Lane. Keep to the right and you will come to Amherst.

2. Angling 2000
Over 20 beats on the Tamar, Taw, Torridge & Camel. Please telephone 01566 784488.

3. Arundell Arms Hotel
Leave the A30 Dual Carriageway east of Launceston and follow signs for Lifton. The Arundell Arms is in the centre of the Village.

4. Avon Springs
Please phone 01980 653557 or 07774 801401 for road directions.

5. Bake Lakes
A38 to Trerulefoot. At roundabout (half way between Plymouth & Liskeard) take minor road to Bake. Turn right at T-junction, then take first left. Fishery is 200 yards on right.

6. Bellbrook Valley Trout Fishery
From Tiverton roundabout on A361 head towards Barnstaple. Take 3rd right (6 miles) signposted Bellbrook & Spurway. Continue down lane for 2 miles then sharp right signed "To the fishery" then 200yds on the right. From Oakford leave uphill, bear left at Pinkworthy Post (signposted Rackenford). Follow lane down hill, cross stream then fork left. Fishery 200yds on right.

7. Blakewell Fishery
Take A39 from Barnstaple towards Lynton. 1.5 miles from Barnstaple turn left on to B3230 and follow signs to the fishery.

8. Bridge House Hotel
The fishing is located just upstream of Oakford Bridge on the A396 approx. 15 miles from junction 27 on the M5. The Bridge House Hotel is in Bampton on the B3227 (A361 to Tiverton – A396 to Bampton). Please phone 01398 331298.

9. Bristol Water Fisheries
a. Barrows. b. Blagdon. c. Chew. d. Litton. Bristol Water fisheries are well signposted from major roads. Telephone 01275 332339.

10. Cameley Lakes
Situated 10 miles between Bristol, Bath & Wells. Off A37.

11. Clinton Arms
Situated between Bideford and Great Torrington on the A386. Turn right to Frithelstock and follow signs to Clinton Arms.

12. Drakelands
From Exeter take the main road to Plympton. At Newnham Industrial Estate take the Cornwood Road to Hemerdon Village. Turn right past Miners Arms, the fishery is signposted 0.75 miles on the left.

13. Drift Reservoir
Take A30 towards Lands End. In Drift village, turn right (signposted "Sancreed"). Reservoir car park is approx. 1/4 mile along this lane. Ticket sales enquiries: Adjacent.

14. Eggesford Country Hotel
At Eggesford on the A377 midway between Exeter and Barnstaple.

15. Environment Agency Fisheries
a-Exe & Creedy fisheries. b Watersmeet & Glenthorne fisheries. Directions are supplied with permits.

16. Exe Valley Fishery
M5 exit 27 to Tiverton on A361. Take A396 towards Minehead at Black Cat Junction, continue on A396 towards Minehead, at Exebridge turn left at garage on B3222, over bridge at the Anchor Inn take first right to fishery.

17. Fenwick Trout Fishery
From Bodmin take A389 toward Wadebridge, continue to village of Dunmere and turn immediate left off river Camel Bridge. Fishery is signposted.

18. Flowers Farm Fly Fishery
Situated mid way Dorchester and Yeovil off A37. From Dorchester take A37, travel for approx. 7 miles look out for green dome on right, 0.5 mile turn right to Batcombe, 0.5 mile turn right at T junction marked to the Friary, take second left at fishing sign, then right at bottom of hill. The fishery is at the side of St Francis Friary. From Yeovil take A37 for approx. 6 miles, turn left at crossroads marked Batcombe, take 3rd left along top Batcombe Downs at fishing sign, right bottom of hill. Continue 0.5 mile to Fishery.

19. Fly Fishing in Somerset
Please contact Mr Robin Gurden on 01643 851504. Based in Winsford. Somerset. Exmoor.

20. Fosfelle Country Manor
Please telephone 01237 441273 for directions.

21. Half Moon Hotel
Sheepwash lies 1 mile North of Highampton (A3072) between Hatherleigh & Holsworthy.

22. Highbullen Hotel
Please telephone 01769 540561 for directions.

23. Higher Cownhayne Farm
Please phone for directions. 01297 552267.

24. Innis Inn & Fly Fishery
M5 to Exeter, A30 to roundabout west of Bodmin. A391 follow signs for Eden. Two miles from Eden, follow Innis Inn & camping signs to fishery.

25. Manningford Trout Fishery
On A345 midway between Pewsey & Upavon, next to the Woodbridge Inn. Phone 01980 630033 for more details.

26. Mill Leat Trout Lakes
Take the A388 north from Holsworthy. Turn right following signs for Thornbury. The fishery is half a mile past Thornbury church.

27. Nick Hart Fly Fishing
Follow A358 out of Taunton, then the B3224 signposted to Exford.

28. Prince Hall Hotel
From M5 - pass Exeter, then take A38 signposted Plymouth. Take second Ashburton turn-off, the B3357 signposted Two Bridges and Princetown. Hotel is situated one mile from this point on the left and one mile before Two Bridges Junction. From Plymouth - Take A386 to Yelverton, follow signs for Princetown, continue towards Two Bridges, turn right and stay on B3357. Hotel is one mile on the right.

29. Rising Sun Inn
The Rising Sun Inn is on the A377 opposite T-junction with B3227 to South Molton.

30. Rockbourne Trout Fishery
Please telephone 01725 518603 for directions.

31. Roddy Rae's Devon &UK Fly Fishing School
Please telephone 01647 24643 for directions.

32. South West Lakes Trust - Game
a-Kennick, b-Siblyback, c-Wimbleball, d-Fernworthy, e-Colliford, f-Roadford, g-Burrator, h-Stithians, i-Crowdy, j-Wistlandpound, k-Meldon, l-Avon Dam, m-Venford, n-Tottiford. South West Lakes Trust fisheries are well signposted from major roads.

33. Sutton Veny Fishing
Please Telephone 01985 212325

34. Tavistock Trout Fishery
Entrance on A386 one mile from Tavistock.

35. Tree Meadow Trout Fishery
Off B3302 Hayle to Helston

36. Two Bridges Hotel
Leave M5 southbound at Junction 31 and join A38 signposted Plymouth. After 18 miles take exit signposted B3357 Princetown/Two Bridges. After 11 miles the Hotel can be seen on left hand side at junction of the B3357 & B3212. Please telephone 01822 890581 for alternative Dartmoor route.

37. Upavon Farm Fishing
From centre of Upavon take the Salisbury road A345 & access to River is on the left within walking distance from village pub.

38. Valley Springs
Half a mile from Cider Press, follow official tourist signs from Frogmore or Totnes Road.

39. Wessex Fly Fishing School
In Tolpuddle turn off A35 signed Southover. You will see our signs 0.25 mile along lane.

40. Wessex Water - Game
a Clatworthy. b Hawkridge. c Sutton Bingham. Please telephone 0845 600 4 600 for further details.

41. Wiscombe Park Fishery
Leave A30 at Honiton, take A375 towards Sidmouth, turn left at the Hare and Hounds cross roads towards Seaton, after 3 miles turn left towards Blackbury Camp, fishery signposted on the left.

Road Directions
COARSE

1. Acorn Carp Fishery
Lampley Road, Kingston Seymour. Please Telephone 01934 833760/834050.

2. Alcove Angling Club
Please telephone 0117 9025737 or 07941 168116 for directions.

3. Avallon Lodges
From Launceston B3254 towards Bude town turn left at Langdon Cross (just before the Countryman Pub) then next right signed Clubworthy. Avallon is 1.5 miles along this road, up a short drive on the left.

4. Avalon Fisheries
Please phone 01278 456429 or 0966 363413 for directions.

5. Badham Farm Holidays
A30 Liskeard turn off - Follow signs for St. Keyne. At St. Keyne take left hand turn just before church signed St Keyne Well & Badham. A38 at Dobwells – Turn for Duloe & St. Keyne, then from St. Keyne as A30 route.

6. Bickerton Farm Fisheries
Please telephone 01548 511220 for road directions.

7. Bridgwater Sports & Social Club
Please telephone 01278 446215 for directions.

8. Bristol, Bath & Wiltshire Amalgamated Anglers
Please phone 0117 9672977.

9. Brokerswood Country Park
Please telephone 01373 822238

10. Bullock Farm Lakes
From Junction 20, M5 follow B3133 for Yatton. Drive through village of Ken, turn right for Kingston Seymour. Follow signs for Bullock Farm Fishing Lakes.

11. Bush Lakes
Over Tamar Bridge, at Saltash roundabout turn right (A388). Continue 3 miles to Hatt, turn left onto Pillaton road. Continue for 1.5 miles up over 1st hill, turn left at red brick corner cottage by fishery sign.

12. Christchurch Angling Club
Please telephone 01425 279710 for directions.

13. Clawford Vineyard
Take A388 from Holsworthy to Launceston. Turn left at crossroads in Clawton. After 2.5 miles turn left at T junction. Clawford is a further 0.6 miles on left.

14. Cofton Country Holiday Park
From Junction 30, M5 Exeter, take A379 signed Dawlish. Park is on the left half mile after small harbour village of Cockwood.

15. Coombe Fisheries
Leave the A386 (Plymouth to Tavistock road) at Yelverton and then follow signs to Buckland Abbey. The Fishery is signposted 100yds past the Abbey entrance on the left.

16. Coombe Water Fisheries
Half a mile from Kingsbridge on road to Loddiswell, B3210.

17. Coombelands Coarse Fishery
Only 15 mins. from junction 28 M5. Approx. 3.5 mls from Tiverton, .75 mls from Butterleigh on the Silverton Rd, 3.5 mls from Cullompton, 1ml from Bunniford Cross on the Silverton Rd and 3 mls from Silverton on the Butterleigh Rd.

18. Cranford Inn & Holiday Cottages
Please telephone 01805 624697 for directions.

19. Creedy Lakes
Travelling south down the M5 exit at junction 27. From Tiverton take the A3072 Exeter/Crediton road. At Bickleigh bear right towards Crediton. At Crediton town sign turn right. Follow blue and white fishery signs.

20. Darts Farm
Leave M5 at junction 30. Follow signs to Exmouth (A376). After 2 miles follow brown tourist signs to Darts Farm Shopping Village.

21. Diamond Farm
Fishing is on river Axe at Brean. Site can be found from M5 junction 22. Follow signs for Burnham-on-Sea, Brean. On reaching Brean turn right at junction for Lympsham and Weston Super Mare on the Weston road. Diamond Farm is approx half mile from junction on left hand side.

22. Dutson Water
From A30 turn off at Launceston onto the A388 to Holsworthy road. Continue for 1.5 miles from town, passing Homeleigh Angling Centre on your right. The lake is at end of 30mph sign at Dutson on right hand side down a lane.

23. Eastcott Lodges
From B3254 take turning signposted North Tamerton. As you come into village take first right to Boyton. Eastcott is 1.5 miles along on the left hand side.

24. Edneys Fisheries
Please telephone 01373 812294 for directions.

25. Elmfield Farm Coarse Fishery
From Launceston take the Egloskerry road found at the top of St.Stephens Hill. About 1 mile out of Egloskerry look for the Treburtle turn off to the right. Follow Fishing signs for 3 mls, signposted on the left.

26. Emerald Pool Fisheries
Off the A38 at West Huntspill, turn into Withy Road by the Crossways Inn. Take the next right Puriton Road. Travel for approx. 0.5 mile, over Huntspill river, take the next track on the left. Pool on the right at the top of the track.

27. Exeter & District Angling Association
Please tel 07970 483913 or enquire in local Tackle Shops.

28. Follyfoot Farm Fisheries
We are on main A38, on the Taunton side of North Petherton. Entrance to lake in first layby on the right heading south.

29. Glenleigh Farm Fishery
From St. Austell take A390 towards Truro, after approx. 3 miles second hand car garage on left, turn left to Sticker, follow road to top of hill, immediately before bus shelter turn left, past mobile homes park, over bypass to bottom of hill, car park on right.

30. Godney Moor Ponds
Please telephone 01458 447830 for directions.

31. Gold Oak Fisheries
Hare Lane, Cranborne. Please telephone 01725 517275 for directions.

32. Goodiford Mill Fishery
From Cullompton take the Honiton road, continue for over a mile past Horns cross. Turn left at signpost for Wressing, Goodiford, Dead lane. Right at end of lane, fishery on left.

33. Hidden Valley Coarse Fishing
Easily found 4 miles west of Launceston, just off A395, 0.5 mile from Kennards House junction with A30. Follow Hidden Valley signs. Please note Hidden Valley can now be approached from new access road. Follow Hidden Valley signs.

34. Ivy House Lakes
From Swindon to Wooton Bassett, bottom of hill turn right down Whitehill Lane. Fishery is approx. 2 miles on the left hand side.

35. Kingslake Fishing Holidays
From Exeter at end of M5 take A30 to Okehampton, in the centre of Okehampton at the lights, turn right onto A386 to Hatherleigh. At Hatherleigh (7 miles) take left onto A3072 Holsworthy/Bude. Travel 7 miles then turn left at sign 'Chilla 2 miles' Kingslake is 0.75 mile along this road on left.

36 Lands End Fishery
From M5 junction 22, turn left at first roundabout, then first left and follow road to T junction, turn left signposted Wedmore, continue through village of Mark, then into Blackford where you turn right by the school signposted Heath House, follow road to crossroads, turn right, then second right, fishery is at bottom of lane.

37. Little Allers
From Exeter: Take Wrangaton Cross exit off A38, take 2nd road on left. From Plymouth: Take Ivybridge exit off A38. Go through Ivybridge to Wrangaton. Turn right and take 2nd road on left.

38. Longleat & Shearwater
From Warminster take 362 towards Frome, follow signs to Longleat. Further information from the bailiff, Nick Robbins on (01985) 844496.

39. Lower Hollacombe Fishery
Please telephone 01363 84331 for directions.

40. Luccombes Fishery
From Exminster, enter Exminster from Exeter on A379, pass the shops on right and Victory Hall on left, take first right into Days Pottels Lane, then next left into Towsington Lane, the fishery is situated approx. 0.5 mile on the left.

41. Mangerton Valley Coarse Lake.
Please telephone 01308 458482 for directions.

42. Meadowside Fishery
Located on A39, just south of the roundabout junction with B3274 at Winnards Perch, within the Cornish Birds of Prey Centre at St. Columb Major.

43. Mellonwatts Mill Coarse Fishery
From St. Austell take A390 Truro road to end of Sticker bypass, then road signposted Tregoney and St. Mawes. Turn left after 1 ml for Mevagissey. Fishery 2nd farm on rt.

44. Middle Boswin Farm
Take Scorrier exit off the A30, follow signs to Helston (B3297) through Redruth. Take B3297 for approx. 5 miles passing Four Lanes, Nine Maidens, Burras and Farms Common. Turn Left at sign to Porkellis, follow for less than a mile. Turn left after White Bridge Weare 0.5 mile on left.

45. Milemead Fisheries
From Tavistock take B3362 (old A384) towards Launceston. Take turning left just outside Tavistock signposted Mill Hill. Entrance is 1 mile down lane on right.

46. Millbrook Fishery
Approach Millbrook on B3247, follow brown Tourist Signs from Tregantle Fort.

47. Millhayes Fishery
2 miles from junction 28 (M5) on the A373 towards Honiton turn left at Post Cross to Kentisbeare. 1 mile to village centre, turn right at Post Office and go down hill for 300yds, turn right at sign for Millhayes.

48. Minnows Camping & Caravan Park
From the North or South exit M5 at junction 27 onto A361 signposted Tiverton. After about 600 yards take first exit signposted signposted Sampford Peverell. Turn right at next roundabout, cross bridge over A361. Straight across at next roundabout signposted Holcombe Rogus. Site is on left. From N. Devon on the A361 - go to end of A361 to junction 27 of the M5. Go all the way round and return back onto the A361. Then follow the above directions.

49. Nanteague Farm
We are situated on the main A30 between the Chiverton & Carland Cross roundabouts. From South on main A30 pass Zelah on dual carriageway and 2 miles further on through the hamlet of Marazanvose on the brow of the hill opposite Town & Country Nissan Garage you will find our entrance.

50. New Barn Angling Centre
From Paignton bypass traffic lights, take the A385 to Totnes/Plymouth. Turn left after 2 miles into farm track signposted New Barn Angling Centre. From Totnes take the A385 to Paignton, turn right 200 yards past the Texaco garage into farm track signposted New Barn Angling Centre.

51. New Forest Water Park
From Ringwood head towards Fordingbridge on A338. After 4 miles you will see signs on the left.

52. Newberry Farm Coarse Fishing
On A399 western edge of Combe Martin village.

53. Newcourt Ponds
Take junction 28 M5 into Cullompton town centre, follow B3181 towards Exeter for 2 miles. At Merry Harriers Inn turn left. After hump backed Bridge turn right, at top of road turn right. Ponds 100yds on left.

54. Newton Abbot Angling Association
Please telephone 01626 331613/200198 for directions.

55. Northam Farm
Leave the M5 at junction 22. Follow signs to Burnham-on-Sea, Brean. Continue through Brean village and Northam Farm is on the right half a mile past Brean Leisure Park.

56. Oakside Fishery
From Newquay take road to Quintrell Downs, at roundabout at Quintrell Downs take A3058, continue to Dairyland, first left, past Dairyland (signposted White Cross). Fishery is 1 mile down road on right hand side.

57. Oaktree Carp Farm & Fishery
From Barnstaple take the A361 to Newtown. Left onto B3227 Bampton Road for 2.5 miles and left at fishery signpost. Down hill and entrance signposted on right. From M5 junction 27 take A361 to Newtown, then as above.

58. Osmington Mills
Approaching from Wareham on the A352 Dorchester road turn left at the A353 Weymouth junction. At the Osmington Mills sign opposite the Garage, turn left and follow the lane to Holiday Park. Approaching from Weymouth, follow the A353 Wareham road. Pass through Osmington and turn right at the sign for Osmington Mills. Follow lane to Holiday Park.

59. Pallington Lakes
On the unclassified road between Dorchester and Bovington Tank Museum (signposted) 1 mile east of Tincleton.

60. Plantation Lakes
From Bristol - Weston-Super-Mare A370. Turn towards Yatton B3133 at Congresbury traffic lights. Go right through Yatton. Turn left towards Kingston Seymour. Just after the Bridge Inn. At village take middle lane. From M5. junction 20. Clevedon. Turn left at both roundabouts onto B3133 towards Yatton, after approx 3 miles turn right towards Kingston Seymour. At village take middle lane.

61. Retallack Waters
Just off the A39 between Newquay and Wadebridge at Winnards Perch, signposted 'American Theme Park'.

62. Rood Ashton Lake
Leave A350 heading through West Ashton Village. Take next left signed Rood Ashton, continue past East Town Farm, turn left. Home Farm is 0.5 mile on left, you will see a sign.

63. Salmonhutch Fishery
A377 to Crediton, turn left after Shell Garage, follow road signed Tedburn St Mary for 1.5 miles, right at junction marked Uton, follow fishery signs.

64. Silverlands Lake
From M4 Junction 17 take the A350 south (Chippenham bypass) continue for approx. 8 miles, still on the A350, you will be on the Laycock bypass. After passing a turn on the left for Lacock and on right for Whitehall Garden Centre, take the next turn on the right Folly Lane West, continue along this lane, under railway bridge to the No Through Road where you will see the sign for Wick Farm.

65. Simpson Valley Fishery
1.5 miles from Holsworthy on main A3072 Holsworthy to Hatherleigh road.

66. South Farm Holiday Cottages
Between Blackborough & Sheldon. Detailed instructions given on enquiry.

67. South View Farm Fishery
From Bristol follow M5 onto A38. After 1.5 miles turn off into Kennford. Continue through village following Dunchideock signs until Shillingford signs are seen. Follow Shillingford signs. Entrance to fishery on left at sharp bend before village. From Plymouth turn left off A38 following Dunchideock until sign for Clapham is seen on right heading down the hill. At Clapham follow signs for Shillingford. From Exeter follow signs to Alphington then Shillingford St. George. Fishery on right after village.

68. South West Lakes Angling Association
Please telephone 01884 256721 for directions

69. South West Lakes Trust - Coarse
a-Slade. b-Jennetts. c-Darracott. d-Melbury. e-Trenchford. f-Upper Tamar. g-Squabmoor. h-Old Mill. i-Crafthole. j-Porth. k-Boscathnoe. l-Argal. m-Bussow. South West Lakes Trust fisheries are well signposted from major roads.

70. Spires Lakes
On the A3072 Holiday Route (HR) from Crediton.Turn right at Newlands Cross towards Sampford Courtney. Spires Lakes are on the left after approx. 0.5 mile.

71. Stafford Moor Country Park
Clearly signposted on the A3124, 3 miles North of Winkleigh, 9 miles South of Torrington.

72. Sunridge Fishing Lodge
Travelling west on A38, just after South Brent take slip road for National Shire Horse Centre, turn left, travel 2 miles to crossroads, turn right onto B3210, continue 3 miles to T junction, turn right onto A379 towards Plymouth, continue 2 miles to second cross roads (just before garage) and turn right. Travel 1 mile and you will find the lodge on left.

73. Thorney Lakes
Directions from A303 to Muchelney. Turn off A303 dual carriageway signposted Martock Ash. Follow signs to Kingsbury Episcopi, at the T junction in village turn right, through the village of Thorney, over river bridge & disused railway. Lakes are on left. Thorney Lakes & Caravan Park.

74. Todber Manor Fisheries
5 miles from Gillingham, Shaftesbury and Sturminster Newton. Just off the B3092.

75. Trebellan Park Coarse Fishery
Take the A30 as far as the main Newquay exit (A392). Follow signs to Newquay until you come to Quintrell Downs. At Quintrell Downs, go straight across the roundabout following signs for Crantock & Cubert. At Trevemper Bridge roundabout turn left onto A3075. For Trebellan Park continue along this road for another 2 miles, turn right at Cubert/Holywell Bay crossroads, 0.75 mile along this road, before the village of Cubert, you will see our sign on the left.

76. Trencreek Farm Holiday Park
4 miles southwest of St. Austell. On the A390 fork left on to the B3287. Trencreek is one mile on, on the left.

77. Trinity Waters
Off M5, Junction 23, take A38 to Bridgwater, take first right turning after Express Park roundabout. First right at traffic lights, over River Parrett, turn right at traffic lights to Chilton Trinity. Take second right down Straight Drove (No through

road).1st gate on right for Wild marsh & Middle marsh lakes, 3rd gate on right for Woodland Lake.

78. Upham Carp Ponds
From J30 on M5, take A3052 signposted Sidmouth. After approx 4 miles, after pasing White Horse Inn on right, sign to fishery will be seen on left. Turn left and after 700 yds fishery will be found on left hand side.

79. Viaduct Coarse Fishery
From Yeovil take the A37 north towards Ilchester and then the B3151 to Somerton. Turn left onto the B3153 (Signposted Somerton) and go up hill to mini roundabout. Go straight over roundabout and take first right through housing estate to T-junction. Turn left and almost immediately first right onto track to fishery.

80. Waldens Farm Fishery
Off the A36 Salisbury to Southampton road near Whaddon. Phone for futher details (01722) 710480.

81. Warren Park Farm
A31, just past Ringwood take B3081, about 1 mile fork right to Alderholt. On entering Alderholt turn left into Ringwood Road, as road bears right farm on the left.

82. Week Farm
From Exeter bypass Okehampton, leave A30 dual carriageway at Sourton junction. At end of sliproad cross A386 at staggered crossroad (signposted Bridestowe). Week signpost on right after 1.5 miles (bottom of hill left 0.5 mile). Or, from Bridestowe village turn right towards Okehampton, pass garage on left & take next left, Week is 0.75 mile.

83. Wessex Water - Coarse
a Durleigh reservoir. b Blashford Lakes. c Tucking Mill. Please telephone 0845 600 4 600 for further details.

84. West Pitt Farm Fishery
Junction 27 off M5, take Barnstaple signed dual way, almost immediately exit signed to Sampford Peverell. Right at mini roundabout, straight over second roundabout. Turn left signed to Whitnage, next right, then at Pitt Crossroads turn left – Fishery is a few 100 yds on left.

85. Witherington Farm Lakes
2 miles out of Salisbury on A36 fork right as dual carriageway starts, then first right again after about 0.5 miles. Follow signs for Downton and Stanlynch. Witherington Farm is about 3 miles on the right.

86. Wood Farm Caravan Park
7 miles west of Bridport on A35, entrance off roundabout with A3052 (access to fishing through caravan park).

87. Wooda Farm Park
From the A39 take the road signposted Poughill, Stampford Hill, continue 1 ml, through crossroad. Wooda Farm Park is 200yds on the right.

88. Woodacott Arms
Proceed north off the A3072 at Anvil Corner, turn right at Blagdon Moor Cross or proceed south off the A388 at Holsworthy Beacon, turn left at Blagdon Moor Cross. After approx 1.5 miles turn sharp left at Woodacott Cross, Woodacott Arms immediately right.

89. Woolsbridge Manor Farm
Please telephone 01202 826369 for directions.